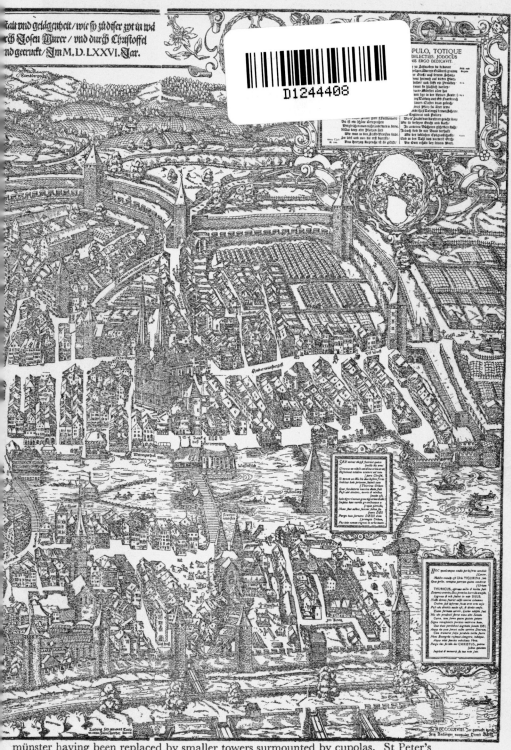

münster having been replaced by smaller towers surmounted by cupolas. St Peter's church, whose huge clock-dial is still a landmark, stands to the left of the Fraumünster. Of special interest is the extensive use made of the water-power of the Limmat flowing from the Lake beyond the right-hand boundary of the plan.

SCIENCE and the RENAISSANCE

An Introduction to the study of the Emergence of the Sciences in the ◊◊ Sixteenth Century

W. P. D. WIGHTMAN

VOLUME I

Published for the University of Aberdeen

OLIVER AND BOYD

EDINBURGH AND LONDON

HAFNER PUBLISHING COMPANY

NEW YORK

FIRST PUBLISHED . . . 1962

PRINTED IN GREAT BRITAIN AT THE UNIVERSITY PRESS, ABERDEEN
FOR OLIVER AND BOYD LTD., EDINBURGH

DUNCANI LIDDELII SCOTI,
MEDICINAE DOCTORIS NECNON DECANI,
ACADEMIAE JULIANAE HELMAESTADIENSIS,
LIBRORUM BONORUM AMATORIS,
IN PIAM MEMORIAM HOC OPSCULUM DICAT AUCTOR.

'Aber kein Ding im ganzen Reiche Gottes
kann ich mich doch überreden ist allein
Mittel—alles Mittel und Zweck zugleich,
und so gewiss auch diese Jahrhunderte.'

HERDER, *Auch eine Philosophie der
Geschichte zur Bildung der Menscheit*

PREFACE

THAT the 'problem of the Renaissance' is still with us probably
few historians would deny. On the one hand it is still possible
to find writers of repute seriously affirming that at a certain
fairly well defined epoch the winds of Hellas set in a westerly
direction and swiftly dispersed the fog which had maintained for a
millennium the Dark Night of Europe's intellectual Soul. At the
opposite pole the opinion is held that the 'so-called' Renaissance
is merely an arbitrary fiction which has for too long obscured the
vision of the unenlightened from the 'modern' achievements of
the Middle Ages. The history of science has been one of the worst
sufferers from this confusion. We are just as likely to be told that
'with the discovery of the Greek classics towards the end of the
fifteenth [sic] century' science was 'free' to throw off the bonds of
'scholasticism', as to learn with some surprise that Francis Bacon,
so far from being the 'founder' of modern science, was a 'typical
medieval'. No apology, therefore, seems to be called for in respect
of the matter of this book; but as to the form, if not an apology,
at least an explanation, is in order.

The corpus of sixteenth-century works relating to the sciences
in the University Library at Aberdeen is of special interest for
two reasons. The University itself was founded in 1494, just at the
time when (so it has been alleged) the fog began to clear; and a
considerable proportion of the books bear the signatures, and
often the glosses, of men who strove in the battle of ideas at a time
when the 'modern' lines of scientific development were far from
having been firmly laid down. Thus it came about that in 1951
this work had its origin in a proposal to the Library Committee
that a *catalogue raisonnée* should be prepared of all such books,
especially in view of the fact that they are dispersed in various
special collections, which are not likely to be discovered except
by someone whose studies take him into the obscurest *penetralia*
of the Library. The remarkably representative character of the
collections revealed by a more thorough search suggested the
possibility of a work on a more ambitious scale, such as might

be found useful both by historians seeking a more comprehensive grasp of the manifold character of the Renaissance problem, and by scientists anxious to discover the relations of their special disciplines to the others which began to separate out at this time. That such a 'synthetic' approach would be fraught with perils was only too evident. That the Library Committee were willing to encourage me to launch out on so dubious a venture was an act of faith, which has been alike a source of anxiety and inspiration, and for which I cannot too strongly express my appreciation. It is hardly necessary to add that the completion of the task was made possible only by the generous co-operation at every stage of Dr. W. D. Simpson, University Librarian.

In order that the work may attain the greatest usefulness it would seem desirable to indicate rather fully the nature of the materials on which it is based, and the manner in which they have been reviewed and related to the whole. In what follows I have tried to sketch the organic structure of the work rather than the order in which the topics have been dealt with.

The kernel of the work is the Bibliography (Volume II), a concise bibliographical catalogue of *all* the printed books in the University Library bearing on science and its related fields, published, roughly, in the sixteenth century. Discretion has been used in varying the *termini* of publication in different fields: thus certain incunables have on the one hand been included, and in the case of alchemy, in particular, a considerable spill-over into the seventeenth century has been permitted, owing to the relatively long-delayed emergence of chemistry as a separate discipline. The selection of bibliographical details included in the Bibliography is indicated in the guide to the use of the Bibliography; such selection was dictated by the view that the Bibliography should be rather a handy check-list of sources for the historian than a compendium of technicalities appealing mainly to the professional bibliographer.

While the provenance of individual books has generally been indicated in the Bibliography, the *scenario* of this provenance has been presented in a sketch of the early history of the Libraries, with special reference to those benefactors whose munificence was largely responsible for that section of them which is the subject of this work. The word 'Libraries' may have reminded the reader that during the greater part of the period under discussion there were two Universities of Aberdeen: this fact will necessitate rather more than passing reference to these foundations themselves.

So much constitutes the primary sources of the work. The lengthy and careful examination of every one of the books listed, however, put me (or so I have dared to hope) in a position whence a new view of the course of scientific thought in the Renaissance could be gained. In the attempt to display this view I have not of course restricted myself to the works listed, but have tried to relate the narrative as closely as possible to the sources by numbered textual references to the Bibliography; many of these are only to the *authors*, and do not necessarily relate to the *topic* under consideration. Since it has seemed to me that it is as an introduction to special studies of the period that the work may find its chief use, I have not hesitated to omit detailed discussions of some of the better-known discoveries, for which rather full references have been supplied in the Supplementary Bibliography. This expedient has made possible rather more thorough treatment of relatively minor figures and movements of thought than is usually accorded to them in the existing histories of Renaissance science written on a similar scale. The due assessment of such trends of thought may be critical for the deeper understanding of the period which is still to seek.

If (as I hope) some students of the sciences should turn to this work to enlarge their knowledge of the genesis of scientific ideas in this fascinating period, they will find that some acquaintance with the background of political and religious controversy is indispensable for the just interpretation of ideas relevant to the sciences. Also much of the picturesqueness of sixteenth-century thought is lost without at least a nodding acquaintance with the princes, prelates, merchants, and ministers of state with whom those conventionally regarded as 'scientists' worked, sometimes in a most intimate manner. I have therefore prefaced the main historical section with a review of those aspects of European history which seem to me most illuminating in this connection. It will be readily understood that such a sketch must be drawn mainly from impressions gained from general surveys and monographs on special subjects, and can lay no claim to originality except in the way of emphasis: historians may indeed prefer to regard it simply as a development of the author's half-supported prejudices!

But assessed even at this level it should be at least not irrelevant in a work of this kind.

It is unnecessary to say anything here about the main section on the growth of scientific ideas in the Renaissance, the arrangement of which—no easy problem—will be indicated in its proper place. It remains only to express the hope that among students of the history of ideas in the Renaissance the scientists will discover some significant details among much that is familiar, and the historians will not find the science too technical nor the history too jejune!

It is particularly appropriate that these two volumes should be published in the series of 'Aberdeen University Studies' since very many of my colleagues have assisted me in ways unfortunately too numerous to acknowledge in detail. There are some, however, who have as it were been at my side throughout the preparation of the work. To Dr. W. D. Simpson, University Librarian, and Mr. H. J. S. Drummond, his Deputy, I owe whatever I have managed to learn of the art of bibliography, and to the patience of Miss K. Walker and the library staff whatever success I may have had in bringing to light unsuspected treasures. Only as a result of the severe scrutiny and kindly criticism of Professor W. S. Watt has the final draft of the Bibliography apeared *ab innumeris mendis repurgatus!* To him must go a very large share of the credit for whatever value this part of the work may be adjudged to have. To Dr. Kathleen Edwards I am more than grateful for having awakened in me a respect, based on greater understanding, for the medieval writings which exercised a marked influence on so many of the authors with whom I have been more directly concerned.

In Volume I the first drafts of Chapters I and III; VI; VII; X; XIV, were read and criticised by Professors J. B. Black, E. M. Wright and H. Dingle, the late Dr. Agnes Arber, F.R.S., and Dr. M. G. McEntegart respectively. So wide ranging a survey would not have been possible without such critical guidance; and in particular I could not have dared to indulge my enthusiasm for Paracelsus had I not had the privilege of being able to call on Dr. Walther Pagel to save me from extravagance. Since none of my critics have seen the final proofs they must not be held responsible for such errors as remain. Finally, in the writing of the earlier chapters especially I was greatly assisted by numerous discussions with my wife, who also undertook a great deal of the arduous task of indexing.

My share of the labour involved in the production of the book was greatly reduced by the care with which Mrs. J. McCulloch prepared the typescript of Volume II, and by the skill with which the copy was followed by the Aberdeen University Press. The photographs from which all but two of the blocks were made testify to the customary skill and care of Mr. Alexander Cain, A.R.P.S.

My thanks are due to the Stadtkanzlei of the City of Zürich for the gift of the facsimile of the sixteenth-century panorama of the city from which the end-paper has been prepared, and to the Trustees of the British Museum for permission to reproduce a folio from MS Egerton 2020 (Plate VI). In connection with the bibliographical study of Paracelsus I was given especially valuable assistance by Dr. L. Forrer, Director of the Zentralbibliothek of Zürich and by Mr. J. Bührer, of the Library Staff; a similar service was rendered by Dr. F. N. L. Poynter, Librarian of the Wellcome Historical Medical Library.

WILLIAM P. D. WIGHTMAN

CONTENTS

ILLUSTRATIONS

END-PAPER DECORATED MAP

The city of Zürich as it appeared in 1576 in a contemporary engraving by Josen Muren published by the printer Christoph Froschower

CHAPTER I

THE RENAISSANCE PROBLEM

THE readiest source of confusion in discussions of the history of the 'Renaissance' is the assumption that the term is uniquely significant. Its literal meaning is of course a 'rebirth', and to the Common Man its usual connotation is even today of a period towards the end of the fifteenth century which witnessed a 'rebirth' of the classical languages with all their grace of diction and wealth of content. This 'rebirth' of polite letters ushered in, so it is commonly held, the 'Modern World', which in the most optimistic version included the birth of 'Modern Science'. For this view the Common Man, who in this respect embraces not a few who write on historical themes, is hardly to blame. The myth was created by men living at the time of, and shortly after, the period to which it refers; it was filled out, though qualified in important respects, by Jakob Burckhardt, one of the greatest historians of the nineteenth century, and it was given a 'local habitation and a name' in the first volume of the first *Cambridge Modern History*. But whereas the first edition accepted, at least in part, the myth, the *New Cambridge Modern History* opens with a warning.

It would of course be impossible, even if it lay within the author's competence, to provide a history of the myth or of its subsequent metamorphosis; fortunately this has been admirably achieved by Wallace K. Ferguson (*The Renaissance in Historical Thought*, Cambridge, Mass., 1948). Nevertheless if the present work is to make any contribution to the history of science in the Renaissance it is clearly incumbent on the author to make clear what he understands by the term. Unfortunately the difficulty of providing such a statement is greatly increased by the absence of any agreement among historians even in respect to the period to which it may apply. For whereas the Renaissance volume of the *New Cambridge Modern History* covers the years 1493-1520,

P. O. Kristeller (*The Classics and Renaissance Thought*, Cambridge, Mass., 1955) defines the Renaissance period as the three centuries starting about 1300. The issue has been further confused by medievalists who, seizing upon the linguistic aspect of the term, use it categorically in such expressions as the 'Carolingian Renaissance' (see below, p. 9), and by implication in many other cases to be referred to later.

With the idea of *re*-birth has also been linked that of novelty, with which the former is so far from being necessarily connected as to constitute, at least formally, a contrast: for the notion of *re*-birth involves an element of backward-looking entirely absent from that of novelty. Superficially this appears to involve a confusion of terms. But the conception of *absolute* novelty arose but slowly— hardly till late in the sixteenth century. Discovery almost in- variably meant *re*-discovery; since it was an essential part of that world-view which was perhaps the most characteristic legacy of the Middle Ages (even of that 'innovator', Roger Bacon, con- demned by his Order for addiction to 'novelties'[1]) that all wisdom had been revealed 'in the beginning' only to be 'lost' through sin and 'deviation'. In a sense this is true, though not quite in the way that men regarded it at that time; for it is difficult on the one hand to find any branch of human knowledge which is not at least referred to by Aristotle, whereas the one activity of which we find little trace—experimental science—makes, as I shall try to demon- strate, but a poor showing in any of the 'renaissances'. Hints and promptings there are somewhere or other throughout probably the whole of recorded history, but there is nothing like a uniform climate of opinion—at least so it seems to me—until near the end of the sixteenth century. With novelty then the Renaissance has no necessary connection; but neither must the fact that its dominant character was a 'rebirth'—if indeed it was— be held to rule out the possibility. A rebirth may be a condition for the subsequent emergence of novelty: at least the French have a word for it—*reculer pour mieux sauter*.

A further difficulty is that no useful discussion of the problem of the Renaissance can be carried on without raising some of the fundamental issues of historiography—to what extent for instance, in the light of history, there can be anything 'new' under the sun. The task then must be undertaken not at such length as to con-

[1] S. Easton, *Roger Bacon*, Oxford, 1952, *passim*.

stitute an examination of the whole question of Renaissance but only as a clarification of its use in the present context—*Science and the Renaissance*.

Our discussion may well begin by removing the main barrier to understanding—the original renaissance myth. Its genesis is unambiguously expressed in the dedication to Leo X of his *De Arte Cabalistica* by Ioannes Reuchlin (No. 565) in 1517: 'Italian philosophy was killed innumerable years ago by the deafening barking of sophists, buried for so long in shadows and deep night, until by favour of the gods the Sun of every kind of good learning, the most famous Lorenzo de'Medici, your father, and offspring of great Cosimo, rose up as ruler of the state of Florence. . . .' Of course this was high-flown nonsense; and a scholar of the range and experience of Reuchlin must have known that it was nonsense; but the kind of extravagance that is found in dedications is usually a distortion of fact rather than arbitrary fiction. Reuchlin would not have written this had it borne no relation to the facts. The facts were of course that nearly two centuries before Lorenzo il Magnifico was born (1448) the 'Sophists' had included Dante, Petrarca, and Boccaccio, while the 'shades and night' witnessed the spread of Greek studies from the time of the arrival in Italy of Manuel Chrysoloras (1396). Nevertheless it was true that only under 'great Cosimo' and to an even greater extent under his grandson, Lorenzo (d. 1492) did the patronage of arts and letters reach a level previously unparalleled in the West. But the tradition of 'darkness' having been started even before the time of Reuchlin and broadcast by that great European, Desiderius Erasmus, it became a fixation in the minds of scholars of all disciplines. Thus Georg Tanstetter introduces his edition of the astronomer Georg Peurbach in 1514 with the claim that he had 'restored' astronomy after it had almost disappeared;[1] Gelenius in his edition (No. 538) of the medical writer Theodorus Priscianus refers to the 'collapse' of the Latin tongue, ignoring or being ignorant of the fact that the 'barbarians' of the eleventh and twelfth centuries wrote with such clarity and elegance as easily to deceive an inexperienced reader into the belief that their works were the product of the fifteenth century. Characteristically the

---

[1] Peurbach's pupil, Regiomontanus, used a similar expression about his own 'mission' in 1471. See D. B. Durand, *The Vienna-Klosterneuburg Map Corpus*, Leiden, 1952, p. 38.

myth appears in France nearly half a century later. Here in the dedication of his *De Abditis Rerum Causis* (1548, No. 251) to Henry II, Jean Fernel anticipates something like the modern version. Since this is the expression of opinion by a physician of high standing, educated in the best traditions of French renaissance humanism, and moreover is not rendered suspect by any associated flattery, it is worth while quoting rather fully. After emphasising that progress would be possible only if men were willing to go beyond previous thinkers he continues: 'And so that I may speak candidly about this our age, the discipline and arts which had been buried nearly twelve hundred years ago, and which had really fallen into a state of complete extinction, have now completely revived and regained, I might even say surpassed, their former splendour, so that this age need envy that former time in hardly any respect. Rhetoric and the greatest eloquence now flourish everywhere; every kind of philosophy is cultivated; musicians, geometers, craftsmen, painters, architects, sculptors, and other artificers have so to say deployed in a line of battle of the mind so that all of them have displayed their several arts by distinguished and magnificent works, which yield nothing to those more ancient ones whose fame is on everyone's lips.' And so on in the same vein, naming not only works of art and letters but military engines, fire bombs, printing (a century old!) and the discovery of new lands. One could hardly find a better blazon of the Renaissance myth both in its absurd exaggeration of the utter desolation of the whole period from the decline of the Roman Empire to the 'present day' whenever that might be, and on the other hand the *feeling* of a new spirit abroad and of enterprises surpassing those of the ancients.

So much for the establishment of a myth of the Renaissance promulgated late in the fifteenth century and thereafter at intervals during the sixteenth century, the times varying according to the nationality of the promulgator: the essence of the myth being that the *arts* [1] had lain in Stygian darkness for roughly a millenium and had been revived in the *second* half of the fifteenth century. I have emphasised the restriction of the judgment to the *Arts* which at that time would include the art of literature and also

---

[1] Cf. the memorial to Giotto (d. 1336!) in the Duomo at Florence which bears the inscription 'Ille ego sum per quem pictura extincta reuixit.' For the peculiar case of the Fine Arts, see below, p. 20.

what we should call the 'sciences'. There was in general no implication of a historical discontinuity; in only one context [1] earlier than the seventeenth century is there a reference to a 'middle period'. The division of *History* into three periods—Ancient, Medieval, and Modern—began only with Christoph Keller, who introduced these terms definitely in three separate volumes published 1685-96. The volume on the Middle Ages (*Medium Aevum*) extended from the time of Constantine the Great (fourth century) to the Fall of Constantinople (1453). This period he continued to regard as one of cultural darkness which was followed by the dawn of a new age. Keller was a pioneer in the writing of *textbooks*, and the fact that successive editions continued to be called for until 1735 is evidence of the wide acceptance of his schematisation. This depreciation of the Middle Ages found an echo in eighteenth-century rationalism which, however, gave an extra turn to the screw. For not only the Middle Ages, though admittedly the most ineffectual of all, but every previous age was regarded by the self-complacent optimists of the Enlightenment as being merely a 'preparation' for the 'Age of Reason' in which all wrongs would be righted in the Parliament of Mankind. This particular attitude has little enough relevance to our problem: it is mentioned on the ground that it was probably from such comparatively recent denunciations that the author of the first comprehensive group of studies on the growth of science, William Whewell, drew his inspiration for the following remarkable pronouncement: 'We have now to consider more especially a long and barren period, which intervened between the scientific activity of ancient Greece and that of modern Europe; and which we may, therefore, call the Stationary Period of Science. . . . We must endeavour to delineate the character of the Stationary Period, and as far as possible, to analyse its defects and errors; and thus to obtain some knowledge of the causes of its barrenness and darkness,' but though Whewell referred in passing to 'the revival of letters' he did not suggest any more than had Keller that there was any Renaissance *Period*.

---

[1] G. Andrea in a preface to an edition of Apuleius (Rome, 1469) referred to Nicholas of Cues as 'vir ipse . . . historias idem omnes non priscas modo sed medie tempestatis tum veteres tum recenteriores . . . usque ad nostra tempora memoria retinebat.' Quoted by Ferguson, *op. cit.* p. 74. But as Nicholas died only five years before this was written the sense is hardly that of today.

A*

This final stroke, Ferguson believes, was effected by Michelet who so far disengaged the idea from the literary and artistic flowering in Italy as to regard the *sixteenth* century as that of the Renaissance which 'started from nothingness. It was the heroic outburst of an immense will' (*Histoire de France, 1832-1862*, VII, 13, quoted by Ferguson, *op. cit.* p. 177). This disengagement was important, but it introduced a new source of confusion in applying a term, previously restricted to a narrower field, to a much more fundamental notion; also Michelet's interpretation suffered from a too restricted concern with the history of France.

The work which finally established the concept of *Renaissance*, and generated all subsequent thought both positively and negatively, was of course Burckhardt's *Die Cultur der Renaissance in Italien* (1860). As in the case of Michelet the strength and weakness of this monumental study were that it greatly enlarged the connotation of the term, introducing such subsidiary concepts as *The State as a Work of Art, The Development of the Individual, The Discovery of the World and of Man*, of great significance in so far as they represent the facts but having no necessary connection with *The Revival of Antiquity*—another of the major divisions of the essay. Of special interest also was the demonstration that Italy was the *fons et origo* of what was now revealed rather as a cultural epoch than as a division of European history. That his disciples made of the Italian culture a paradigm of 'the' Renaissance was hardly to be laid to Burckhardt's door. In any case this thoroughgoing interpretation of the term led to an enormous amount of revaluation of the history of the time-span which Burckhardt's period comprised. One major consequence of this was what Ferguson calls the 'revolt of the medievalists', which in its extreme form proclaimed the Renaissance to be a mere continuation (and for some a mere decadence) of the Middle Ages. The result of this *antithesis* has been most salutary, and not least for the history of science, in which the critical importance of certain medieval movements of thought has only recently been at all widely realised. But although the shallowness of the original conception of the rebirth of the sciences has been thus demonstrated, a new element of confusion has been introduced by the postulation of a series of earlier renaissances. Burckhardt himself admitted the omission of any discussion of the progress of science in which he felt himself too little instructed. Economic factors, in which it is far from evident that any 'rebirth' occurred during his period,[1] he tacitly ignored: in this, since he called his work *Cultur* he may have been justified; but, since the English versions use as equivalent the word 'Civilisation', the omission is one to which attention now needs to be drawn.

One of the results of this intensive research into the origins and varieties of *Renaissance* in history was naturally to raise the question whether there was any period at all to which such a term could usefully be applied; and, if so, whether there was more than one. The question could also be, and in fact was, raised at the deeper level as to whether the concept of *Period* itself was a mere fiction of the mind and generated more problems than it solved. The first set of questions was peremptorily disposed of by several medievalists by referring to the period to which Burckhardt had addressed himself as the 'so-called Renaissance', several adding the rider that if there had been one there had been many. The second question could not be disposed of so easily. An answer which goes beyond a mere expression of opinion must be based on a thorough examination of the nature of history: it is not a historical question at all, but a philosophical question; though historians, like 'scientists' (I refrain from raising another philosophical question, whether 'History is a science—no less no more'), are chary of admitting that the solution of any problem relating to history may lie outside the categories of their own discipline. Since these questions can certainly not be solved by mere appeal to the facts it is unlikely that any final answer will ever be given. But what can not be tolerated is that *interpretation* of historical data referring to the fifteenth, sixteenth, and seventeenth centuries should be based on a confused prejudgment implicit in the mind of the interpreter, but to which the reader is given no access. It will therefore be necessary to devote the rest of this chapter to a statement of such conclusions as I have been able to come to, and to deploy such assumptions as I have felt myself justified in making. It is unlikely that the opinions of a student of such a 'fringe' subject as mine can be anything but one-sided; hence it is not suggested that these conclusions constitute a 'solution' of the Renaissance problem. But in the absence of such an explicit statement of belief any judgments

---

[1] For an instructive case of 'modern' manipulation of the factors of production see D. Herlihy, *Pisa in the Early Renaissance*, New Haven, Conn. 1958.

about *Science and the Renaissance* might be little short of meaningless.

I take first the question of periodisation. The easy solution is of course to deny absolutely that the concept of a historic period is anything more than a fiction. If this is so then there is no more justification for introducing terms like 'Renaissance' or 'Middle Ages' than for chopping the narrative up into centuries. Both such modes of division might be used as pedagogic convenience but both would be equally arbitrary. The argument for this radical view is that the scroll of history is without break or seam, a continuum upon which the mind imposes its own categories. As an *aspect* of historical knowledge this is undoubtedly true; but if pressed to its ultimate conclusion it recoils upon the heads of those who embrace it. For the scroll of history is not given as a continuum, but in the form of discrete documents and oral testimonies. Until the category of causality is impressed upon these units of experience there is no history but merely annals. But if the continuity is not given, neither is causality—except by the 'mind' in the form, as Hume put it, of 'custom and a felt necessitation'. It would of course take far too long to attempt to analyse the implications of this view: but it is unnecessary. All that I am maintaining is that since history has in any case to be *constructed*, the decision as to whether the course of history is uniform or not can not be made *a priori* but must be judged on the historical evidence. Though the concept of 'history' implies continuity, it does not imply uniformity. The flight of an aeroplane is normally continuous, but non-uniform: at times it is climbing, at times descending; so it may be in the course of human history. The fact that it is impossible in the last analysis to decide at what instant a climb changes to straight and level flight can not be accepted as evidence against the *fact* that the latter state succeeded the former. The same principle applies to the very much slower changes which have been discovered in human institutions. It must, however, be admitted that the revolt against periodisation and the attribution of special characters to periods, such as the 'Renaissance', the 'Age of Reason' and the like, has had the salutary effect of bringing these categories under a much more critical scrutiny, which has revealed their hasty and misleading application: they have been based upon a much too narrow view of the evidence. This re-examination has in no case been more searching or more profitable than in the case of the *Renaissance*. And this brings us to the second question: If it be granted that time-lapses of *relative* homogeneity in the structure and attitudes of societies are to be found of such a magnitude as to justify division of the whole course of history into *periods*, what is the evidence justifying the postulation of such a period called the 'Renaissance'?

In regard to this question I can do no more than state my own conclusions, together with such meagre justification as space permits. If they are ill-founded, then a great deal of the broader interpretation tentatively offered in the following chapters will collapse. Fortunately the survey of the material will not be similarly undermined. But ill or well founded, it is in my view essential that these conclusions should be stated, since they embody the assumptions upon which the interpretation has been based.

My main conclusion can be briefly stated: namely, that a recognisable period can be delimited in which occurred that transvaluation of values which produced the ultimate gulf between the world of Roger Bacon and that of Francis Bacon, the aims and atmosphere of the Council of Constance and those of the Congress of Vienna; between the intellectual climate in which the *Summae* of St. Thomas Aquinas were written and that which saw the publication of the *Principia* of Isaac Newton. Doubtless I shall be told that 'all ages are ages of transition'; of course they are. But that does not preclude the possibility that some ages are more transitional than others! And such an age I take the 'so-called Renaissance' to have been. For the traditional recognition of a period marked by exceptionally radical revaluations, despite the weighty arguments recently ranged against it, there seems to me to be conclusive evidence. But that this period should have been called a 're-birth' was the source of such a tissue of confusions as historians of 'fringe' subjects, as I have already suggested, have hardly yet escaped from. A rebirth of what? When? Where? There would probably now be no disagreement with the view that there occurred at the Court of Charlemagne (*c.* 800) the first revival of a recognition of the importance of secular literacy. Simultaneously in Baghdad there was a probably much more important awakening of the Moslems under the Abbasid Caliphate to the immense potential wealth of knowledge in the Greek manuscripts, which had been preserved by the Nestorian Church as it was driven eastward under successive persecutions.

When Toledo was reconquered from the Saracens the translation of these Arabic versions into Latin by devoted scholars from many Western countries ushered in what was probably the most significant rebirth of learning of which there is any evidence. But one has only to compare the style of, say, John of Salisbury or Thierry of Chartres with the best writers *outside Italy* during the subsequent three centuries to realise that a rebirth of *learning* is no guarantee of that of *letters*. The mention of Chartres is not of course casual: in the schools attached to that famous cathedral there was the brightest hope of a *general* rebirth embodying the best that the Roman writers could offer together with an awakened curiosity concerning the natural world. But the first universities came into being at Bologna (with a bias towards Law and Medicine) and Paris, where Theology and 'philosophy' gained the ascendency over the other disciplines embodied in the Roman conception of 'Liberal Arts'.

It is probably safe to say that, although ultimately of varying degrees of importance to the progress of 'science' in the Renaissance, the 'rebirths' so far reviewed had little or no connection with the traditional 'Renaissance', which was in its beginnings a purely Italian affair. Southern Italy had always been much nearer to Greek ways than the rest of Western Europe. About thirty years before Gerard of Cremona in Toledo translated the *Arabic* version of the *Almagest* into Latin the Greek-speaking 'admiral' [1] Eugenius had in the Norman kingdom of Sicily helped the self-styled translator, Henry 'Aristippus' with a *Greek* codex of the same work brought as a gift from the Byzantine Emperor, Manuel, to the King of Sicily. How much the course of European learning might have been changed had not this outpost of Greek language and thought passed not many years later into the hands of the German House of Hohenstaufen it is impossible to say. But in the event, when Petrarca, who is usually reckoned to be the man chiefly responsible for the return to the Latin style of the great Romans, regretted his ignorance of the Greek authors so much admired and cultivated by Cicero there was no one to teach him the language. For such a teacher Italy had to wait the coming of Manuel Chrysoloras in the train of the Emperor

---

[1] For the origin of the name 'admiral' (Arabic 'emir') and of the association of the office with Greek Christian families, see E. Jamison, *Admiral Eugenius of Sicily*, London, 1957.

Manuel Paleologos in 1396.[1] It was, however, only as a consequence of the Council of Florence (1439) that enthusiasm for
Greek learning spread rapidly throughout Italy. This was mediated mainly by Gemistos Plethon,[2] whose charm and eloquence
initiated a study of the authentic Plato, previously known only
at second hand. Greek manuscripts also entered Italy at this
time—largely by the good offices of the Greek (Cardinal)
Bessarion whose patronage was so much valued by Georg
Peurbach and Regiomontanus (p. 13). It is significant that all
this happened about thirty years before the sack of Constantinople
(1453) drove numerous Greeks with further manuscripts to
Italy, thereby accelerating the work already well begun.

The outcome of these events was the 'Humanistic Renaissance'
which spread throughout Italy. Of its subsequent dissemination
throughout Europe it is impossible to give in any reasonable
compass an account which would not be highly misleading. It can,
however, be said without reservation that a corresponding movement in other countries was invariably stimulated by visiting
Italian scholars or by the return to those countries of men who
had sought inspiration and teaching in Italy itself. Occasionally
the route was less direct, as for instance when Beatus Rhenanus
took back to south Germany the fruits of the teaching of Lefèvre
d'Etaples at Paris, who had himself studied in Italy. It may also be
said that in few cases was the new (linguistic) learning received
without opposition; though the quarters from which this opposition came were not uniform in character. The relative slowness
with which general acceptance came may be judged from the
reference by Andreas Laguna, a scholar of some standing, to the
'recent rebirth of polite disciplines at Paris' (No. 373). This was in
1548: Francis I had, on the advice of Guillaume Budé but
contrary to the wishes of the theologians of the Sorbonne, founded
Chairs of Latin, Greek, and Mathematics in 1530.

Something must now be said about that much abused word

---

[1] The development of a new conception of Greek studies in Byzantium (consequent
on the stagnation of education during the sixty years following the taking of the city
by the Franks, 1201-4) when Greek was taught virtually as a dead language is described in Bolgar, *The Classical Heritage and its Beneficiaries*, Cambridge, 1954, pp. 82 f.
[2] Paradoxically Plethon was the master of Chrysoloras who had blazed the trail
fifty years earlier—a paradox explained by the fact that Plethon was now nearly
ninety years old. This may be the reason for Bolgar's slip in stating that it was to the
Council of Constance (1414) that Plethon came.

'humanism'. In relation to the Italian Renaissance and its beneficiaries there was in its connotation no suggestion of an *opposition*
of the 'human' to the 'divine': this is a modern perversion which
can only be regretted as a new source of confusion. Those who
begat the original idea of 'humanism'—Petrarca, Guarino,
Filfelfo, Marsilio Ficino, for instance—and those who carried it
abroad—Reuchlin, Lefèvre, Erasmus—were men of the utmost
piety. Its arrival in England at the turn of the century was marked
by the lectures of John Colet on the Pauline Epistles and those of
William Grocin entitled *De Ecclesiastica Hierarchia*. According to
Kristeller [1] the word 'Humanismus' was first used to designate a
form of education emphasising the study of the classical languages
only in 1808 (F. J. Niethammer). The nearest approach to a
similar usage in the centuries of its birth was the colloquial term
Humanista current in the Italian universities in the early sixteenth
century: this name for the teacher or student of classical grammar
and 'rhetoric' corresponded to the long established custom of
referring to the teachers of other disciplines as 'artista', 'civilista',
etc. The association of 'humanitas' with the new emphasis in the
'arts' may have been a reference to Cicero's use of the expression
'studia humanitatis' for a similar discipline. At most, then, the
the Italian Renaissance was 'humanistic' in its explicit recognition
of an immensely rich literature in Latin and Greek (the latter
being especially a 'new discovery', though the former was not
without its 'novelties', such as Lucretius and Sallust) which
demanded study for the better understanding of the power of
the human spirit. 'Humanism' not unnaturally acquired overtones
of the 'modern' emphasis on the cult of the individual character
which is present in the writings of Petrarcha and achieved prominence in those of Coluccio Salutati. Kristeller's view is that this
association is non-essential, and that the further extension to
embrace Burckhardt's characterisation of the Renaissance as
embodying the cult of the *outstanding* individual is wholly un-
justifiable.

Such, I conclude, was one of the dominant characteristics of
the so-called Renaissance—it was a re-birth of classical *literature*;
or rather as will appear hereafter a new evaluation of that
literature by men who, though they felt themselves in the closest

[1] *The Classics and Renaissance Thought*, Cambridge, Mass., 1955, pp. 8 f.; also *Studies in Renaissance Thought and Letters*, Rome, 1956, pp. 11-15.

sympathy with the ideas expressed in it, saw it from the point of view of their own time. But though a dominant characteristic it was not the only one. In the decade following the Council of Florence (1439) there appeared successive instalments of two books—Leonardo Bruni's *History of the Florentine People*, and the slightly later *History from the Decline of the Roman Empire* by Flavio Biondo. Though written by 'state officials' and consequently coloured by contemporary political philosophy, these works set a new standard in historiography—legendary origins are rejected; sources critically examined; and evidence weighed. Owing to the date at which these works appeared it is difficult to decide whether they were the by-products of the new passion for seeking out and critically evaluating classical sources, or whether they in turn played the chief part in establishing this critical outlook;[1] nor is it necessary, since for our purpose all that needs to be established is the appearance during the Renaissance of a new standard of criticism of documents of any kind. For this, I believe, was the most important influence of the humanistic renaissance on the subsequent progress of science. In this connection it had the most immediate effects in Astronomy in the attempt made by Georg Peurbach and Ioannes Mueller (generally referred to as Regiomontanus from his birthplace at Königsberg in south Germany) to establish a critical text of Ptolemy's *Almagest* (see below, p. 108 and No. 558). Not only had these Germans studied in Italy as the humanistic Renaissance was approaching its climax there, but they acknowledged the patronage of Cardinal Bessarion, who put them in the way of obtaining *Greek* manuscripts. Other examples will be provided in their proper places, and will show, especially in regard to medicine, that the influence was not always for good since energy was diverted to the task of exposing linguistic errors in the texts which would have been better employed in the direct study of nature. The importance of a critical estimate of witnesses and their reports is shown by the persistence of legends such as that of the 'Barnacle Goose' (p. 181) for a century after historians had shown the way to a proper scepticism. But here, as in the cult

---

[1] That the two functions were admirably united in Bruni is beautifully expressed by his epitaph in Sta. Croce, Florence:

Postquam Leonardus e vita migrauit
Historia luget, Eloquentia muta est
Ferturque Musas tum Graecas tum Latinas
Lacrimas tenere non potuisse.

of classical literature, the new ways were not readily followed. Half a century after Biondo, Hector Boece had no compunction in basing his *Historia Scotorum* on an apocryphal origin of this people; and obversely Polydore Vergil's history of the House of Tudor was at first looked upon with considerable disfavour. Vergil was an Italian, Boece had been no nearer the fountainhead than Paris.

The third dominant characteristic of the traditional Renaissance —one most powerfully stressed by Burckhardt—was the concept of the cult of excellence in every human enterprise—a concept finely illustrated in his famous character-sketch of Leon Battista Alberti (quoted below, p. 17). Of this concept I shall say no more here, since the Art of Statecraft (of which the classic exposition is held to be Niccolò Machiavelli's *Prince*) will be touched upon in connection with the political relations of the sixteenth century.

In respect of the fine arts the men of the Renaissance looked back upon Giotto as the one who having 'abandoned the crudeness of the Greeks' [*sc.* Byzantine influences] 'introduced the new art' [*sc.* of painting]. Though this contains an important element of truth, it does not do justice to the extraordinarily complex course of the 'renaissance' of art. That Ghiberti's [1] words represent the usual *quattrocento* over-simplification is revealed by a striking passage from the *Chronicle of Monte Cassino* written by Leo of Ostia more than two centuries before Giotto (d. 1336). After mentioning that the abbot Desederius had 'sent envoys to Constantinople to hire artists who were experts in the art of laying mosaics and pavements', and that as a result of their work 'one would believe that the figures were alive and that in the marble of the pavement flowers of every colour bloomed in wonderful variety', Leo goes on to say: 'Since *magistra Latinitas* had left uncultivated the practice of these arts for more than five hundred years . . . the abbot in his wisdom decided that a great number of young monks in the monastery should be thoroughly initiated into these arts in order that their knowledge might not again be lost in Italy' (*Doc. Hist. Art*, p. 13). Here is quite another view of the 'Greeks', who themselves appear as the 'restorers' of a lost art. Note especially the 'liveliness' of the figures and flowers: within the

---

[1] Lorenzo Ghiberti, quoted in *Documentary History of Art*, Vol. I, New York, 1957, p. 153.

formal arrangement and pervasive symbolism of Byzantine composition the details reveal a degree of naturalism based on observation seldom to be achieved by the 'Latins' until the *quattrocento*. Only in the delightful panel of St Francis preaching to the birds does Giotto display such naturalism, and the lively poses of the birds have much in common with those (V-2) in the so-called Mausoleum of Galla Placidia at Ravenna. In other respects—a closer approximation to true perspective, the creation of adequate space, and more 'personality' and variety of physical expression in the figures—all achievements traditionally associated with the Renaissance—it is less to Giotto that we look than to the frescos by Masolino and Masaccio in the Brancacci Chapel of Sta. Maria del Carmine in Florence.

If Ghiberti's judgment has thus been shown to be over-simplified in respect of time, it must also be held as parochial. For in drawing attention to the growth of naturalism as the Humanistic Renaissance approached and passed its climax in Italy, enthusiasts bent on regarding this movement as the re-birth of everything modern ignore the early fourteenth century sculptured foliage in England (see below, p. 78) and the monumental figures of the same period at Bamberg, Naumburg, and elsewhere. And naturalism in Italy began, though it did not end, with the copying of the work of Flemish artists associated with the Court of Burgundy.

CHAPTER II

INDIVIDUAL AND COSMOS

IF there is any characteristic by which the Renaissance can be recognised it is I believe in the changing conception of Man's relation to the Cosmos. I therefore make no apology for borrowing Ernst Cassirer's title and applying it to the present chapter, even though it is here to be put to uses rather different from his. Nor, in the examination of the background of science in the Renaissance, shall I seek to justify the precedence given to Individuals in relation to States; for as I have already indicated I accept Burckhardt's implication that in the contemporary consciousness of the Renaissance, Men were more important than Institutions. This does not, however, imply the acceptance of Burckhardt's further thesis of the emergence of an entirely new type of personality—'Renaissance Man'. A correlate to the revaluation of the Individual was the gradual acceptance in the absence of adequate evidence—indeed almost in defiance of the evidence—that the cosmos is unimaginably larger and richer than had hitherto been dreamed of, and that there is no sufficient reason for regarding the earth as its pivot and centre.[1] In this respect the fourteenth century 'barbarians'—notably Nicole Oresme—had been more *scientific* than Copernicus: they had raised the question 'utrum terra semper quiescat in medio mundi' and had either decided it in the affirmative or suspended judgment, not, as is sometimes suggested, at the behest of disapproving theologians, but on the grounds of the inconclusiveness of the evidence. The uncanonical hymn to the sun in which by contrast Copernicus indulged (No. 171), sprang from no newly observed facts, nor was the sun's pre-eminence in any way 'proved' by the application of a 'new' hypothesis to the old ones: it was an ex-

[1] There was never in medieval cosmology any suggestion that the earth was other than the *lowest* body in the scale of value; for it was furthest from the *primum movens* and the 'Divine' in both Aristotelian and Christian sense. Cf. A. O. Lovejoy, *The Great Chain of Being*, Cambridge, Mass., 1936, pp. 101-2.

pression of a new *philosophy*. It was a phase—perhaps the most important phase— in a 'naissance' of ideas: not a *re*-naissance since, if Plutarch's testimony may be accepted, the only Greek who had gone as far as Copernicus was frowned on.[1] It is more difficult to decide to what extent the new challenge put forward by Copernicus was related to the renaissance of letters; for though it was published only in 1543, the idea was conceived, and even privately circulated, at latest by 1509; and significantly after many years study of law, medicine and astronomy in Italy. We shall return to this question (*infra.* p. 111). It has been touched on here to illustrate the view—which has still to be substantiated—that the key to the scientific 'renaissance' of the sixteenth century is ultimately philosophical: for it concerns the emergence of a new conception of the relation of the human individual to the cosmos.

As an approach to this problem we can hardly do better than try to recapture the 'feel' of the period by sharing something of the lives of one or two of those prodigal individuals who, taking all knowledge for their province, saw old problems in a new light and prepared the ground for those who later actually created the sciences in something like their modern form.

Burckhardt's tribute to Leon Battista Alberti is of course a classic: 'In all by which praise is won, Leon Battista Alberti was from his childhood the first. Of his various gymnastic feats and exercises we read with astonishment how, with his feet together, he could spring over a man's head, in the cathedral he threw a coin in the air till it was heard to ring against the distant roof; how the wildest horses trembled under him. In three things he desired to appear faultless to others, in walking, in riding, and in speaking. He learned music without a master, and yet his compositions were admired by professional judges. Under the pressure of poverty, he studied both civil and canonical laws for many years, till exhaustion brought on a severe illness. In his twenty-fourth year finding his memory for words weakened, but his sense of facts unimpaired, he set to work at physics and mathematics. And all the while he acquired every sort of accomplishment and dexterity, cross-examining artists, scholars and artisans of all descriptions, down to the cobblers, about the secrets and pecul-iarities of their craft. Painting and modelling he practised by

[1] *De Facie in Orbe Lunae*, quoted by T. L. Heath, *Greek Astronomy*, London, 1932, p. 108.

B

the way, and especially excelled in admirable likenesses from memory. Great admiration was excited by his mysterious "camera obscura",[1] in which he showed at one time the stars and the moon rising over rocky hills, at another wide landscapes with mountains and gulfs receding into dim perspective, and with fleets advancing on the waters in shade or sunshine. And that which others created he welcomed joyfully, and held every human achievement which followed the laws of beauty for something almost divine. To all this must be added his literary works, first of all those on art, which are landmarks and authorities of the first order for the Renaissance of Form, especially in architecture; then his Latin prose writings—novels and other works—of which some have been taken for productions of antiquity; his elegies, eclogues, and humorous dinner-speeches. He also wrote an Italian treatise on domestic life in four books; and even a funeral oration on his dog. His serious and witty sayings were thought worth collecting, and specimens of them, many columns long, are quoted in his biography. And all that he had and knew he imparted, as rich natures always do, without the least reserve, giving away his chief discoveries for nothing. But the deepest spring of his nature has yet to be spoken of—the sympathetic intensity with which he entered into the whole life around him. At the sight of noble trees and waving corn-fields he shed tears; handsome and dignified old men he honoured as "a delight of nature" and could never look at them enough. Perfectly formed animals won his goodwill as being specially favoured by nature; and more than once, when he was ill, the sight of a beautiful landscape cured him. No wonder that those who saw him in this close and mysterious communion with the world ascribed to him the gift of prophecy. He was said to have foretold a bloody catastrophe in the family of Este, the fate of Florence, and the death of the Popes years before they happened, and to be able to read into the countenances and the hearts of men. It need not be added that an iron will pervaded and sustained his whole personality; like all the great men of the Renaissance, he said, "Men can do all things if they will".'

---

[1] There is reason to believe that this more nearly resembled a 'peep-show' than the modern 'camera obscura' first unambiguously described by Giambattista della Porta about a century later. See (Leon Baptista Alberti) *On Painting*, trans. edn., J. R. Spencer, Yale, pp. 51, 57. The idea may however be traced back at least to ibn al-Haitham. See H. and A. Gernsheim, *History of Photography*, London, 1955.

Although this passage is so well known, it has been quoted in full so that we may have before us what seems to me so vital in any study of the Renaissance—the universality of its greatest representatives and, what is less taken note of, perhaps through some unconscious guilt-complex for our failure to conserve them, the existence of 'virtues', in these men, which we have lost. But even Burckhardt's catalogue of virtues misses something in this, perhaps the most attractive, hero of the Renaissance—the humanity with which not every 'humanist' was endowed. This has recently been put in a very clear light by a brief study of his little known and—for most of those even well acquainted with him— quite unexpected work, the *Vita S. Potiti*,[1] first published in 1954. Sometime between 1432 and March 1434 Alberti wrote the first, and as it turned out the last, of a projected series of the lives of the saints. Faced with the task of writing 'history' on the basis of legends for which there was no documentary evidence and in which as a 'humanist' he could not believe, it is not surprising that the 'series' ended where it began. But it is the resolution of the problem within the sole member of the series that is so extraordinarily interesting. Alberti not only makes no attempt to authenticate the legends, but actually distorts them in such a way as to cast light on the new approach to Individual and Cosmos of which he was so notable a leader. The speeches in which the saint and the pagan emperor blazon forth their incompatible faiths become components of a Thucydidean dramatisation; and in so doing achieve a much higher level of realisation than in the crude dichotomy of Good and Evil of the legends. Here is no longer a blood-lusting beast opposed to the mouthpiece of Divine vengeance, but a human being who can not yield without losing his all. Fable has become tragedy; a problem of ethics has been made to serve the purposes of Art. There is, of course, both gain and loss: righteous wrath has given place to *caritas*, the Old Covenant to the New; but the parable of the Rich Young Man [2] will have to be told again in Wittenberg before a new resting point can be reached for humanity.

This universal genius Burckhardt has crystallised in a phrase: He 'held every human achievement which followed the laws of

[1] Guido A. Guarino, 'Leon Battista Alberti's Vita S. Potiti', *Renaissance News*, Vol. III, No. 2, p. 86.
[2] Mark x. 17.

beauty for something almost divine'. The seeking out and formulation of these 'laws of beauty' constituted his contribution, not only to art but to science. In his *De Re Aedificatoria* (No. 14) occurs the oft quoted passage 'Architectum ego hunc fore constituam qui certa admirabilique ratione et via tum et opere absoluere didicerit quecunque ex ponderum motu corporum que compactione et coagmentatione dignissimis hominum usibus bellissime commodentur' (' I shall hold him to be an architect who has learnt to determine by means of accurate theory, and to complete by practice, all those things which, as a result of the movement of weights and the juxtaposition and conjoining of bodies, may most aptly serve the noblest uses of men'). But whereas the work on architecture has the more direct relation to a particular science (mechanics) it is his treatise on painting that throws out ideas more significant for our present problem. For the transfer of the 'work of nature' to the two dimensional counterpart, which is often the only possible 'work of man', he devised the 'perspective net' and examined the geometrical theory underlying it. But again, for us, his special significance lies not so much in his establishment of the theory of linear perspective as in the achievement of what might be called *freedom* and *vitality*. In respect of the former he derided the practice, common enough in the preceding centuries, of painting Man inside a small building as in a closed casket. To attain this liberation he describes how to build up 'free space' by the variation of light and colour—distance is to be shown by an increased haziness, since light being 'borne by rays' becomes 'tired' by passing through humid air: here he shows himself closer to nature than do the 'naturalistic' Flemish masters (see below, p. 78). But he goes further:—'It would be useful to isolate each bone of the animal, on this add its muscle, then clothe all with its flesh.' As the former device *constructs* 'free space' so the latter *reveals* the 'form' of the living creature. Had Vesalius read this when he planned his *Fabrica*, displaying the 'living' body from the supporting skeleton outwards ? (See No. 709 and below, p. 228.)

In the *practice* of these canons Alberti had to some extent been anticipated! Giotto had begun the liberation of groups of human figures from the 'casket' (e.g. in the *Death of St. Francis*; to a greater extent in the exterior architectural setting of the *Salome*;[1]

[1] M. Kline, *Mathematics in Western Culture*, London, 1954.

and pre-eminently in *St. Francis preaching to the Birds*. Brunelleschi's systematic measurements of ancient buildings had yielded him the key to the geometry of linear perspective; Donatello had, in his *David*, created the first free human nude since antiquity, yet one which was no mere 'copy' of a classical form;[1] Uccello had struggled with the problems of perspective as with an incubus. But in Alberti these lines of development met, were fused and evaluated[2]—man may by taste and judgment improve on nature—and, above all, attained to explicit enunciation in an ordered system of thought.

Alberti's path was crossed, probably more than once, by that of Piero della Francesca. Piero's treatise on perspective is more severely mathematical than the *Della Pittura* but it gives little hint of his conception of the art of painting. Fortunately there are extant from his hand, as is not so in Alberti's case, numerous pictures of surpassing beauty and significance. In these we can see, as in a kind of Hegelian dialectic, the thesis of the concrete scene broken by the antithesis of perspective separation, and once more synthesised by the calculated harmonies of form and colour—'of the crupper on a horse and the shoulder of a hill, the fluting of columns and the hanging folds of a dress' as Adrian Stokes exemplifies it in a deeply observed and sensitively phrased study (*Art and Science*, London, 1949, pp. 30-2). 'Thus', he observes, 'geometry is at peace with a deep-rooted organic structure, product of chromatic sense. Franchescan forms are brothers and sisters at ease within the ancestral hall of space.' And in the noble naturalism of Piero's human figures there is a timeless vitality: the labourer leaning on his mattock in the *Finding of the Three Crosses* is resting his muscles while his mind is intent on the revelation which is proceeding before his eyes; it is almost a combination of the two famous Vesalian poses of the skeleton—labour and contemplation. Also, in what is claimed to be the first picture of a scene in moonlight—*The Dream of Constantine*—the mystical *silence* of moonlight is evoked by the visual suggestion.

Since Alberti's *Della Pittura* was not *printed* until 1540 it is

---

[1] L. Olschki, *The Genius of Italy*, London, 1950.

[2] The *Della Pittura* was 'dedicated' to Brunelleschi, Donatello, Ghiberti, Luca della Robbia, and Masaccio. In regard to Giotto, as elsewhere, the influence of a parallel and somewhat earlier 'renaissance' in Byzantine art has too often been overlooked. (Cf. D. Talbot Rice, *Byzantine Art* (Pelican Books, Harmondsworth, 1954), pp. 102, 107. I am indebted to my wife for drawing my attention to this matter.)

almost impossible to determine what exactly may have been its influence on his contemporaries and early successors. Sir Kenneth Clark ('Leon Battista Alberti on Painting', *Proc. Brit. Acad.* Vol. 30, quoted by Stokes) believes that Leonardo da Vinci must have had the work at his elbow as he wrote his own more widely quoted treatise. With Leonardo the deep significance of the artists of the *quattrocento* for the subsequent development of science receives its final illumination. An attempt will be made to assess this relationship after we have considered another universal mind from an entirely different though not wholly unrelated setting.

The figure of Albrecht Dürer [1] is of particular significance to our study in that he carried forward the tradition of Alberti in Germany, but only after he was far advanced in his own development and without any direct influence from Italy. He was born in Nürnberg, whither his father had migrated from Hungary in 1471, the year in which Regiomontanus also settled there to be, as he affirmed, in close touch with the instrument makers for which the city was already famous.[2] Nürnberg, though an Imperial City (see below, p. 47) had since 1420 been entirely self-governing. Its society was markedly stratified, and the basis of its craft-guilds in metalwork was the market for decorative gold and silverware provided by the most prosperous merchant-patricians: Aeneas Sylvius was astonished at the display of gold and silverware which he saw in German houses below those of the highest rank. In respect of its craft, its social structure, and its traditions it was of course truly German. Nevertheless through the agency of a few men and by virtue of its comparative tranquillity (in comparison for instance with England and France) southern Germany had been brought so intimately in touch with the peak of Italian Humanism as to justify the description used above. Of the men who brought this about *suae aetatis facile princeps* was Ioannes Reuchlin, whose declamation of Thucydides brought from his teacher, Argyropoulos, the remark, later quoted with pride by Melanchthon, 'Hellas has flown over the Alps'. Reuchlin's activities were mainly in Tübingen, Heidelberg and Ingolstadt, but among the leading burghers of Nürnberg was

---

[1] This account is based on W. Waetzoldt, *Dürer and his times*, trans. by R. H. Boothroyd, Phaidon Press, London, 1950.

[2] There are three instruments, still extant at Cues, said to have been bought at Nürnberg by Nicholas of Cues in 1444. D. J. Price in *Hist. Tech.*, Vol. III, p. 585.

Bilibald Pirckheimer, who was perhaps Dürer's most intimate friend. His fame as a Latinist was such that when Beatus Rhenanus came to edit the Epigrams of St. Thomas More, printed by Froben, it was to Pirckheimer that he dedicated the work.

Bilibald was only the best known of a learned family; and his contemporaries in Nürnberg also included Conrad Celtis, founder of Academies somewhat resembling the Italian prototypes, the printer Koberger, Hieronymus Münzer and others. These men were mainly 'humanists', but with interests rather wider than those of the earlier Italians. In 1486 there appeared the famous *Nürnberg Chronicle*, composed by Hartmann Schedel, in which was evident the influence of the more critical historiography recently developed in Italy and here applied to the origin of a city. In addition there were scientific craftsmen, such as Nikolaus Kratzer (who left for England in 1517 to become Astrologer-Royal to Henry VIII after a sojourn of two years in More's household), Martin Behaim, the navigator who constructed the first recorded terrestrial globe ('Weltapfel') for the City Fathers, and Etzlaub and Waldseemueller the cartographers. Two questions naturally arise from these facts—why should Nürnberg, where there was no university, be the home of such eminent scholars, and why should a city so far distant from the sea be for a time the most active centre of geographical and carto-graphical activity? Though it would be stretching the evidence too far to seek the solution to these problems in a single event—the arrival there in 1471 of Regiomontanus—he may well have provided the focus for the activities of a number of gifted individuals. It has been claimed that Regiomontanus was one of the outstanding figures of the scientific renaissance despite the fact that he neither made any original discovery nor put forward any suggestive theory. Accumulating evidence from medieval sources casts some doubt on the adequacy of his advances in observational technique to warrant the claim whose justice Thorndike in particular has questioned (see below, p. 103). What perhaps has never been sufficiently stressed is his combination of humanistic learning, persistence in the revision of the Greek text of the works of Ptolemy (Nos. 558 and 543 .d), outstanding attainments in pure mathematics (see below, p. 96) a more systematic use of instruments than anything which can be attested in the West before his day, and the exploitation of the newly invented printing press.

His name, and that of his young master, Georg Peurbach, has not escaped the eye of Bolgar in his search for the seeds of humanism in Germany (the garden where these seeds came from was not of course Nürnberg but Vienna, No. 669). Here at any rate is a possible reason for the emergence of great scholarly activity in a centre previously renowned for its metalwork. The excitation of an interest in geography may likewise have been at least mediated mainly by one man, even though the four years' stay of Regiomontanus provided the first stimulus. This was Hieronymus Münzer, whose library (see below, p. 74) contained three works presented to him by Bernhard Walther, the wealthy young patron of Regiomontanus, on the departure of the latter to Rome in in 1475. Münzer, born in 1437, had learnt his medicine at Pavia, and wrote to John II of Portugal the famous letter on the possibility of a western circumnavigation: this will be discussed in its proper place. Such may have been the individual impulses to Nürnberg's intellectual development, but the economic motive doubtless played its part. The ruling caste of the city were not for the most part scholars; nor would most craftsmen aspire to such learning. It was as merchants that the burghers had gained wealth and power. The main source of this wealth was the strategic position of Nürnberg (together with Augsburg, Ulm and Frankfurt) for the distribution to the northern countries of the oriental merchandise entering Europe mainly through Venice.[1] That they were sensitive to the need for expanding markets is suggested by the presence of Germans in the employment of Prince Henry 'the Navigator' (see below, p. 133). When the advance of the Ottoman Turks closed the trade route through Venice the merchants bankers of Nürnberg and Augsburg were quick to establish agencies at Lisbon and later at Antwerp to profit by the switch in the trade routes from the Mediterranean to the Atlantic. At the very beginning of the sixteenth century there appeared at Nürnberg two editions of a broadside describing the route from Lisbon to Calicut.[2] Moreover it is easy to exaggerate

---

[1] A lively description of the *Fondaco dei Tedeschi* (Warehouse of the Germans) now the Central Post Office near the Rialto Bridge at Venice, and at Alexandria, is given by the Ulm Minorite, Felix Fabri, in his *Evagatorium in Terram Sanctam* (1483?) an attractive summary of which is given by H. F. M. Prescott in *Once to Sinai*, London, 1957.

[2] *Den rechten Weg ausz zu faren von Liszbona gen Kallakuth*, translated as *From Lisbon to Calicut*, Univ. Minnesota Press, Minneapolis, 1956.

the static condition of inland populations in the centuries before powered transport: Münzer travelled widely towards the end of his life, and Martin Behaim made his 'apple' only after an absence of many years, some of which were spent at Lisbon as navigational adviser to John II.

Such then was the little world in which Albrecht Dürer, son of a goldsmith, opened in 1497 his own atelier from which went out not gold indeed, but the more precious products of his fertile genius—the copies pressed from the wood blocks and engraved copper plates of his portraits, biblical scenes, and fantasies. He entered passionately into every aspect of it: drew armillary spheres for Pirkheimer's new edition of Ptolemy's *Geography* from the Greek; displayed the pair of compasses in his 'problem' picture *Melencolia* as only one familiar with their use could have done; made innumerable designs for ornaments in metal; expressed in their portraits the temperaments of wealthy and powerful patrons in a manner never before approached. But for Dürer, as for the earlier Italians at whom we have glanced, this was not enough. It was good to be able to model the plastic human form upon a flat surface as it was to project the curved surface of the earth upon a sheet of paper; but better far was it to know the laws connecting the shadow with the substance. In 1512 he wrote: 'It has been instilled into us by Nature that we should wish to know much, that we may thereby perceive the real truth of all things' (Waetzoldt, *op. cit.* p. 206). This truth he believed (as did so many of his contemporaries) to have been known to the ancients and partly rediscovered by the Italians. He learnt much from Italy, as may be gauged from the greater approximation to 'vanishing perspective' in the landscapes painted after his return from that country: the confusion of planes and lack of a point of rest in his earlier views of Nürnberg have in these later works been corrected. But this was only intelligent copying; what was the *law* of it? He hoped to learn this from the Italian, Jacopo de'Barbari,[1] who had dropped hints as to the 'secret'. But in the end Dürer had to turn to the Ancients themselves—Euclid and Vitruvius—and to experiment on the drawing board with perspective lines, proportional intercepts, strange

---

[1] Jacopo's feeling for geometry is shown in his portrait of Luca Pacioli, surrounded by instruments and models. (Reproduced in G. Sarton, *Six Wings*, Bloomington, Indiana, 1957.)

cubic units of solid body; to apply his theories by means of sighting nets or glass frames. None of this was wholly original: he may have heard indirectly of Alberti's sighting net (the *Della Pittura* had not then been printed); passages from Pacioli's and Piero della Francesca's works he reproduced almost verbally. Dürer clearly knew of Leonardo's investigations, though he mentions him (and Piero) only in passing. Nevertheless, great artist as he was, he made his own use of the material. He would never have subscribed to Alberti's view that man may improve on nature: if he is less profound than the Italians he is also closer to nature, at any rate to nature concretely observed, in which he surpassed that consummate 'naturalist', Leonardo. Lovely as is the floral setting to the *Madonna of the Rocks* there is a suggestion of contrivance about the plants—it has the orderliness of a 'model rock garden' at a flower show. When Dürer on the other hand painted the *Grosse Rasenstück* he himself became a denizen of that world of grasses and familiar weeds of pasture which form the subject of the study—the trivial takes on immortality. Who before him or since has seized the quivering sensibility of the *Young Hare* as did Dürer? It is no accident that the first book to portray explicitly 'living' plants (No. 111 and below p. 190) was built upon the lovely colour sketches of his pupil, Hans Weiditz. If the famous Rhinoceros is an apparent exception it may be said, as Professor F. J. Cole has urged (Singer, *SMH*, Vol. I, pp. 337 f.) that the 'portrait' renders with a high degree of fidelity what Dürer had heard about the creature. The only criticism which might be levelled at him is that he should never have attempted to paint a real animal which he had never actually seen.

Between the birth of Alberti and the death of Dürer there was almost exactly a century: the not uncommon belief that a great part of this century was relatively barren in the history of science over- looks the fact that a period of gestation is to the casual observer one of barrenness. It is true that this century was almost devoid of any addition to the positive knowledge of the natural world: highly effective histories of science could be, indeed have been, written without mentioning a single investigator whose life span fell mainly within those limits. The only exception would probably be Leonardo, of whom our imaginary author would probably say that because none of his discoveries were 'published' he was without influence on the actual course of scientific discovery.

It is still impossible to refute this claim categorically. But, as has already been suggested, a re-orientation of observation, a reconstruction of the framework in which the idea of Nature took shape, was already far advanced before Leonardo began to record his ideas in his hardly legible mirror writing; and what he achieved was only the perfecting of this process. In what then did this reorientation and reconstruction consist? In nothing less than a technique for the reversal of emphasis from subjectivity to objectivity; nothing less than the demonstration that a science of Nature is *possible*. To say that this was effected by the solution of the problem of 'perspective' is to convey less than half the truth to anyone ignorant of the earlier struggles towards a similar end, yet perhaps not consciously conceived as such. For to numerous thinkers in the centuries immediately preceding the fifteenth, *Perspectiva* covered a great deal more than the geometrical theory which was found to give such power in forecasting the character of shadows and images formed by reflection of mirrors of every kind. From the εἴδωλα of Demokritos so vividly described by Lucretius to the *actio* of Grosseteste (No. 319) light and vision were thought to be at the heart of man's comprehension of Nature. The Italian painters of the *quattrocento* discovered that for the *representation* of Nature geometry is necessary but—equally important—not sufficient. The eye does not 'see' a uniform distribution of 'points' on a precisely calculated cone or pyramid: distant objects, even in the clearest field, are not seen merely as smaller, but as blurred, confused, even distorted. And the beauty of what is seen is heightened by the confusion and distortion of the colour values. The pictures of Piero della Francesca exhibit this; but the triple distinction of linear (really angular), areal (not aerial!), and chromatic relationships appears explicitly first in Leonardo's *Note Books*. This conception—particularly that of chromatic polyvalence in shadows—was later given precision and detailed application through the studies of the *Plein air*, and *Pointilliste* Impressionist, schools of France four centuries later; though the first impulse may have come from Constable's 'snow'. The highly significant feature of Leonardo's conception was in a sense the virtual *denial* of Alberti's theory of infinite divisibility. The 'body' felt in the paintings of Leonardo and his successors (what Berenson called the feeling of the feet being planted firmly on the ground) is related to his (Aristotelian) idea of space as 'substantial', it being actually generated by the movement of planes, etc. This was not the road subsequently taken by natural science, whose spectacular progress was the consequence of the simplification brought about by Galileo's (and Descartes') 'geometrisation' of space. Maybe the last word has not yet been said: the ghost of substantial space—the 'ether'—effectively laid by the negative result of the Michelson-Morley experiment, has been walking again. Also the problem of visual perception is still very much with us, transformed and rejuvenated by the phenomenological analysis of Husserl, despite the antiphony of half-truths announcing its 'reduction' to a mere linguistic confusion. Maybe, like the 'flower in the crannied wall', if we could grasp it 'all in all' natural philosophy would once again come to mean the philosophy of nature instead of, as in our age, merely the powerful but highly abstract category of physics. But whatever the outcome, the discovery by the *quattrocento* painters of what we are today painfully relearning, through the study of the problems raised by relativity physics, that space is not merely nonentity but a system of ordered relations to be *constructed* must rank as one of the greatest discoveries in the history of *science*. How Dürer would have delighted in these questions! He was engaged on them in the last years of his life, the *Anderweysung der Messung* (No. 217) being published the year before his death, the *De Symmetria Partuum Humanorum Corporum* (No. 218) only posthumously. But many years before his death he had achieved that other pre-requisite of science, begun indeed by Alberti and Piero della Francesca, namely the conquest of objectivity—the creation of the object, be it hare or sod of pasture, as it is in itself and neither swollen, bemeaned, or endowed with imaginary powers, at the whim of human subjectivity.

In thus conquering space had the artist-scientists lost touch with motion? Whoever looks attentively at Piero's battle scenes or Verrochio's (?) *Tobias and the Angel* will doubt the justice of such a suspicion. But before motion could be *analysed* as space had been, a new kind of mathematics—dimly recognised by the Mertonian logicians of the fourteenth century—had to be called into existence. In this no thinker before the seventeenth century was effective; and then only after the simplification of space by abstraction. This was the almost unique contribution of Galileo. We shall return to it again in later chapters.

The omnicompetence of Dürer naturally embraced that branch of applied science—fortification and artillery—which became more and more insistent in its call during the sixteenth century. As one would expect, Dürer took the large view—defensive batteries will be of little use to a town short of water or depleted of stores or distracted with dispersed sick, wounded and infirm. So he planned not merely a fort, but a complete town in which, alas!, the amenities of civilisation have to take second place to the demands of defence: it is the first example of a polygonal fronted plan to be created in Germany.[1] A fragment of his ideal town—not the military part, which was on a scale far beyond the means of the impecunious rulers of his day—persists in the *Fuggerei* at Augsburg, which seems to have been financed by the sons of Jacob Fugger about 1519. Incidentally, cannon in Dürer's day played a part similar to that of aircraft and armour in ours: distinguished artists were commissioned to paint their portraits, and scholars to find appropriate names—at least for those of the Emperor Maximilian (see below, p. 48). Dürer would have been used to seeing these cannon in the making, for the foundries of the Behaims were among the most important industrial establishments of Nürnberg.

If Alberti and Dürer represent all that is best in the prodigality of the beginning of the scientific renaissance, Girolamo Cardano (1501-76) reveals much of the perversity with which it developed. This is one reason for choosing him as our next representative of the outstanding figures of the time; more important is the fact that he wrote an autobiography almost without rival in the frankness and detail of its self-analysis—a phenomenon in itself a distinguishing character of the Renaissance. Unfortunately it is the work of his old age, bearing the marks of impaired memory, which probably implies a certain amount of highly imaginative reconstruction. But it is the fact that the book was written at all in this particular form which gives it such importance; and one can read a good deal between the lines for hints as to the general tenour of the life of a sixteenth-century Italian *savant*, checking details, as occasion demands, from other sources. Space does not permit of even a summary of *De Vita Propria*, which should be read by everyone with a serious interest in the Renaissance.

[1] The earliest use of the polygonal bastion is believed to have been by Sammichele in the city walls (still to be seen) of Verona.

What principally emerges from a perusal of the book is the portrait of a man capable of reporting as facts such absurdities as that three rings on his finger once fused into one, yet at the same time displaying a persistent determination to report all unfavourable instances in relation to a theory. Of the latter none is more striking than his life-long faith in astrology combined with his admission that the fact that his own horoscope implied almost certain death at about his fortieth year had not only played havoc with his early life, but was completely inconsistent with the ultimate event—namely that it was only in his forty-third year that he really began to 'live'. This happens over and over again. He is a great believer in signs and portents, giving numerous examples of their validation by the event, but freely admitting that in other cases there has been no such correlation between the sign and the event signified. His inconsistency of judgment it is more difficult to assess. He is boastful of his attainments in some respects, yet could write about his independently attested brilliance in debate and disputation that it was 'no more a special dispensation to my own nature or to my own distinction than it can be counted glorious for the cuttlefish to eject the shadows of its inky humour about the dolphin and force it to flee; that is merely the result of being born a cuttlefish'.[1] Here is a remarkable anticipation of the modern (though in ethics it goes back at least to Spinoza) notion of innate capacities for the fruits whereof no special praise—or in the case of misshapen fruits—blame, is due to their owner. Perhaps in the last analysis there is still the final consistency of revealing everything; for if he is boastful—well, does he not admit that he is by nature prone to every vice and evil save ambition? He is the 'renaissance man', then, in the range of his vices as of his virtues. In the sweep of his intellect does he measure up to an Alberti or a Dürer? A glance over the bibliography of his works, which he included in his *Life*, reveals a range of interests which is positively astounding; a glimpse of the ten folio volumes of the surviving works (1650) exhibits a sheer bulk which is incredible— and he may well have destroyed almost as many manuscripts as were ultimately printed. Incredible, since he was no cloistered scholar, but by profession a physician who undertook many journeys, one even as far as Scotland. And he admits that he wasted an unconscionable time in games of skill (particularly

[1] *The Book of my Life*, trans. and ed. by Jean Stoner, London, 1931, p. 45.

chess) and of chance. Yet, through the labours of Oystein Ore [1] it turns out that 'waste' is not a wholly appropriate term; for whatever Cardano's attainments were in algebra—the 'sideline' in which his most permanent creative work was done—Ore concludes that in his *Liber de Ludo Aleae* he broke ground for the first time in the theory of probability more than half a century before Fermat and Pascal, to whom the taking of the first crucial step is usually attributed. His *De Subtilitate* deploys a massive learning in relation to natural philosophy—real and imaginary—against which even the elder Scaliger dented his reputation. It would be idle to claim that Cardano made any attempt to base natural knowledge wholly on well attested observations and approved methods of reasoning—there is still an enormous hangover from Pliny. But where he puts forward a new item of knowledge, or corrects an old one, his method differs markedly from that of Ermolao Barbaro (No. 58) whose concern is mainly the balancing of rival authorities. In one or two places Cardano is specific about method, as for instance in his *Regulae* (which remind one of those of Descartes), the sixth of which is 'to observe all things and not to think that anything happened fortuitously in nature'.[2] In another place his insight seems to go deeper: 'Although there are many arts, one is the master of all: that fundamental precision by means of which one may explain many things through a few cases or render vague facts clear, or state in certain form facts formerly doubtful. However, there are three requirements: that all these general principles fall in with that one master theory, that they harmonise one with the other nicely, mutually inclusive and exclusive, and that each may be peculiarly adapted to its own special usage.'[3] How much of this foreshadows Descartes, or even J. S. Mill, it is difficult to say.

In the final assessment of Cardano's character it is essential to take account of the tragedy which blasted his latter years—the execution of his son for having poisoned his wife. The *Life* makes it evident that Cardano—then at the height of his fame—became obsessed with this to such an extent that it may well have clouded his reason. In view of the accessibility of the father's detailed

---

[1] Oystein Ore, *Cardano, the Gambling Scholar*, Princeton, N.J., 1953.

[2] *Op. cit.* p. 83. He applies this also to medicine where 'chance is not to be counted on', but the complexity of the art may obscure the appropriate practice. *Op. cit.* p. 181.

[3] *Op. cit.* p. 269.

account of the matter—the essential accuracy of which has not been questioned—it seems extraordinary that historians of science have been content to imply that Cardano himself was a blackguard—a blackguard all the more detestable since he 'stole' from Niccolò Tartaglia the solution of the family of equations expressible as $x^3 + ax = b$.[1] The facts of this case are admirably set out by Ore in the work already alluded to. Cardano not only never claimed the invention of this solution, but in his *Ars Magna* gave Tartaglia full credit for it.[2] The 'sin', of which it is impossible to clear him, is his publication of the solution, after promising Tartaglia on oath that he would never do so. But what was Cardano to do? His own researches involving the demonstration of the three roots of a cubic could never be developed except on the basis of Tartaglia's rule. Cardano sought no material profit by it. Today his behaviour would be regarded as normal, Tartaglia's as reprehensible. But the matter is not settled quite so easily; for in the first half of the sixteenth century there was no *Mathematical Gazette*. It was considered perfectly honourable to keep up one's sleeve a particularly potent intellectual weapon for the discomfiture of a rival candidate for an academic post. This bitter dispute is thus revealed as a conflict between an academic etiquette which was dying and the more liberal one replacing it. Also there was a purely personal side to it. Tartaglia had been horribly disfigured since childhood when he was slashed by the soldiery in the Sack of Rome. He was doubtless the victim of an inferiority state consequent on this and upon the unfortunate circumstance that although he was a remarkably able mathematician, Cardano was far the greater. The case of Hooke and Newton presents some parallel features.

In his exuberance, many-sidedness, sheer virtuosity in medicine and algebra, mechanical resourcefulness (the universal joint is

---

[1] It is still erroneously referred to as 'Cardan's Rule'; actually it was first discovered by Scipio del Ferro.

[2] Verum temporibus nostris, Sc. Ferreus Bononiensis capitulum cubi & rerum numero aequalium invenit . . . Nicolaus Tartalea Brixellensis amicus noster [!], cum in certamen cum illius discipulo Antonio Maria Florido venisset, capitulum idem, ne vincerent, invenit, qui mihi ipsum multis precibus exoratus tradidit. . . . Inde autem, illo habito, demonstrationem venatus, intellexi complura alia posse habere. Ac eo studio . . . per me partim, ac etiam aliqua per Lodovicum Ferrarium olim alumnum nostrum, inveni. Porro, quae ab his inventa sunt, illorum nominibus decorabuntur, caetera quae nomine carent, nostra sunt.' *Ars Magna*, Cap. 1, quoted from No. 134, Basel, 1570.

still known by his name), blatant self-assertiveness and self-criticism, love of marvels, feelings for warnings from a supra-physical sphere—even to the extent of believing in a familiar spirit—delight in animals, a medley assortment of which he kept about his house—in all this he represents an age into whose spirit it is difficult but important for us to enter. In surveying what he believed were his most notable achievements he says: 'Other doctrines too numerous to mention I have propounded, but this especially: I have taught that a contemplation of the natural universe leads to an artistic expression and to creative labour, although no others before my time have undertaken to offer such a suggestion.' In this he was in fact more representative of his age than he imagined: such a suggestion had indeed been implicit in many of his immediate predecessors. Not a few of them as we have seen had demonstrated in their lives and works far more completely than did Cardano the faith enshrined in his words.

The three individuals I have tried to characterise were chosen as men as nearly representative of their time, roughly 1450-1550, as could be found. In the many facets of their individuality they reflected the versatility of their age. None, though this is not quite true of Alberti, could be singled out as a prophet of a new world-view. It has been urged at the beginning of this chapter that the origin, or at least a highly significant factor in the origin, of the Renaissance was in the main a, probably unconscious, reassessment of Man's relation not only to 'nature' as then understood but to the cosmos. If this was in fact the case we should expect to find at latest about the middle of the fifteenth century a change in the philosophical climate of opinion of Western Europe. Moreover, since, as we have already noted, what is most important about the scientific culture of the Renaissance is precisely that it was not merely a re-naissance, we should expect to discover in this change of philosophical climate not one of those movements designated as 'Back-to-Someone-or-other' but a mode of thought with at least some strikingly novel characteristics. It has in the past been too readily concluded that the scientific renaissance was predominantly a consequence of the marked revival of interest in Greek literature which reached effective proportions with the foundation by Cosimo de'Medici in 1462 of the so-called Platonic Academy at Florence. By 1468 its leader, Marsilio Ficino, had translated the whole of the extant works of Plato into Latin. This was in itself an entirely novel factor in the learning of Western Europe, which throughout the Middle Ages knew Plato, if at all, only through the Neoplatonists Proklos, Plotinos, and especially the *pseudo*-Dionysios. But if the Florentine circle did once again read Plato himself it was still in the light of the Neoplatonist tradition that they interpreted his teaching. To look for the origins of modern science in the discussions of the Platonic Academy is to *overlook* the fact that it was not to the *Theaetetus, Sophist,* and *Timaeus* that they chiefly turned, but rather to the *Phaedo, Symposium,* and *Republic.* In other words there is no evidence that the Academicians had any but an incidental interest in the problem of knowledge of the external world, the structure of the cosmos, or the mathematical concepts which alone, according to Plato himself, could render an account of the intelligible word. Indeed the so-called philosophical works of the Academicians betray a looseness of texture, a superficial eclecticism and facile optimism which must have caused their idol to turn in his grave. Giovanni Pico della Mirandola alone in his *Oration on the Dignity of Man* (composed as a prelude to the nine hundred theses which he proposed to defend) shed light, not indeed on the philosophy of nature as such, but on the uniqueness of Man in relation to the cosmos by virtue of the divine gift of liberty of thought. But Pico's discourse was pronounced only in 1486. Apart therefore from the fact that he is chiefly remembered not as a Platonist but as the one member of the Academy convinced of the possibility of displaying a fundamental concordance between the teaching of Plato and that of Aristotle, Pico's manifesto came too late to be anything like a starting point of a new cosmic consciousness. Ranking, as I believe it does, among the most fruitful products of the Academy for the future of learning in general it should more properly be regarded as a singularly lucid reflection of a point of view fairly widely dispersed. If this was in fact the situation, then its origin may rather be sought not in the Medicean Academy but perhaps in the first Italian 'Academy' of which we have any record: this was the group which met under the direction of Luigi Marsigli (d. 1394),[1] a pupil of Petrarca, in the cloister of San Spirito,[2]

[1] Nesca. A. Robb, *Neoplatonism of the Italian Renaissance*, London, 1935, p. 31. This work (especially the earlier chapters) still forms an indispensable guide to the evaluation of the influence of the Platonic academy on renaissance thought in general.

[2] The cell of Fra Marsigli was in a part of the church accidentally burnt during a miracle play performed on the occasion of the visit of Galeazzo Maria Sforza to Florence

Florence. Here, if we may judge by the writings of Marsigli and Coluccio Salutati, its most prominent member, was first emphasised the view that a divinity pervades the whole natural order and that Man can attain to his full stature only by participation in this order, knowledge of which is comprised in no final static form but is in process of continuous development. From such teaching of course there could come no clue to natural knowledge as such; but it was the inspiration of the liberal conception of the education of the young carried out in the 'boarding schools' of Vittorino da Feltre. From here also or rather from Petrarca himself, came the 'news' that it was possible to be a Christian without being bound by the empty formalism of scholasticism.

If then it is impossible to regard the activities of the Platonic Academy as providing the philosophical background from which men might ultimately come to look out upon the cosmos, where else are we to look? Among the immediate precursors of the Academy was one figure who may lay claim to having expressed the new outlook in its most universal form. The universality was in a sense emphasised rather than contradicted by the fact that, though his eyes surveyed the boundless cosmos the acceptance of which was one of the products of the Renaissance, his feet were firmly planted in medieval custom; for we can not too often remind ourselves that the rejection of the rationalism which characterised the High Middle Ages was one of the factors which rendered so much renaissance thought ineffective. Everything about Nicholas Krypffs, born at Cues in 1401 and ending his days as Cardinal and Bishop of Brixen (Bressanone), conspired to generate this combination of universality and rigour. His home was that of a prosperous merchant lately risen from peasant stock, but he gained his early education at Deventer in one of the schools of the Brethren of the Common Life.[1] He passed his childhood and

in 1471. (E. G. Gardner, *Florence and its Story*, revised edn., London, 1953, pp. 68, 275-6.) Before the end of the fifteenth century Vespasiano da Bisticci could write of Marsigli and Salutati that 'of their lives we have no detailed record' (quoted *Documentary History of Art*, Vol. I, Doubleday Anchor Books, New York, 1957, p. 181.)

[1] The first of these schools was founded before the end of the fourteenth century. Though ordered on monastic lines they sought to provide a Christian education to meet the needs of the increasing numbers of men not concerned mainly with ecclesiastical affairs. The spirit which infused them is finely revealed in the *Imitation of Christ* of St. Thomas of Kempen. Erasmus was also one of their pupils but by his day they were perhaps out of harmony with the times; at any rate he has little good to say about the education they gave him.

adolescence in the heart of Germany, but completed his studies at Padua. Of a naturally studious habit, he nevertheless spent his days in Councils and on diplomatic missions. Soaked in the medieval tradition which held theology to be queen of the sciences, he yet found time not only to write a comprehensive pamphlet on the history and theory underlying the problem of the reform of the calendar, but also, if not actually to perform, at any rate to describe, experiments with the balance as an aid to discovery in a wide field. What a contrast is this environment of a growing intelligence to the hot house atmosphere in which so much of the output of the literary coterie of Florence was produced! Even his limitations are revealing; for though he recognised the significance of appeal to the balance in his search for the nature of things, his reasoning in relation to hydrostatical problems would disgrace a modern schoolboy.

The nature of the Cusan revolution is easily misunderstood. The bald statement that he affirmed (Nicole Oresme only considered it an hypothesis) the motion of the earth a century before Copernicus is as undoubtedly true as it is as grossly misleading. The truth which lies hidden in the mere affirmation is far more interesting. His reasons were metaphysical—or perhaps epistemological—and his aim theological. His argument achieved such high generality that it gave no hint of any possible verification or falsification. The aim of Copernicus on the other hand was methodological; he proposed an hypothesis which was based on no new evidence and in flat contradictian (as his contemporaries were not slow to point out) to common sense [1] and the accepted natural philosophy; but it was sufficiently specific to allow of a degree of verification or falsification. Its advantages were a simplification in the traditional geometrical apparatus and a slight increase in predictive power. The contrast between these two men, when viewed from our point of vantage, is highly illuminating. Whereas the *mechanism* proposed by Copernicus was thoroughly medieval and his actual hypothesis almost completely superseded within less than a century, that of Nicholas of Cues, reinterpreted in non-theological terms, is effectively a particular formulation of the restricted principle of relativity. If Nicholas 'anticipated' anyone, it was not Copernicus but Einstein.

[1] Which, I believe, removes the apparent contradiction between this paragraph and the view put forward near the beginning of the chapter.

It will repay us to look a little more closely into this matter. The novelty of Nicholas's approach lay in an entirely new application of mathematical analogy to cosmic relations. In this approach he was in the Christian-Neoplatonist tradition, reaching back to the first cosmic 'synthesis' in the works of the *pseudo*-Dionysios (cf. Plate No. III); but this static hierarchical system for the propagation of the creative power of God had been transformed into a more subtly dynamic pantheism by Ioannes Eriugena and Eckhart. It was Nicholas who gave precision to this conception by means of a deeper understanding of the authentic Platonism on which the so-called Neoplatonists had cast a mystic and distorting light. For Nicholas, as for Plato . . . 'nihil certe habemus in nostra scientia, nisi nostram mathematicam, et ille est aenigma ad venationem operum Dei' ('There is no certain knowledge except in mathematics, and that is the clue in the chase to discover the works of God'). Truth, though never wholly attainable, is the *adaequatio rei et intellectus*. To this end he makes skilful use of two principal concepts: *maximum* and *coincidentia oppositorum*. The former is ill-described by his name, for it signifies, not the greatest term in a sequence, but the term between which and any other term there is *no proportion*, and one to which therefore no measure can be assigned. And since it has no 'parts' it is also the minimum—hence the 'coincidence of opposites' which may also be illustrated by the indistinguishability of the straight line and the 'infinite' circle.[1] Although it must be conceded that the derivation of further relationships is not wholly convincing, the denial of any local centre to the infinite sphere, the relativity of time and movement as consequences of their creation by the active intellect, constitute *tours de force* whose significance was not realised by cosmical physicists for more than four centuries. It is not however with the rather pointless game of discovering 'anticipations' that we are here concerned, but with the more fundamental question of seeking a transition point in general culture. That Nicholas of Cues in any sense 'started' the renaissance of philosophy in the wake of the already expanding renaissance of letters is by no means claimed; but rather that in Cassirer's suggestive phrase his world-view represents a point of 'labile equilibrium' between 'the religious and philosophical concept of truth (*Wahrheitsbegriff*), between faith and knowledge,

---

[1] In this connection see Kepler's comment quoted on p. 38.

between religion and world-construct'.[1] In him the authentic
Greek Plato met Augustine's Christian Platonism, German mysticism met Italian scholarship, experimental enquiry joined with
mathematical speculation (perhaps an echo of Grosseteste's
rather uncertain call), papal legate (of Eugenius IV) opposed—to
maintain the integrity of Christendom—the conciliar tendencies
of some of his ecclesiastical contemporaries. Here surely is a focal
point in the transition. That the subsequent course (or courses)
of the Renaissance was the direct consequence of Nicholas's
teaching it would be unhistorical to maintain: the influential
'Academicians' mention him only casually, if at all. But Peurbach
and Regiomontanus acknowledged his lead. Lefèvre of Etaples
thought it worth while to have his works printed in Paris in 1514;
and Kepler, who stood in a similar relation to him with regard
to the transition from 'renaissance' to 'modern' science, wrote in
the *Mysterium Cosmographicum* 'divinus mihi Cusanus'.[2] If, to
return to a point pressed earlier in this discussion, the 'climate
of opinion' in the Renaissance is characterised *chiefly* by a
change in man's appraisal of his relation to the cosmos, then
Nicholas of Cues expresses this appraisal in the most significant
way.

To leave the discussion at this point might be to give the impression that somehow or other the 'Renaissance'—especially as
regards science and cosmology—was a consequence of the final
triumph of Plato over his erring disciple Aristotle.[3] In respect of
the assessment of mathematics as the paradigm and archetype of
knowledge this was certainly the case; though the immediate
effects were limited in range of application and the extent to
which it was accepted. Nothing is more striking to the student of
sixteenth century scientific works than the almost universally
Aristotelian setting of a geocentric universe in which is drawn the
absolute distinction between the 'sublunary sphere' of the four

[1] Ernst Cassirer, *Individuum und Kosmos in der Philosophie der Renaissance*, Berlin, 1927,
p. 63. I am greatly indebted to this work for clarifying and giving substance to my
uncertain conjectures.

[2] Kepler, *Opera*, ed. Frisch, I (1858), 122. See also Max Caspar, *Iohannes Kepler*,
Stuttgart, 1948, pp. 46, 66.

[3] In this connection see Kristeller, *op. cit.* on p. 12. Dr. Kristeller's recent researches
on early unpublished manuscripts by Marsilio Ficino show a markedly Aristotelian
point of view in the latter. This, as Dr. Kristeller emphasises, is explained by the fact
that the Aristotelian *education* provided by the Universities was due not to inertia but
to the absence of any suitable alternative.

elements suffering generation and corruption, and the 'aetherial sphere' of eternal and uniform circular motions. Reference to the records of the universities confirms that departure from this rigid discipline was probably less encouraged than had been the case in the early fourteenth century. The limited relativity introduced by Copernicus had few adherents, and it should be noted that in this he was following not Plato but the Pythagoreans;[1] it has never been established that Plato positively accepted the theory of a moving earth. The immense vogue for Plato in the Florentine Academy had but a delayed action and even then not always for the good—as Kepler was to bewail.

It is coming to be recognised that one of the most valuable services of the fifteenth century Platonists was to stimulate a much more critical approach to Aristotle. Petrarca's objection to the domination of Aristotelianism in his day was not to Aristotle, but to 'the stupid Aristotelians who day by day in every single word they speak do not cease to hammer into the heads of others Aristotle whom they know by name only,'[2] also to 'that frantic dog Averroes'.[3] The second reference may give a clue to the first. Italy had been dominated by the Averroist version of Aristotelianism to an extent which the North had not.[4] The teaching of Averroes on the existence of a sole universal active intellect which acts only through the bodies of individual human beings was one which no Christian could accept—least of all an 'individualist' like Petrarca. St. Thomas had an answer to this Averroistic interpretation, but, involving as it did the resort to a belief in special creation, it was unacceptable as *philosophy*. The subsequent history of 'Aristotelianism' in Italy was greatly modified by the Aristotelians' realisation that, as J. H. Randall Jr. puts it, Aristotle as well as Plato spoke Greek. The study of the Greek manuscripts gave a stimulus to Aristotelian studies, the importance of which has until recently been too little appreciated. In 1497 a new Chair was created at Padua for the teaching

---

[1] It is important to avoid here the not uncommon error of ascribing to the Pythagoreans the view that the motion of the earth was round the *sun*.

[2] *The Renaissance Philosophy of Man*, ed. E. Cassirer *et. al.*, Chicago, 1948, p. 107.

[3] *Op. cit.* p. 143.

[4] For the need for caution in the application of the label, 'Averroist' see F. van Steenberghen (*The Philosophical Movement in the Thirteenth Century*, Edinburgh, 1955), who emphasises the fact that 'everyone' *used* Averroes's exposition and commentary on Aristotle in the Middle Ages.

of Aristotle in Greek: Aristotle, freed from the taint of the translation by the 'barbarians', thus achieved respectability. We have already noted how Pico della Mirandola had lived up to his title of *Princeps Concordiae*; it was now possible to be an 'Aristotelian' while opposed to both Averroism and Scholasticism. The master of the 'new' Aristotelianism was Pietro Pomponazzi, who used St. Thomas's argument to dispose of the Averroistic principle of a single World Soul. For the progress of philosophic thought, however, it was fortunate that a vigorous Averroistic school had persisted at Padua, since he was forced gradually to realise the inadequacy of the Thomist solution as *philosophy*. During his subsequent teaching at Ferrara he elaborated the great work *De Immortalitate Animae*, which showed the possibility of a solution of this famous problem [1] and which was printed in 1516 soon after his appointment at Bologna. The solution is admittedly a compromise, but a compromise in which clearly appears what implications of the displaced rival view no longer hold. Its implications for the science of the Renaissance have yet to be assessed;[2] but it is significant that it was mainly in the universities where he had taught—Padua, Bologna, Ferrara—that occurred the great advances in medical science at the end of the sixteenth century. It was at Padua that Fabricius ab Aquapendente began the teaching of embryology, which his pupil Harvey elaborated a generation later: and their work is Aristotelian through and through. Of more importance perhaps were the other Aristotelian problems raised by Pomponazzi's pupil Zabarella. Since these must be discussed in some detail, and their methodological importance seem first to have been appreciated in the Faculty of Medicine, consideration of them will be deferred.

The last general characteristic of the Renaissance with which we are here concerned is the rending of the seam of Christian unity—or rather of what is commonly claimed to have been Christian unity—in forgetfulness of the fact that a considerable rent had been made in the earliest centuries by the monophysite secession, and a major divorce in the establishment of the Byzantine secession. Within a few years of the last effort to

---

[1] The problem is involved and overlaid with subtleties. A very clear outline is provided by J. H. Randall Jr. in his introduction to Pomponazzi's essay in *The Renaissance Philosophy of Man*.

[2] For another aspect of Pomponazzi's influence, see below, p. 287.

reunite Byzantium and Rome the former was destroyed;[1] but
before this ultimate tragedy the fabric of Western Christendom
had shown signs of disintegration. No one would probably now
be so naïve as to suggest that the ultimate rending was either a
cause or an effect of the Renaissance; only a biassed enthusiast
would still regard the 'Reformation' as having done for religion
what it was once supposed the 'Renaissance' had done for culture
in general: much that was immeasurably precious was destroyed
in both spheres. While it is none of our concern to consider either
the history or the merits of the Reformation we may profitably
attempt to determine its relation to the general cultural movement
of the times and its consequences, if any, for the progress of science.

We have already seen that the Lutheran explosion was only
the most widespread and most effective of many movements for
reform. That there were many might be due merely to the pressing
abuses within the Roman Church; but in addition to his attack
on the immorality of the traffic in indulgences is Luther's insistence that the authority of the Bible is above that of popes,
cardinals, bishops and even councils. This implies, what in other
contexts he explicitly states, the Priesthood of all Believers.
But the words of the Bible must be interpreted, and who, we may
ask, is to be the final arbiter of the interpretation if not the Vicar
of Christ and his servants? There is a fundamental weakness here
which Luther himself never adequately cleared up. All we are
concerned with is this application of what I have called the new
conception of man's relationship to the cosmos. Obversely,
Luther's teaching concerning the sacrament of the mass involves
a new conception of *God's* relation to the cosmos. Although Luther
rejected the Roman belief in a change of 'substance' in the sacred
elements (which nonetheless, he thought, retain their 'accidents')
he held that the Real Presence followed from the *omni*presence of
God throughout the universe. Doubtless that devout and optimistic servant of Eugenius IV, Nicholas of Cues, would have been
profoundly shocked if he had been able to forsee that his deep
philosophic insight might lead to the greatest heresy the Church
had ever had to face. But perhaps in his wisdom he might also have
seen that this way of tragedy was the only way to arouse the
Church to such a pitch of self-examination as to purge itself of

[1] But not, of course, the Eastern *Church*, the heart of which was thereafter to be the
'Third Rome', that is, Moscow. (See Barraclough, *op. cit.* p. 40.)

the corruption whose further spread would have rent the garment of Christianity not merely in twain but into shreds.

It is now fortunately rare to meet such crude statements as that the progress of 'science' was prevented by the obscurantism of the (generally Roman) 'Church', or that Copernicus was prevented from publishing his views by the 'Inquisition'; but the exact facts of the case are still far from universally known. Confining our attention to essentials and mainly to printed documents we need only refer the reader to the introductory pages of the *editio princeps* of his final work, the first copy of which, there is good reason to believe, reached him as he was dying. There the reader will see reproduced the letter addressed by Cardinal Schoenberg to Copernicus, urging him to publish his great work of whose existence many scholars of the Church had long been aware. The reader will see also that the work was dedicated by Copernicus to the reigning Pope, Paul III. So much is self-revealing. But an unsigned foreword explaining that what the work proposed was only a mathematical hypothesis which might have no actual replica in the physical world is at complete variance with certain passages in the text. The anonymous writer of this face-saving piece of casuistry was revealed later by Kepler to be the *Lutheran*, Andreas Osiander, to whom had finally been entrusted the task of seeing the work through the press. As to the reception of the central idea that the unmoved centre of the universe is a point near the sun, there is no evidence that any attempt was made to suppress it, or to cast the aspersion of heresy on Copernicus. It was one of Luther's circle at Wittenberg, Andreas Rheticus, who was mainly responsible for getting the work printed, another, Erasmus Reinhold, who published the Prutenic Tables, based on the New Theory. As regards Luther himself, the only evidence of his views is a remark in the *Table Talk*:[1] there seems little doubt that this was meant as a reproof of an innovator who was attempting to upset the world-view established by philosophy and supported by scripture. Apart from a report that Paul III was 'not amused' by Copernicus's rather slighting reference to Lactantius there is no evidence that the Roman Church was at first at all disturbed by the new view. The

[1] 'Der Narr will die ganze Kunst Astronomiae umkehren. Aber wie die heilige Schrift anzeiget, so hiess Josua die Sonne still stehen und nicht das Erdreich.' See W. Norling, *Isis*, 44, 273.

case of Giordano Bruno, who was burnt at the stake as a heretic half a century later, is still the subject of a good deal of ill-informed comment. To some he was an irresponsible visionary of no interest to the historian of science and best left to the judgment of theologians. To others he was a 'martyr in the cause of science', who was burnt because he spoke the 'truth' about the structure of the cosmos. Both these views seem to me hasty and ill-considered. There is no need to argue the case in detail: we have recently been provided with lucid reviews of the evidence upon which each person may base his own judgment.[1] Here it may be pointed out that though superficially Bruno was largely repeating the views set forth a century earlier by the Cardinal Bishop of Brixen (p. 36) it must be added that the spirit in which he made these claims was very different. Whereas Nicholas of Cues had shown that the infinity of the cosmos followed necessarily from certain concepts involving assumptions as to the nature of mathematical truth Bruno based his claim on the principle of plenitude—a dogma concerning the nature of God. Neither he nor Nicholas had any means of verifying their conjectures, but whereas Nicholas's were rather concerned with the conceptual apparatus of natural philosophy, Bruno's views on the plurality of 'worlds' were announced not as hypotheses but as matters of fact and real existence, whose unverifiability was the result of the imperfection of human senses. The importance of Bruno in the history of science is that he was the first to give a detailed exposition of a cosmos without centre or boundaries, in which the stars were freely dispersed instead of being restricted to a separate sphere; and each star was to be regarded as a sun surrounded by planets similar to the earth. Irresponsible dreaming this may have been, yet Kepler (who denied most of it) dreamed no less, but his dreams, unlike Bruno's, turned out to be deceptive and barren.[2] Was Bruno's prescience mere chance? We do not yet know enough about the psychology of discovery to be able to decide such questions. But we do know that without such dreams the great breaks-through into new realms of natural knowledge seldom take place. In scope and daring Bruno's was an imaginative leap comparable to Newton's 'extending gravity to the orb of the moon'. The reason we rate Newton far above Bruno as a man of

[1] See supplementary Bibliography.   [2] But see below, p. 284.

science is that he was able to reply truthfully to Halley's query as to how he knew, 'Why, I have *proved* it'.

That Bruno gave the ultimate expression—probably, like Leonardo, too soon to have exerted any direct influence—to that cosmic transvaluation of values which I have regarded as the most characteristic feature of the scientific renaissance I have no doubt. That he was not a 'martyr in the cause of science' I have equally no doubt. Whether he suffered for the sake of free thought is another matter which I need not consider. The case of Miguel Servet is similar. A fellow student with Vesalius in Paris, he was a skilled dissector and may well have been the pioneer of the new views on the circulation of the blood.[1] But these views were presented in a theological setting, and it was for his theology that he was burned by Calvin.[2] To clarify these issues is of course not to defend the ecclesiastical powers. Of the two faiths the Roman, as was to be expected, was at first generally the more liberal in regard to learning and the arts. The mass destruction of everything giving grace and beauty to life, whether at Zürich in the time of Zwingli or in the Scotland of John Knox, was the work of protestant fanatics and undisciplined mobs such as may always be expected to attach themselves to any 'reforming' movement, though neither at the behest nor even with the approval of the leaders. What both Churches were determined to crush was free speculation on the ultimate things. Each would doubtless have justified this on the grounds of preventing moral corruption. Unfortunately there was, and is, no universally acceptable criterion of what constitutes corruption.

[1] It is extremely unlikely that he was aware that similar views on the pulmonary circulation had been put forward before the end of the thirteenth century by Ibn al-Nafis.

[2] Cf. C. D. O'Malley, *Michael Servetus—A translation of his geographical, medical, and astrological writings*, Philadelphia, 1953. Servet is put in a more favourable light in J. F. Fulton, *Michael Servetus—Humanist and Martyr*, New York, 1953.

CHAPTER III

PRINCIPALITIES AND POWERS

THAT the course of discovery and development in science
is to a large extent moulded by social conditions and economic drives is now so far assumed as often to cause less than
justice to be done to the converse relationship. It is my purpose
here not so much to attempt to mediate between these not necessarily rival views, but to provide materials on the basis of which
scholars of various disciplines may approach this and related
questions. In no period is it more important to keep this aspect
of the history of science more sharply focused, and in no period is
it more difficult to do so. For in no previous period did *scientific
questions* obtrude themselves over so wide an area of human
endeavour—in the counsels of the Prince, in the counting-house,
in the fine arts, on the battle field, on the high seas, in the cham-
bers of the sick and of those about to make their first entry on
this earthly stage—to name but a few. I say advisedly 'scientific
questions', for though, as in astrology, the aim was knowledge of
the influences of natural bodies, yet the method employed was
often so ill-conceived as to render impossible anything that
would now be regarded as a scientific *answer*.

If the primary assumption be allowed, it will be further agreed
that the nature of the scientific renaissance—using the term in
the manner already elaborated and without any implication of a
universal 're-birth'—can be fully understood only in the light of a
fairly comprehensive picture of social structure, and particularly
social trends, during the period under review. A glance through the
dedications of the books here considered reveals the fact that only
few were in any way sponsored by universities. Indications are
frequent that the writer owed his livelihood to rulers—secular,
ecclesiastical, or municipal—and that his association with them
might be of a degree of intimacy varying from that of personal
physician or co-worker in research to that based rather on hope

45

than actuality. It is further remarkable that national boundaries, though gradually hardening with the intensification of power in central governments, still meant much less than they do today. A striking example of this is the grovelling dedication of Tartaglia's work on ordnance to Henry VIII (No. 673). And this of course is quite apart from the frequent cases of more or less permanent employment of foreign nationals, as for instance of Hans Holbein the younger as Court Limnologist, Polydore Vergil as Historiographer Royal, and Nikolaus Kratzer as 'King's Astrologer and Horologer' (the post of Astronomer Royal was of course created by Charles II in 1675). Even when universities took a prominent place in the conduct of a particular research or in the dedication of the book describing it, the very various origins of sixteenth century universities have to be borne in mind. Some, like Paris and Bologna, dated from the twelfth or thirteenth centuries; others, though more recent, were still essentially papal promotions; Helmstadt was founded by a Noble who had embraced the reformed religion; Douai was to provide missionaries for the *Counter*-Reformation; Leiden was a 'war memorial' to the victory of the Protestant Dutch Republics over Catholic and Imperial Spain. In such a medley there could be no such thing as complete 'academic freedom'; censorship, whether of speech or writing, was not restricted to the Holy Office, whose activities are merely more widely known for being overt, based after 1559 on an *Index Prohibitorum*, established by a public body—The Council of Trent.

In these circumstances it seems desirable to sketch as briefly as may be consistent with clarity the broad political alignments, that 'transvaluation of all values', of which the 'Reformation' was the most spectacular evidence, and the shift of economic power both socially and geographically. This will be the subject of the present chapter; in the next it will be convenient to discuss separately the special problems of the new sources and means of communication of knowledge, especially the part played by that which was perhaps the most potent of all the new factors—the invention of printing from movable type.

It will be readily understood that what is aimed at in the present chapter is no 'history' of Europe in the sixteenth century— such would be altogether outside the scope of this book and beyond the competence of the author. It is rather to provide a spatio-temporal framework into which the 'scientific events' may be appropriately fitted. This should be chiefly of service to readers whose scientific interests have left them insufficient time to study the social background of the century. While it is unlikely that any historians in the customary sense of the word will find anything new in its pages, it may be of interest to them to discover what historical facts seem to be of special significance to at least one historian of science. And whether these revelations be regarded as insights or prejudices, their explicit statement is necessary for the full comprehension of the study of the sciences which follows.

A glance at a map delineating the Europe of the year 1500 reveals, at the heart, the sprawling feudal conglomeration of territories owning allegiance to ecclesiastical or secular princes, of cities claiming liberties, and Imperial Knights license, known at this time as the Holy Roman Empire of the German Nation, stretched from near Dantzig to Trieste in the east and from Zeeland to Nice on the west; though it must be admitted that the kingdom of Bohemia, the Swiss Cantons, the States of the Netherlands, and those states of northern Italy which fell within its boundaries, were little more than nominal in their allegiance. The significance of the title; the structure and the relations, both internal and external, of the entity to which it referred, must be accorded more than passing notice in any study of the Renaissance. For even at the present day the not uncommon attribution to the Empire of a universality and continuity which it never in fact possessed is pressed [1] into service as part of the indictment against the Renaissance as a period of disruption of culture and fragmentation from which the spirit of European Man has never recovered. Whatever may be the truth of the indictment it can to only a very limited extent be associated with the alleged decay of the Empire. For it was during the century in which, beyond the frontiers of Italy, the culmination of the Renaissance occurred, that the Empire both in respect of its relations to the Church of Rome and of the extent of territory and power at the command of the Emperor attained an importance hardly equalled during any part of its history. This was brought about largely by means characteristic of 'modern' statecraft—administrative and dynastic—rather than by feudal rewards or adherance to the creed

[1] For a critical examination of this question see G. Barraclough, *History in a Changing World*, Oxford, 1955, ch. vii. *The Medieval Empire: Idea and Reality.*

of a Universal Church. The man mainly responsible for laying the
basis of this renewal was Maximilian I, who, crowned as 'King
of the Romans' in 1486, had already impressed his personality
on many of his domains when, on the death of his father, Frederick
III, in 1493, he automatically took over the rule of the German
Reich. He would ordinarily have assumed the title of Emperor
only after coronation by the Pope in Rome; but, owing to the
state of war with his 'subjects' the Venetians who barred his
passage to Rome, Julius II conferred on him the title of Emperor-
Elect. The altered status of the Empire was shown by the fact
that no Emperor was thereafter crowned in Rome, and only one
(Charles V) by the Pope.

Part of the importance of the Empire was the fact that the
office of Emperor was not necessarily hereditary but was ultimately in the hands of seven Electors. To avoid the hazards of
an empty throne it had long been the custom for the ruling emperor to attempt to secure the election of his son during his own
lifetime; if he succeeded, his heir-apparent was crowned at
Aachen as King of the Romans,[1] but exercised no rule during his
father's presence in the Reich. The electoral principle was fraught
with grave risks since the Emperor might fail to obtain the confirmation by the Electoral Council of his designated heir; in
such circumstances the election subsequent to his death might be
brought under pressures of a nature far from holy: it is hardly an
exaggeration to say that in the case of Maximilian's grandson,
Charles V, the fate of Europe hung on the size of the 'consideration' which the banking firm of the Fuggers was able to raise to
buy a majority of electoral votes.

As an effective ruler Maximilian I was not a success. Only a
man strong in genius and character could have hoped to be, under
the preposterous conditions in which the emperor was expected
to function: to wield authority throughout the dominions of the
Reich; but, for the means to make his writ effective, at the
mercy of the jealousies and intrigues of the princes and towns
composing the Reichstag. Nevertheless Maximilian established a
fairly effective administrative machine at Innsbruck and exploited the mineral wealth of Tirol by selling to the Fuggers the
monopoly to work its ores. But it was by his series of shrewd

[1] For a more detailed account see J. Bryce, *The Holy Roman Empire*, 8th edn., London,
1886, pp. 432-7.

marriages—above all to Mary of Burgundy, and of their son Philip the Fair, to Juana, daughter of Isabella of Castile, that Maximilian laid the foundations of the Habsburg empire. For on the death of Isabella, Juana succeeded to the throne of Castile, and owing to the early death of her husband, Philip, their own son Charles ultimately became ruler of Castile. Finally, what Maximilian could not have forseen, Ferdinand of Aragon, the husband of Isabella, named Charles as heir to his own kingdom. Thus when Charles, on his grandfather's death in 1518, was a candidate for the Imperial throne, he was already king of a united Spain, and through his own tactful handling of the Netherlands (his outlook has been described as typically Burgundian, and on his accession he was unable to speak Spanish) he was able to pledge the Netherlands as the 'surety on which the Fuggers bought the Empire from the Electors'.[1] The Empire of Charles V was thus Habsburg and Germanic: for though Charles himself was crowned by a pope (at Bologna) his was the last coronation to signalise this always tenuous claim to the attribute 'Holy'. Also, for the future, though in Charles's life-time playing an unsuccessful part in the effort to maintain the alleged unity of Christendom against the Reformers, it was to become, what it had not been for centuries, a powerful political bloc, the last vestiges of which disappeared with the Austro-Hungarian Empire in 1918.

Important as was Maximilian's reign in the establishment of the conditions in which Renaissance thought developed outside Italy, even more so for our purpose was the character of the man himself. Dazzled as we are apt to be by the splendour of the princely courts of Italy, whether of the papacy of Julius II or the Florentine of Lorenzo il Magnifico, it is easy to overlook the glamour in which the young Maximilian was invested by his contemporaries, such as Dürer. 'Medieval' indeed was the light in which he was wont to be seen as the 'last of the knights', the conservator of the long cherished ideal of a *Pax Christiana*, which, it had long been hoped, would transcend the vanished *Pax Romana*. But his astonishing versatility provides some excuse for seeing in him the manifestation of a new urge to make of the individual life a work of art. Handsome, athletic, courageous and headstrong, he won

---

[1] *New Cambridge Modern History*, p. 257.

D

the hearts of his humbler subjects by his urbanity and ease of manner. Anxious for personal glory he could nevertheless (on the rare occasions when the money was available) hire Swiss mercenaries to undertake war as an instrument of policy; and he had the professional's insight into the growing importance of the infantry soldier, whose training he personally supervised, no less than that of artillery, in the collection of which he took an almost childish delight. Yet exploits of arms in no way excluded the desire to be surrounded by creative artists and men of learning. If Dürer and other Nürnberg artist-craftsmen had to provide him with the famous Triumphal Arch—a fantastic collection of wood-cuts in a single unit almost ten feet square—it was to feed his love of nature that Dürer designed the *Prayer Book* illustrated with hunting scenes, birds, beasts, and flowers. The moralist might see in the circumstances of his death a portent of the failure of Renaissance Man: the visitor to the Hofkappelle at Innsbruck may still look with awe and wonder at the effigies finely wrought in wood and brass, of knights and noblewomen, kings and queens, assembled round the great tomb in which Maximilian intended that his remains should lie. But the tomb is empty: the burghers of Innsbruck, remembering only the unpaid bills, refused to admit the dying emperor with his retinue; so he passed to a humbler resting place near his birthplace at Wiener Neustadt.

Before leaving (for the present) the Empire we may take note of the fact that when an effort was made to arrest Luther for trial at Rome he was saved by the intervention of Frederick the Wise, Elector of Saxony, not because the latter liked Luther's theology, but because he liked a good deal less the prospect of one of his subjects being tried in a foreign court.[1]

Turning now from the 'heart' of Europe we may first deal rather summarily with its eastern neighbours. In the relatively far east lay at this time the virtually Asiatic mass of Muscovy. Though the movement towards centralisation of government under Ivan III made great strides in the second half of the fifteenth century, the Byzantine solidarity of the Church and the preoccupation of the secular power with the Tartar invaders in the south and east effectually prevented any infiltration of ideas from the West,

---

[1] A complementary case was the invocation in England of the Statue of Praemunire two years *earlier* than Luther's manifesto. Feiling, *History of England*, London, 1950, p. 341.

whether of 'Renaissance' or 'Reform'. Only towards the end of the sixteenth century do we find references to 'Muscovy' in any scientific works, and then only in connection with the problems of navigation and travel which faced the traders of London and elsewhere intent on 'venturing' into Muscovy (No. 555).

With Poland, also a Slavonic country and next to the Empire the largest state in Europe, it was quite otherwise; for was it not from Frauenburg[1] that came the greatest manifesto of the century? Though it is at least doubtful whether Mikolaj Kopernik would have promulgated his System of the World without a journey to Italy, there is ample documentary evidence [2] that Cracow, where he received his early training in mathematics and astronomy, was as active a centre of study and teaching of natural philosophy in the broadest sense as anywhere else in Europe. The persistence of this activity during the sixteenth century is confirmed by the numerous dedications to members of the Jagellon dynasty among the books under consideration.

South of Poland lay Hungary, where strange to say, despite the presence of the magnificent library collected by Matthaeus Corvinus, there appears to have been made a much smaller contribution to the emergent scientific culture. It would be unwise to assume that this was due to the anarchic state of government; for the national spirit had been great enough to check decisively the advance of the Ottoman Turks before 1490. But on the death of Matthaeus (1490) a final rot seems to have set in,[3] culminating in the disastrous rout of Mohacs (1526). Two years later the sound of Turkish artillery was heard at the gates of Vienna.

To the north of the Empire a superficially similar situation existed. The unit here is the Baltic sea surrounded by the loose confederation of Norway, Denmark, Sweden and Finland, and the ecclesiastical states of Esthonia, Kurland, Livonia and the area round Königsberg which was one of the cells whose coalescence later formed the kingdom of Prussia. From the early

[1] The German name indicates that this city was in a region disputed between Poland and the Teutonic knights.
[2] E.g. J. Rudnicki, *Nicholas Copernicus*, Quatercentenary Publication, London, 1943, pp. 3-4.
[3] Matthaeus's successor the weak Wladislaw, was reduced to selling items from the great library to meet the expenses of his court. (*New Cambridge Modern History*, p. 387). Some of these volumes came finally into the possession of the Royal Society (1667).

fifteenth century onwards the centre of power gradually shifted northward: the 'free cities' of the Empire constituting the Hanseatic League gradually yielding before the determination of Denmark to control the whole Baltic trade. By the end of the sixteenth century Sweden was emerging as a major military power whose armies operated far into the 'heart' of Europe. From the Scandinavian countries there came no token of scientific activity until near the close of the sixteenth century; and when it came it was unconnected with any university, but was the product of an 'eccentric' nobleman's insistence and a king's munificence. The pious horror with which the young Tycho Brahe's decision to devote his life to the study of astronomy was met by his outraged kinsfolk was in marked contrast to the enthusiasm of many men of gentle birth in other lands.

The western border of the Empire consisted of the Low Countries and France. The former, as has already been noted, were nominally within its bounds; but the looseness of the bond is best demonstrated, as Grant[1] puts it, by the fact that a detailed history of the struggle for communal liberty can be written without any allusion to the fact that they were 'subjects of the Kaiser and members of the Reich'. Though the seventeenth century must be reckoned the period of flowering of the intense political consciousness, military skill, and economic enterprise of the northern Netherland confederation of towns, nevertheless throughout the sixteenth century there is evidence of increasing activity in science and learning of every kind. Was not Erasmus of Rotterdam the ambassador of the Humanistic Renaissance to all nations? Was it not to Antwerp that, after Italy, Dürer felt bound to turn for inspiration and perhaps more urgently a ready market? Are not Vesalius of Brussels and Simon Stevin of Bruges outstanding figures in renaissance science? Finally was it not in Antwerp and Leiden that one of the greatest scholar-printers, Christophe Plantin, established himself and played a dominant part in the dissemination of works of the famous botanical 'family'—De l'Ecluse, de l'Obel, and Dodöens—all natives of the Netherlands?

The emergence of the 'Benelux' association in recent times may serve to remind us that the present political boundaries are not

[1] Grant, *op. cit.* p. 380.

very much older. In the sixteenth century the 'Low Countries' comprised seventeen independent 'states', which included Brabant, Hainault, Artois, and Flanders, all or part of which are now within the frontiers of France. Luxembourg was, as it is now, an independent Duchy. 'Holland' was then merely one, but, perhaps the most important of the seven northern states, the kinship of whose language to German (*Hoch Teutsch*) was indicated by the name of Nieder Teutsch—or 'Low Dutch' [1] as distinct from 'High Dutch' as they were rendered in English. An important factor in the emergence of these political units was the recent dismemberment of the feudal conglomeration of Burgundy (see below, p. 55).

The later Middle Ages had seen the emergence of urban wealth and power with some of the appurtenances of modern capitalist organisation first in Bruges and later in Ghent. At the beginning of the sixteenth century it was Antwerp which took the leading place. In 1560 the Italian chronicler, Ludovico Guicciardini, then resident in the city, wrote a vivid and balanced account of its inhabitants and their occupations.[2] The origin of its phenomenal expansion he saw, and there is no reason to doubt the accuracy of his judgment, in the diversion of the oriental spice trade from Venice to Lisbon: this had come about at the beginning of the century as a result of the successful organisation of regular sailings across the Indian Ocean to Calicut. In answer to the further question as to why Antwerp, so far from Lisbon, should have become the port of entry he pointed to the special concessions for international fairs, and to the thriving industries, both of wool and high grade craftsmanship, already established in the hinterland. Not least in importance was the central position of Antwerp with respect to the northern markets of England, Scotland, France, Scandinavia, and even Germany, which, though distant, was more accessible from Antwerp than from Venice, shut off as it was from the latter by mountain barriers. Later in the century but before the date of Guicciardini's chronicles the gold and silver bullion

---

[1] 'Low Dutch' was not of course restricted to 'Holland': thus the printer of the English translation of Christoph Wirsung's book on general medical practice (No. 733), refers to its previous translation from 'high Dutch or Germaine' into 'low Dutch or Flemish'.

[2] The Italian edition revised by Guicciardini was printed by Plantin in 1567. This may be conveniently read in the French edition of 1581 reprinted in R. H. Tawney and E. Power, *Tudor Economic Documents*, Vol. III, London, 1924, pp. 149 f.

D*

from the New World poured into Antwerp. Thus it came about that the Low Countries were for a time a guarantee of solvency of Portugal, Spain, and the Empire first of Charles V and after 1556, when Charles was succeeded as Emperor by his brother Ferdinand, of the Spain of Philip II, Charles's son. That it was no more was due to the Spanish incapacity for economic affairs which 'seemed almost inspired' (R. H. Tawney, *Religion and the Rise of Capitalism*, London, 1926, p. 72) whereby the greater part of the wealth accruing in the first place to Portugal and Spain slipped through their hands into the coffers of Welsers, Fuggers, and other international bankers, who had established themselves in Antwerp in the early days of its expansion. But before the end of the century it was even less; for the wealth of the southern states of the Low Countries, including Antwerp, was drained away by the wastage of a war, whose brutality was matched only by its futility. The stamping out of heresy had been initiated by the ruthless *placards* of Charles V; but the blood-bath which Philip II inflicted upon the Netherlands was the outcome of his refusal to recognise a new factor in politics—national conscious-ness. For though it was with the devout intention of maintaining the Catholic Faith unsullied by infection by the Calvinism which was gaining ground in France, it was the unimaginative and irresponsible manner in which the campaign was directed by Philip from Spain, without any consideration for local pride, whether of nobles or people, that drove Catholic and Calvinist alike to band together against the threat of foreign domination. The terrible sack of Antwerp in 1576, which ended the commercial supremacy of that city, was the signal for united action without regard to differences of religion. Unity was not however sustained (see below, p. 56): the mainly catholic South was subdued to Spanish hegemony and formed the nucleus of the future Belgium. The Calvinist North continued the struggle as the United Pro-vinces, out of which grew the unique Dutch civilisation of the seventeenth century. One of the first signs of this coming glory was the foundation in 1575 of the University of Leiden as a memorial, chosen by the citizens themselves, of the stubbornness with which the city had been held against the Spanish besiegers. One of the first distinguished *émigrés* to seek temporary asylum there was the printer, Plantin; in the next century, in various cities, they were to include Descartes, Spinoza and John Locke.

To a modern reader it may appear strange that from this long and desperate struggle the United Provinces emerged richer than when they entered it, not only in riches of the mind—Athens had achieved no less in the Peloponnesian War—but in tangible assets and military, or rather naval, power. The explanation of this apparent enigma lies in the fact that 'economic warfare' of a whole *people* as distinct from the sovereign power is a comparatively modern expedient. The Dutch merchants continued to trade with Spain greatly to their material advantage. Such behaviour was merely a continuation between different parties of a principle among the provisions of the *Grand Privilege* granted by Mary of Burgundy to the Estates General in 1477 which distinguished between the sovereign's interests and those of his subjects and specifically mentioned trading with the former's enemies. The application of such a principle to a democratic union of communities fighting for their existence is harder to swallow; yet swallow it they did, with their consequent enrichment in material wealth and the subsequent rise of Amsterdam to something like the pre-eminence previously enjoyed by Antwerp.

The French are apt to claim, not without reason, that they are the only really civilised Europeans. Whatever may be the justice of this claim, it is certainly the case that France was the first European country to achieve national sovereignty. This was mainly the work of Louis XI, who, ascending the throne in 1461, in the course of twenty-two years achieved a considerable part of the ambition expressed in the following preamble to an act of his chancellery: '. . . Le roi a voulu, et veut toujours soutenir et maintenir, que le royaume s'étend d'une part jusqu'aux Alpes où est enclos le pays de Savoie et jusqu'au Rhin où est enclos le pays de Bourgogne.'[1] The key word is of course 'Burgundy'—a feudal anachronism which had been a thorn in the side of France throughout the exhausting Hundred Years' War against England. Anachronism it may have been; it was nevertheless in 1461 an exceedingly powerful one—'the greatest power in Western Europe' (Gilmore, *The World of Humanism*, New York, 1952, p. 78). Fortunately for Louis, Charles the Bold, the reigning duke, over-reached himself and was defeated and killed by the consequent coalition, leaving no male heir. The subsequent break-up of

---

[1] Quoted by Pierre Champion, *Le Roi Louis XI*, Paris, 1936, p. 298.

the Burgundian territories greatly enlarged the kingdom of France. Of greater interest from our point of view is the fact that the Flemish-speaking parts of the Netherlands had had close cultural and economic ties with Burgundy: the city of Brussels arose mainly as a result of being for some time the capital of the Duchy. Hence, when, after some territorial adjustments, these territories came to be numbered among the seventeen Netherland provinces they enriched that confederation with a national consciousness quite different from that of the 'Dutch' provinces of the north. This of course had its disadvantages, as was first apparent when, as a result of a resurgence of extreme Calvinism and Anabaptism in Brussels and Ghent the southern catholics formed a confederation to protect themselves 'against the barbarous and worse than Spanish tyranny'. This led to the Union of Arras—the beginning of the final disruption into Holland and Belgium, a state ultimately stabilised only in 1839.

After this digression we return to that part of the policy of Louis XI which has special relevance to our discussion. This was his fostering of old industries—mines and wines—and introduction of new ones—silk and glass; above all the establishment of printing at the Sorbonne.

Looking back at the solid achievements of this remarkable and fascinating man—a long stride towards the goal of geographical inclusiveness, financial stability, industrial progress and diversification, the final liquidation of irresponsible feudal adventurers, the raising of the *bourgeoisie* (in its modern sense) to a leading consultative body, the freeing of the Gallican Church from the incubus of absolute control (in respect of taxation and appointments to benefices) by the Pope—all this with comparatively little war and even bloodshed. How was it possible? Luck, cunning, bullying, perfidy, superhuman energy—all these have been variously assigned by historians as the main cause. All indeed seem to have played a part. Perhaps Joseph Calmette has put the matter most fairly: 'Subtilité, mensonge . . . c'est bien par ces procèdes que Louis s'est assuré dans l'histoire cette solide réputation d'astuce et de mauvais foi qui n'est point surfaite, mais qui fait trop souvent oublier la mauvaise foi égale de ses partenaires: car la génération au milieu de laquelle il a vécu et manoeuvré est celle qui a inspiré a Machiavel par une simple transposition de la realité en principes, sa theorie célèbre du Prince.' [1] Louis has in short a strong claim to be numbered among those rulers of the renaissance who by dubious and often reprehensible means were opening up new vistas of political life. It is only fair to add that Louis's achievements could hardly have been possible but for the establishment of a standing army by his predecessor, Charles VII, who also took the first steps towards achieving ecclesiastical independence.

If the reign of Louis XI has more than a little resemblance to that of the English king Edward IV and, even more, to that of Henry VII, the Italian venture which followed it dissipated its fruits as surely as did Henry VIII his father's colossal fortune. It is possible to see in Charles VIII's invasion of Italy in 1494 the beginning of 'modern' *Weltpolitik* in the overt recognition of the principle of the maintenance of the 'Balance of Power' between national sovereign states. But it is also possible to regard this adventure as a retrogression from the idea of extending the frontiers of a compact domain, imperfectly envisaged by Louis XI, to the feudal ideal of having a foot in as many camps as possible, to which real or imaginary title-deeds gave a claim capable of formulation. This may serve to remind us of the danger of attempting to isolate any date or event as 'the' end of the Middle Ages.

Three French kings in succession wasted their substance on the attempt to add at least the Kingdom of Naples to the French domains. The opposition came, not from 'Italy', since there was not then, nor for another three centuries, any such state, but from the Habsburgs; which meant Spain with the somewhat fickle assistance of the Empire. All these efforts resulted in ultimate failure; they are of interest to the historian of science on three counts. First stands the impact on the French nobility of the artistic splendour of the Italian towns, which resulted in the aging Leonardo da Vinci's ending his days near Amboise in the service of Francis I. Second, it was in the numerous battles on Italian soil that was demonstrated the final eclipse of the armoured knight by gunpowder and field fortification. [2] Last—a

---

[1] J. Calmette, *Les Derniers Etapes du Moyen Age Français*, Paris, 1944, pp. 133-52.

[2] This is true only in a broad sense. For though Ravenna (1512) was the first battle in which cannon settled the event of the day, at Marignano (1512) it was the hitherto invincible Swiss *infantry* (standing or charging in serried ranks of pikes) which was broken by gunfire; and, even here the result was complicated by the treachery of their allies: moreover they ultimately effected their retreat in good order. (C. Oman, *A History of the Art of War in the Sixteenth Century*, London, 1937, pp. 130, 148. For the

fact which does not appear to have penetrated into the standard works on the period—it was in Naples that the great pandemic of syphilis started, giving rise to a considerable special literature, and an immense number of references dealing with the *Morbus Gallicus, Hispanicus, Neapolitanus,* according to the nationality or whim of the writer. Of this scourge it will be necessary to speak at length in a later chapter.

The last of the French 'excursionists' to Italy, Francis I, with all his faults as a national leader, stands highest as patron of arts and founder of Colleges and Chairs for the teaching of Latin, Greek, Hebrew and the 'new' mathematics (but see below, p. 70). Nevertheless, though for a time he and his sister, Marguerite of Angoulême, Queen of Navarre, had viewed sympathetically the movement towards reform within the Gallican Church initiated by the great scholar, Lefèvre d'Etaples, and nurtured by Briçonnet, Bishop of Meaux, he was ultimately won over by the reactionary fervour of the theologians of the Sorbonne and the constitutional orthodoxy of the *Parlement* of Paris, so that his reign ended with a rigid censorship and an orgy of persecution which brought about the relative extinction of Paris as a centre of learning.

From this time onward to the Edict of Nantes (1598) France was racked with a succession of civil wars of religion bringing the country to a state of destitution to which the dedications of many contemporary works bear pathetic witness (No. 213). The Edict itself, negotiated after Henry IV had been 'converted' to the Roman faith, was one of the greatest, if not moral at least political triumphs of the sixteenth century. For, although affirming the necessity of religious unity for the complete health of the state, it permitted, as an unavoidable compromise, freedom of conscience and, under not unreasonable conditions, of worship to the Huguenot minority unwilling to profess the State religion.

Leaving France emerging from destitution we pass on to the nation which had taken the place of England as her traditional enemy. For some centuries before 1480 there had been more than one kingdom in the Iberian Peninsula—not to mention the Moorish caliphate in the south. In 1470, when the kingdom of

development of firearms and its influence on military history see Singer, *Hist. Tech.* II, and III, and the interesting study by D. Ayalon, *Gunpowder and Firearms in the Mamluk Kingdoms,* London, 1956.

Portugal was just reaching its zenith, the kingdoms of Castile and Aragon were joined by the marriage of their respective rulers Isabella and Ferdinand. Had Isabella married the king of Portugal, as had more than once seemed likely, the whole course of world history might have been changed. The fruits of the great discoveries would have been shared; the draining of Iberian blood and wealth into Italy *via* Naples avoided. The first major consequence of this unification was the final extrusion of the Moorish power from Europe (1492) for which service the Pope conferred on the Spanish sovereigns the title of 'Catholic'. The establishment of the Inquisition which gave effect to this policy had the consequence of driving away the Jewish merchants—a consequence of special gravity for the already declining trade of Barcelona.

Of the Portuguese navigators, as a consequence of whose initiative and organisation geography and cartography came to be in the sixteenth century such an important part of science, it will be convenient to speak when we deal with the history of that science. Though men of Portuguese birth continued to play an important part in the critical diffusion of classical and medieval knowledge, which formed so large a part of the scientific activity of the early sixteenth century, of the country itself, even of Lisbon, we hear comparatively little. Of Spain on the other hand, as we have already seen, we hear a good deal too much. At least if we restrict our consideration to political and religious activities, for here the legions of Spain seem always to be on the side of reaction and oppression. But such a judgment would be unfair to the memory of such men as Hernando Nunez, Elio de Nebrija, and Cardinal Ximenes, founder of the new University of Alcalà, at which the production of the first polyglot (Complutensian) Bible realised the aim of Erasmus earlier than in any other European country.[1] In Castile, at least, Italian Humanism flourished as early and as vigorously as in other countries and by similar means. Nevertheless the revival of classical scholarship in Spain was mainly restricted to what may be called 'Erasmian Humanism'; of critical editors of the classics of science and medicine, such as Linacre, Guinther of Andernach, and Jacques Goupyl there were none. In the highly conservative soils of Aragon and Portugal Humanism failed to

[1] The Greek text of Erasmus was, however, actually printed some years earlier than the polyglot.

strike roots. In the vernacular literature did the Spanish Renaissance flower most brilliantly; but so late that in the most famous work of all—*Don Quixote*—Cervantes was able to laugh not only at the extravagances of Chivalry but also at the scholarly futilities of the Renaissance itself.

Even in the military sphere the near invincibility of the Spanish infantry was due to the perfection of an instrument with only a limited application. The rout of the Armada was in a sense the outcome of this very efficiency: so long as the enemy agreed to play the same game, then even on the sea, as at Lepanto, the Spaniard was invincible. But against an enemy with a new conception of warfare, possessing the instruments and the training to handle them, reliance on an outworn tactic, however efficiently and courageously it might be applied, was to invite disaster, which came in an unexpectedly terrible form.

We now return to the Empire, or rather to that part of it in which so small was the influence of the Emperor that no one seems to have thought it worth while to draw up an official repudiation of his claims. The last effort to influence the thirteen cantons of Switzerland from without was made by the Swabian League: its failure was sealed in the Peace of Basel in 1499. Of the thirteen cantons, six were agrarian, exhibiting a form of primitive communism. But not unnaturally it was in the remaining town cantons—Zürich, Basel, Solothurn, Lucerne, Berne, Schaffhausen, Fribourg—that the greatest contribution to renaissance thought was made. Of these, at the beginning of the century Basel and Zürich take the foremost place. In the former Erasmus was to be seen (and doubtless heard) from time to time; in the latter, greatly influenced by Erasmus, Huldreich Zwingli was slowly developing his attack on the Church of Rome independently of Luther's theses; but it was only in the year following that event that he was appointed 'people's priest' in the Grossmuenster. The democratic structure of cantonal government is well illustrated by the way in which Zwingli's challenge was thrown ('flung' is here too strong a word) down. In 1523 the municipal head of Zürich summoned a gathering of public officials and priests. Before this assembly Zwingli proposed sixty-seven articles. Despite some opposition the articles were held to have been sustained thus marking the establishment of a phase of the Protestant Reformation—though the term was first used only after the Diet of Speyer (1529) and refers strictly only to the Lutheran Reform. The Zwinglian phase was indeed only a passing one owing to a radical divergence of views on the nature of the Eucharist.

Prior to 1515 the cantons frequently exerted an influence on European affairs by military intervention; in that year, however, they found themselves opposed to the French instead of, as was more usual, fighting for them. At the battle of Marignano, where they were fulfilling a promise to support the Duchy of Milan against the invasion of Francis I, they suffered a heavy defeat. Thereafter they did not interfere as a body politic but permitted France to recruit mercenaries within their frontiers—an ignoble state of affairs which was one of the spurs to Zwingli's crusade.

Basel and Zürich, and to a lesser extent the other town cantons, were throughout the century a centre of intellectual activity second to none in Europe. In the former Ioannes Froben, to name but the greatest of a number of great scholar printers, published the works of his friend Erasmus and employed the young Hans Holbein; Paracelsus anathematised Galen and his sycophants; Felix Platter and Caspar Bauhin anatomised to such good effect as to surpass Padua; Bauhin also laid the foundations of a science of systematic botany. The house of Froben (occupied by his son, Hieronymus, after 1527) where Erasmus ended his days (1536), still stands as a living memorial. Zürich on the other hand is dominated by the encyclopaedic genius, Conrad Gesner, and by his publisher (who also printed the Bible of 1550 for the London printers) Christof Froschover. At least it *was*; today Gesner's house, among the winding alleys of the Altstadt, has to be sought out with the aid of the helpful officials of the Rathaus; and no plaque announces to the searcher the end of his quest. Reparation is however made in the Botanic Garden.

Nearly at the last we reach the country where perhaps we might have been expected to start. But in this chapter we are concerned only with setting the stage for the sixteenth century—a century in which the *predominance* of Italy soon passes—except in regard to her medical schools. The 'Italy' which Charles VIII proposed to annex to his domains was in the first place the Kingdom of Naples—the only kingdom in the peninsular. It was ruled—if 'ruled' is the word—by the illegitimate branch of the House of Aragon, but in no part of Italy had feudalism—especially the disruptive aspects—been so well established. The antagonisms between Naples and the Duchy of Milan promised a good chance of assistance by the latter to France. Milan, however, together with all the Italian states except Venice, Naples and the Papal territories, was a fief of the Empire, which could therefore not fail to be dragged into the French adventure. Milan was at this time subject to the military dictatorship of Lodovico Sforza ('il moro') ruling nominally for, but contrary to the will of, the young duke Gian Galeazzo. Of life in Milan in the first half of the century we may learn a good deal (always with a pinch of salt) from Girolamo Cardano (see above, p. 29).

The exact nature of the leading northern 'states'—Venice, Florence and Milan—is difficult to determine. Their genesis, each from a single city and its immediate neighbourhood, led to the names by which they were known for centuries. It is also the only justification for the custom of referring to them as 'city states'. When it is recognised that the territory included in the Republic of Venice was in 1500 comparable in extent to the whole of contemporary Switzerland, and that it embraced within its borders, in addition to Venice, the cities of Verona, Vicenza, and Padua, the misleading character of the term is at once apparent. Nevertheless the dominant position of the name-city placed these states in a category unlike any others in Europe. Doubtless the splendours of their civilisation was not unconnected with their relatively early detachment from the feudal and religious struggles which retarded the development of other European *states*, though comparable municipal splendour was to be seen in the Flemish wool towns and some of the Hansa cities. It is important nevertheless not to be blinded by the subsequent brilliance of this civilisation to its earlier deficiencies; for, as Olschki has emphasised,[1] no first rate thinker or artist was active in Italy from Gregory the Great (d. 604) to St. Thomas Aquinas (b. 1226); and it was to Paris that the latter had to go to school himself for his great synthesis.

Almost unique in its political constitution, in its early years almost entirely free from foreign entanglements—feudal, dynastic

---

[1] L. Olschki, *The Genius of Italy*, London, 1950. Though he notes that the earlier universities (especially Bologna) were either exclusively or predominantly concerned with Secular and Canon Law, he perhaps does not do full justice to the importance of these studies as a basis of subsequent developments in the structure of scientific and philosophical thought.

or military—was Venice. Its government, both on account of its aristocratic structure and by the frequent use of the lot, approached most nearly that of the Greek πόλις; moreover it owed its existence to sea-power. As Venice acquired more landward territory and was thus drawn more into the ambit of fifteenth-century power politics it came to make more and more use of its merchant service as an intelligence service—a device which had its beginnings in the consuls maintained in Alexandria and other Levantine ports from the late thirteenth century. Berenson has called the Venetians 'the first modern people in Europe'. 'Since there was little room for personal glory in Venice owing to the oligarchical structure of the government the perpetuators of glory, the Humanists, found at first scant encouragement there; and the Venetians were saved from that absorption in archaeology and pure science which overwhelmed Florence at an early date'.[1] Since Venice depended for its existence on trade—mainly seaborne—from the East, it is not surprising that the Venetian rulers disposed of a 'true science of statistics'.[2] At the beginning of our period the Iron Curtain thrown across the East by the Ottoman Turks, combined with the opening up of the Western Approaches, foreshadowed the decay of Venetian power. Nevertheless there is evidence to show that despite the Humanist Academies at Florence and the Papal Curia at Rome, Venice had by 1500 ten times the number of printing presses as the former and three times as many as the latter.[3]

Although Florence was nominally a 'republic' with a government ostensibly more 'democratic' than the Venetian oligarchy, Grant (*op. cit.*) draws an illuminating parallel between the Medici and a modern 'Press Lord' with no official position but controlling the organs of government through the money market and the press. The most famous of these 'Banker-Princes', Lorenzo il Magnifico, died in 1492, from which time they lost their grip. The first sign of this was the extraordinary 'dictatorship' of the fanatical friar Girolamo Savonarola. The advent of the French gave the enthusiasts their chance of ending the tutelage to the Medici; but with the temporary retreat of the French the latter returned to power. In 1527, however, things took a strange turn, well illustrating the political confusion of the period. The Imperial armies

[1] B. Berenson, *The Italian Painters of the Renaissance*, London, 1953, p. 8.
[2] Burckhardt, *op. cit.* pp. 45-6.   [3] Putnam, *op. cit.*

which had been responsible for the defeat of the French decided to recoup themselves for their long arrears of pay by sacking Rome. As a consequence of this hideous affair, in which the Spanish appear to have specialised in murder and rapine while the Lutheran elements in the Imperial army made the best of this glorious opportunity to desecrate the Holy Places of the modern Babylon, the power of the Medicean pope, Clement VII, appeared to be broken. So the Florentine Republic made a second—and last—appearance. But in 1530 Clement was 'reconciled' to the Emperor, Florence was betrayed and handed over to Alessandro de' Medici with the title of Duke of Florence (1532). Florence finally disappeared as a political entity after 1574 when Francesco de' Medici was styled Grand Duke of Tuscany. Thus it came about that it was in connection with a pump working on the water supply of the 'Grand Duke of Tuscany' that Galileo banished for ever the Aristotelian fiction of the *horror vacui* The Medician patronage of learning—this time with a severely practical bias—persisted until 1655 when it appeared again in the leadership of the *Accademia del Cimento*.

Of the Papal States—hardly more coherent than the 'Empire'—it is unnecessary to speak here, except to call to mind that it was in the Papal Curia that the labours of Flavio Biondo went some way towards the founding of critical historiography. No attempt will be made here to strike a balance between the good and evil consequences of the papal magnificence and papal corruption between say 1458 (Pius II) and the end of our period.

We come finally to that 'sceptred isle', which if it had not yet achieved 'splendid isolation' did during the sixteenth century manage to release itself of entanglements on the continent of Europe to a degree never before achieved. This at least is true of England and Wales, less so of Scotland, which after the disaster of Flodden and, later, the marriage of James V to Marie de Guise, hovered for most of the century on the brink of civil war, and for many years fell over it. The genesis of this relative isolation must be sought in the failure of the English arms in the closing stages of the Hundred Years' War; its maintenance was due to the fact that Henry VII loved money more than glory. In honour bound he was obliged to make a show of military force to deter Charles VIII from his invasion of Italy: but his 'honour' appears to have been quickly satisfied—though at a considerable price. Once only was there a threat of the renewal of feudal entanglement—when Henry VIII's boundless egotism provoked his candidature for the Imperial crown. Presumably the price offered came nowhere near the figure which the Electors might reasonably have expected to cover this transparent absurdity. The issue, at any rate, was never a serious one. This relative isolation had both its good and its bad sides. On the credit side was the stability of the throne, in startling contrast to the previous century; the almost unbroken peace within the realm; and, apart from Henry VIII's mainly futile wars in France, a century in which foreign *conquest* was not the dominant passion. All this sounds like special pleading in respect of a century which saw Perkin Warbeck, the Pilgrimage of Grace, the Marian Persecution, and the assaults on Cadiz and the Spanish Armada. But set in the balance against the invasions of Italy, the French civil wars of religion, the Peasants' War in Germany, the Holy Inquisition in Spain, and Alva in the Netherlands, they are seen to be merely incidents—critical as they undoubtedly were at the time. Nothing is more remarkable than the course of the Reformation in England. Not only was a new heaven introduced but a new earth also; for in the dissolution of the monasteries the power of the ecclesiastical magnates disappeared with that of the Lords temporal already broken by Henry VII. Despite isolated barbarities and the actual or potential conflicts engendered by the two Marys, this religious and social revolution passed off without the holocausts and massacres committed everywhere on the Continent in the name of the Prince of Peace and the Gospel of Love.

So much for the credit side of relative isolation. The debit shows itself in the comparative slowness with which the glow of the renaissance lit up the English landscape—Scotland it hardly reached at all until, with the turn of the century, it flashed briefly as the continental graces grew over the forbidding keeps of Crathes and Keith Hall, and the formal garden of Edzell revealed a new graciousness of living. Printing indeed reached England within twenty years of its appearance at Mainz; but an examination of Caxton's and even Wynkyn de Worde's productions reveals an almost complete lack of learned works, for which presumably there was no market—and this despite the fact that Caxton was a not inconsiderable scholar, whose translations of

E

(mainly French) romances were finely printed. Oxford, which in the thirteenth and fourteenth centuries had generally equalled and sometimes surpassed any university on the Continent, was at no time during our period the scene of new enthusiasms such as those which arose at Wittenberg, Erfurt, Basel, Montpellier, Alcalà, Salamanca and a dozen others. Neither Oxford nor Cambridge lacked Greek scholars of the highest rank, but their teaching aroused but moderate enthusiasm: with one exception (p. 305) Linacre's translations were done for continental printers. Painting was supplied by Hans Holbein, the rich ornament of the Henry VII tomb by Torrigiani. Though the transition from defensive to domestic architecture was carried out with skill and no little sense of beauty, the classical orders which Alberti introduced into Italy were unknown. This in itself is no discredit: there is no aesthetic law demanding a return of ancient forms however noble. But it was not that the vigour of native art rendered their return superfluous; for return they did in over-flowing measure in the centuries which followed. Lastly an Italian, Polydore Virgil, had to be called in to 'write up' the history of the House of Tudor. All this is not to be reckoned pure loss. For if no new ideas emerged from the universities, Erasmus was at least able to find a spiritual home in one of them; and when new ideas from the continent began to filter through in the second half of the century their reception was on the whole more en-lightened than in the places of their origin. If the universities gave their *juvenes optimae spei* no marked inspiration they seem to have avoided the clogging of their minds with the lumber of a debased Aristotelianism or Galenism such as was still a common practice on the Continent. In the sphere of political economy there was also in the literature of the so-called 'commonwealth' circle a freshness of approach, which if not yet 'scientific' at any rate recognised the resemblance of the polity to a clock in which no wheel could turn of itself, but must in its motion influence all the others.[1]

Here we may perhaps bring to a close our fragmentary sketch of the sixteenth-century background. If the deployment of facts has of necessity been highly selective, an effort has been made to avoid drawing any dogmatic or far-reaching inferences from them,

[1] J. Hales, *Discourse of the Commonwealth of this Realm of England*, quoted by Arthur B. Ferguson, *J. Hist. Ideas*, **16**, 296.

whether explicitly, or what is far more insidious by implication. Juxtapositions have certainly been made, rather with a view to lighten the burden of bald description and in the hope that they may point to correlations which may be more precisely determined. What has principally been aimed at is the revelation of the author's ideological bias; and on the constructive side the provision of a frame of reference into which the reader may fit the scientific events to be subsequently put before him. No scientific observation is made, far less is any scientific theory put forward, in a purely mathematical continuum, devoid of social and political strains. That the contrary seemed at one time to be possible was the consequence of a very partial examination of the actual circumstances of scientific discovery and communication. The strains inherent in the historical continuum of the Renaissance, though unrecognised at the time, were probably greater than at any other period. It was to make these evident, even if their respective influences can not yet be fully assessed and allowed for, that this chapter was written.

CHAPTER IV

COMMUNICATION

THE 'communication' we are to consider here is not that of bodies, but of ideas. Until comparatively recently it has generally been assumed that such communication has been mediated almost entirely by conventional speech transmitted either orally or visually. But as we have seen, at least one outstanding scholar, Girolamo Cardano, was firmly convinced that 'knowledge' can be acquired by immediate intuition. Also the verbal and pictorial creations of the alchemists can not be merely written off as so much gibberish: rather they represent a sustained effort to evoke an experience of a kind for which the syntactical structure of conventional language is unsuited. The medieval church knew the power of visual symbols for the indoctrination of an unlettered laity. Whether such experience—either immediate or evoked by symbols having a closed semantic—has a significance in any way comparable in importance to that mediated by conventional modes is not here in question. All that is being urged is that no real understanding of the cultural upheaval we call the 'Renaissance' can be hoped for until these widespread characteristics have been studied with greater sympathy than has so far been the case. To the cultural tradition inherited from the so-called 'Age of Reason' they appear as aberrations now happily outlived. But to the Christian Fathers much of Greco-Roman culture took on a similar appearance—and incidentally had a similar lure which was to be resisted. Moreover these 'aberrations' seem far from having been outlived: an advertisement on behalf of the Rosicrucians appears regularly in the most 'respectable' British newspapers; Paris is said to support an unparalleled number of *clairvoyants* of all grades and types. Finally, there is a growing body of scientists and philosophers ready to admit parapsychology as a proper discipline in which some at least of these experiences, though different in kind from those amenable to the traditional methods of science, can nevertheless be subjected to controlled experiment. On a different plane is C. G. Jung's claim[1] that the arcana of the alchemists were so to say a dream acted out in the conscious in symbols revealing the welling up of the collective unconscious. All this is a beginning: possibly the beginning of a retrogression to the 'unreason' such as the Mediterranean world witnessed after the collapse of Greco-Roman civilisation, and from which first medieval Christianity, and later modern science, rescued the West. Jung's thesis embodies the belief that both these modes of 'rescue' were bought at a price too great for the unconscious to bear. The danger is real; but it is one which must be faced by the future historian of the Renaissance if not ultimately by every active member of Western civilisation. Moreover the danger is greatly lessened when, probably for the first time, it can be recognised as such in the light of its past excesses.

It was necessary to emphasise this aspect of 'communication' in renaissance thought, since it has in the past been almost consistently overlooked or passed over as the untypical enthusiasm of a few eccentrics. But if Tycho Brahe and Libavius are to be numbered among the 'eccentrics' the term loses any useful connotation. No more will be said about it here; the subject is far too complex, the paths to be followed as yet too dimly discerned: some indication of the issues at stake will, however, be referred to in the final chapter.

We pass now to the traditionally accepted media of communication through the conventional symbols of speech and the auditory and visual symbols of the arts. Of these the former has quite properly been held to be of paramount importance, so we shall consider it first.

It is tempting to regard printing from movable type as the most potent factor in bringing about the Renaissance, but the temptation must be resisted on several grounds. The earliest date for this invention is 1450, but it was almost a local craft until the Sack of Mainz in 1462 drove the printers to Strassburg, Cologne, Augsburg, Basel, Ulm, and Nürnberg. The first Italian press was set up in 1464. So from what has already been said it is clear that the literary Renaissance at least was well under way

---

[1] C. G. Jung, *Psychology and Alchemy*, trans, R. F. C. Hull, London, 1953.

E*

before the new invention could have exerted any decisive influence. Again if we examine the books themselves [1] nothing is more significant than that the great majority of books printed before 1500 were little calculated to advance either the classical renaissance or the fitful stirrings of the scientific spirit. Missals, Bibles, patristic and medieval commentaries, 'popular' Latin works such as Cicero's *De Officiis*, formed the bulk of the incunables, with here and there a Latin translation of a Greek classic. Printing in Greek type started indeed at a comparatively early date, but made no headway until Aldus Manutius put the enterprise on a commercial basis near the end of the century—a fact pointing to another aspect of the matter, namely that, contrary to what one might expect, few presses were able to hold their own in purely university centres. The pre-eminence of Paris in the early sixteenth century was due to the rigid control exercised by the Theological Faculty, which used the press as a powerful agent of propaganda. The same was true of Cologne and later of Wittenberg. But where this was the case the quality of both printing and subject-matter was apt to decline, unless some genius like Badius Ascensius managed to dodge the control, or like Robert Estienne to enlist for a time the king's support [2] against the Sorbonne.

From another point of view it must be remembered that when the humanist revival was at its height in Italy many of its promoters would not have desecrated their libraries with the 'cheap, mass-produced' substitute for a fine manuscript—the last of the great dealers in which, Vespasiano da Bisticci, lived till 1498. That the machine-made article could ever come to be regarded as a thing of beauty, merely by virtue of its form, was by most connoisseurs hotly denied. Others, like the Abbot Trithemius, thought that in any case such flimsy stuff would not hold together for more than a couple of centuries. Fortunately this contemptuous attitude was not universal, as we shall see.

To be a factor in the *origin* of the Renaissance, then, printing came too late. That it had little influence on the course of the

---

[1] For details see the chapters on the various departments of science.

[2] It is not generally known that the 'Father of Letters', Francis I, actually placed a ban (1535) on all printers, which could only have been as a means of stopping the devaluation of his beloved manuscripts. The ban was never effective; within a month it was changed into a Royal License for about a dozen printers. (*Dictionnaire Larousse*, art. '*Bibliothèque*'.)

Renaissance for half a century was mainly due to the fact that most printers had to make a profit—an object which could be achieved in the fifteenth century only by means similar to those of today, namely the proximity of an adequate market, or alternatively by producing wares appealing to a large but scattered public together with the possession of means of distribution. In the early years the former method was predominant; so the goods had to be well-known lines for which an unsatisfied demand already existed: centuries of ecclesiastical infiltration, especially, the later centuries of devoted preaching by the Mendicants ensured that this demand would be for religious works. The realisation that a contemporary writer might create a demand and thereby advertise the printer shifted the emphasis towards the second form of business: the case of Johann Froben and Erasmus is outstanding. The problem of distribution was solved partly by the opening of agencies by the printer in other countries—Aldus, Giunta, and later Plantin, are examples of this—partly by handing over the job to a banker-colporteur such as the Fuggers (see dedications of Nos. 298, 478). A major difficulty was the absence of any *effective* copyright: the 'privileges' much sought after, though in the case of the Papal and Imperial decrees nominally applying to the greater part of Europe, were for the most part too slow and costly in operation to be effective. This state of affairs accounts for the enormous emphasis placed on indications of 'new' and 'improved' (e.g. *novus, auctus, castigatus*) editions. To the annoyance of piracy was added the restriction of censorship, begun by Alexander VI but spreading quickly to the secular powers. For half a century it was little more than a nuisance to a reputable printer, but the successive *Indexes* enforced by the Council of Trent made it impossible to plan ahead. It can hardly be doubted that this was an important factor in the rapid decline of the Venetian book trade in the second half of the sixteenth century. Finally, in the *cri du coeur* of Aldus, the 'stupidities of war' ensured that the printer's life was not a happy one. But with what zest they must have worked! When one takes account of the type-setting, registration, and gathering, in a work like Avicenna's *Canon Medicinae* (the *Continens* of ar-Razi was much larger, but probably unique), the speed with which editions poured out makes the delays of our mechanised and streamlined inefficiency look rather shabby (see No. 615). Nor were the men who pushed these jobs through mere hard-headed businessmen with no non-sense about them. Of Badius Ascensius Erasmus could say that his Latinity was the equal of Budé's. So accomplished in Latin was his daughter, Petronilla, that the problem of communication in the polyglot household of her husband, Robert Estienne, was easily solved by using that language in the affairs of everyday life.

An important factor in communication was patronage. Nauseating as some of its cruder manifestations appear to us, it must be remembered that with all its faults it played the essential role now performed by governments and other corporate bodies, especially learned societies. Not until about 1510 is there any evidence of an author receiving any payment for his work. Books, when they were not merely editions or translations of classics, served the purposes of the modern learned periodical in making a scholar's views known to a much wider circle than could be achieved by a declamation in his university or other local as-sembly. A considerable proportion of scientific writers were the servants of princes who gained as much prestige by the display of learned works written under their patronage as from the other marks of pre-eminence—castles, retinue, processions and the like—typical of the age. This form of patronage was most in evidence during the period of the Medicis, the Emperor Maxi-milian I, and Francis I, but persisted throughout the sixteenth century. During this century, however, we see a gradual increase in the number of dedications to the 'Senate' of a town. Also we know from the evidence provided in printers' account books and correspondence, as well as from forewords in the books themselves, that the initiative was increasingly taken by the printers, who with the enlarged field of potential customers found that they could afford to commission and pay for a book on a subject of sufficiently wide interest. A form of royalty payment had existed from early in the century (as we know from the jibe of Erasmus against Ulrich von Hutten);[1] Gesner in the middle years speaks of 'writing for his daily bread';[2] so that throughout the period there seems to have been in varying degrees all the forms of author-printer relationship which we know today: only the relative emphasis was

[1] Who replied in kind, with respect to Erasmus's fees for proof-correcting! Putnam, *op. cit.* II, 176, 182, 431.
[2] Putnam, *op. cit.* p. 432.

different. The same is true of the relations of production. From Erasmus [1] we learn that Froben published sometimes at his own risk, sometimes wholly at another's; and sometimes the risk was shared according to the terms of a temporary agreement. It is obvious that the principal difference between renaissance publication and that of today is that each publisher was then most commonly his own printer; today, apart from some of the University Presses, it is the exception.

With regard to the size of editions and the price of books information is somewhat meagre, but so far as it goes it reveals a state of affairs differing from today's less than might be expected. The earliest recorded price-list dates from 1470, but the correspondence [2] and price-list (1489) of Aldus provides the first information of printing on anything like a modern scale—effectuated by his introduction of 'pocket' editions of the classics, of convenient size for leisure reading, and at a reasonable price (estimated by Putnam in 1898 at about $ 2.00). Even at this early date editions might run into several thousand copies—Simon de Colines printed 24,000 of Erasmus's *Colloquies* at Paris soon after 1520—but nearly a century later the *average* edition was of the order of one thousand.

Where did all these books go? From the earliest days of printing there were libraries,[3] both institutional and private, which are either extant or of which contemporary records exist. The Vatican Library effectively founded by Nicholas V (d. 1447) was merely one of a number of great Italian libraries. Louis XI reorganised the Library of the Louvre, which under Francis I became the *Bibliothèque Royale*, and was inaugurated as an effective national library by a decree of 25 Fructidor, an iv. Fortunately it has been possible to reconstruct in large measure catalogues of three private libraries existing at or about the beginning of the sixteenth century. These belonged to Giovanni Pico della Mirandola, Nicholas Pol, and Hieronymus Münzer. Pico's influence on science was indirect, in particular through his diatribe against astrology; and even this was not based on arguments which would now be regarded as scientific. The deed of appointment of Nicolaus Pol as physician to the Emperor

---

[1] Putnam, *op. cit.* p. 429.
[2] Putnam, Vol. I, pp. 418 f.
[3] For details see J. Westfall Thompson, *The Medieval Library*, Chicago, 1939.

Maximilian I (1506) is still extant, and interest in his life centres in his journey to Spain to investigate the guaiac 'cure' for syphilis, of which his report exists in both manuscript and printed form. This will be referred to later (p. 281); what is of special interest in connection with communication is his correspondence with the monk Veit Bild, who acted as a scribe in the Monastery of Saints Ulrich and Afra at Augsburg. Nicolaus Pol, in the deed of appointment as Imperial Physician, undertook to reside at Innsbruck: by 1517 he owned two houses there on the Silbergasse; and it is to Innsbruck that Veit Bild's letters from 1513 onwards are addressed. The importance of this correspondence, copies of which were fortunately made by Bild, is that it casts light on communication in the learned world of the time. Augsburg was one of the chief centres of the book trade; Innsbruck on the other hand was only then rising to the eminence it later achieved. But Pol was by then rich enough to assemble a great library, so he was glad to use Bild as an agent; the latter thought himself sufficiently rewarded for his services by the guidance which Pol gave him in the task of making and calibrating sundials—in which he did a considerable 'mail order' trade—and of compiling calendars and nativities. Pol's literary interests were by no means restricted to medicine. Though a perusal of the list of 467 works, which it is thought may represent only a half to one-third of his library, reveals a comprehensive selection of Arabic, medieval and contemporary medical works, there are far more of a theological nature. If the list can be regarded as a random sample then it is significant that whereas four editions of the *Canon Medicinae* are named, there is no work of Hippocrates,[1] and only one of Galen. Pol was evidently determined to keep up to date with his reading; he ordered several of Symphorien Champier's (Nos. 143) works, and Reuchlin's Hebrew Grammar. Tanstetter's work (No. 669) of 1514 was in his hands in May of the following year.

Hieronymus Münzer (Monetarius) belonged to the Nürnberg of Dürer. He completed his medical studies (begun at Leipzig) at Pavia 1476-8, and in the latter year established himself in medical practice in Nürnberg. Concerning his niche in the history

---

[1] The one mentioned under 'Hippocrates' can not have been by Hippocrates of Cos since there was no 'Ptolemaum regem' living to whom it could have been written. There is a brief quotation of Hippocrates in the Guaiac tract.

of science we shall have to speak at a later stage (see below, p. 135); what concerns us here is the very revealing record of the formation of a private library which E. P. Goldschmidt [1] reconstructed in his most valuable biography. Of the 185 authenticated works possessed by Münzer, 18 are classified by Goldschmidt as Theology, 32 as Philosophy, 26 as 'Exakte Wissenschaften, Astronomie, Geographie', 29 as Medicine, 40 as 'Klassiker', 40 as 'Neulateiner' (original works by Humanists). About ninety other works are also listed, whose names have been derived from the catalogue of books presented by Münzer to his home-town Feldkirch: these comprise very few works on science or medicine. The value of Goldschmidt's reconstruction for the history of science is greatly enhanced by Münzer's frequent habit of noting down where and under what circumstances he acquired the volume. Thus: '. . . quem mihi comparavi dum essem Parisius in peregrinacione Hispanica anno 1494 in diebus Marcii' refers to his journey to Spain to which we shall revert later; 'quem mihi aportari feci ex Florencia . . . 1493 . . .'—a volume ordered from Florence (the *Enneades* of Plotinus, Florence 1492); 'quem mihi comparavi Mediolani et Nurembergam mecum traduxi . . . 1488' evidently picked up at Milan eleven years after its publication and carried with him on the journey home. An earlier purchase at Milan was on his return from Rome in December 1483 at the conclusion of that journey in which he followed his own advice to the populace of Nürnberg on the onset of the severe plague and hurriedly left the city and, somewhat cravenly, his family. Many books were bought by him during his student days at Pavia. He was so enamoured of Cicero that he noted in a composite volume: '. . . dies enim medicinali practice addixit, noctu autem huius lectione se levavit.' Sallust also he read 'for a couple of hours after dinner' and during the watches of St. Simon and St. Jude and All Saints; similarly Ovid (*Opera*, sent from Venice to Nürnberg in 1482) 'ut animum reficerem'.[2] Of all Münzer's inscriptions perhaps of most interest to the historian of science is that in the *Editio princeps* of Euclid's *Elements* (No. 235) to the effect

---

[1] E. P. Goldschmidt, *Hieronymus Münzer und seine Bibliothek*, Warburg Institute, London, 1938.

[2] He added a note (in Latin) to the *Heroides*, XI, 43, to the effect that he had known the wife of a certain physician who finding herself pregnant in the absence of her husband had made many vain attempts to procure an abortion. He mentions the frequent resort to herbs and other things for this purpose.

that it had been given to him by Bernhard Walther, the pupil and patron of Regiomontanus. Bound with it are two works printed at their private press in Nürnberg—Peurbach's *Theoricae Planetarum Novae* (No. 513) and Regiomontanus's *Dialogus contra Cremonensia* (c. 1475).

When we compare these indications with what we have seen in the case of Nicolaus Pol's collection we are struck by the fact that whereas the latter was able to purchase most of what he wanted at Augsburg, Münzer collected a large number on his numerous travels—mainly in Italy. This does not mean that Nürnberg was entirely cut off from supplies from Italy, since there is evidence in several cases of local purchase and binding; but it does seem likely that in the thirty odd years which supervened between Münzer's appointment as *Stadtarzt* at Nürnberg and Pol's employment of Bild as his agent the flow of books from Italy and France had increased.

The life of Hieronymus Münzer sheds a light on the question of communication not only in relation to the movement of books but also by the movements of the man himself, which serve to remind us that despite the great difficulties of travel—especially overland as was necessarily the case from Nürnberg—actual conversation between scholars of different countries played a part in the diffusion of ideas whose relative importance it is now very difficult to estimate. Münzer's was very nearly the age of Erasmus—that Envoy Extraordinary of the Republic of Letters, whose journeys back and forth from Basel to England, France, the Low Countries and Italy spread the gospel alike of Cicero and Christ. It may be that this period was the high watermark of oral communication which was rendered the less necessary by the greater—and cheaper—flow of books. Probably the most important function of printing in the *progress* of the Renaissance was that it made possible for the first time the setting up of definitive texts, available in any number of *identical* copies. (Cf. G. Sarton, *Six Wings*, pp. 116 f.)

Of the last kind of oral and visual communication with which it is possible to deal, the importance can hardly be exaggerated, namely that provided by the *atelier*—a convenient term to cover all places of 'work in progress'. It is only necessary to recall what has already been said of the concentration of metal-working crafts in Nürnberg. Corresponding to this in the realm of the more conventional 'fine arts', was the *atelier* [1] of Andrea del Verrochio in Florence, where from the age of thirteen Leonardo da Vinci developed his many-sided genius. Here artists availed themselves of the knowledge and skill of the best mathematician in town, Paolo Toscanelli (see below, p. 130). Outstanding medical authorities helped the Florentine artists in their study of anatomy, but it is a moot point as to who gained the most in this exchange of views.

The importance of the visual arts in the development of the idea of physical space has already been dealt with (p. 20f.), but even before the problems of perspective had been seriously tackled a growing awareness of the peculiar forms of living things was being communicated from one mind to another by their visual exhibition. I emphasise 'awareness', since the absence of naturalistic verisimilitude does not appear to be due to lack of skill, but rather to a lack of interest. This is brought out in a remarkable manner in one of the masterpieces of (for this aspect of art) the transition period: *The Vision of St. Eustace* by Pisanello (d. 1455). Whereas the floral carpet is much inferior to the best of Fra Angelico (e.g. the *Noli me tangere* in the Convent of San Marco, Florence) who died in the same year, the 'sporting' animals are observed with an astonishing exactitude. Not only are there at least five distinct 'species' of sporting dogs, but the treatment of their bodies and of those of the stags (especially the smaller one) shows an undoubted acquaintance with the relation between tendons, muscles and even bones. [2] Even the horse (though it might fall backwards at any moment) is far better moulded than the wooden rocking horses of the *Rout of St. Romano* by the more sophisticated Paolo Uccello (d. 1475). And here the question of awareness and interest come very clearly into view, for whereas there is in the *Vision* only an imperfect appreciation of linear perspective, Uccello, as is well known, displays in the *Rout* an almost morbid preoccupation with its early triumphs. When we turn to the portrayal of plants an even more striking case of 'awareness' meets us—I mean the sudden irruption of stiff-leaf

[1] Cf. L. Olschki, *The Genius of Italy*, London, 1950, pp. 301 ff. In view of the earlier example of Nürnberg it is an exaggeration on the part of Olschki to say that 'such a communication of artistic and scientific activities did not exist in any other part of the world'. A partial retraction occurs on p. 310.

[2] Even more remarkable are Pisanello's drawings of monkeys (J. Rosenberg *Great Draughtsmen from Pisanello to Picasso*, Cambridge, Mass., 1959).

carving in several English churches, but pre-eminently in the chapter-house of Southwell Minster. Dr. Pevsner[1] thinks that the master mason who directed the work at Southwell drew his inspiration most probably from Rheims as equally probably did the masters of Bamberg and Naumburg. But whatever the immediate model it was little removed from nature itself as evidenced by the facts that the leaves 'grow out of' the piers, that they are accurate representations of distinct species of plants, and that the massing, though by no means haphazard, lacks the formal regularity of all that had gone before. Above all is the evidence of such significant incongruities as the Hemp Nettle (?) leaf in one of the groups. The relevance of all this to the historian of science is that this outburst of floral naturalism lasted no longer than perhaps fifty years, ending early in the fourteenth century. This was over a century before the formalised floral carpet or sandy waste decorated with plants not yet characterised by distinctive botanical features, gave way to plants individually conceived.[2] The two aspects appear in the same picture in the National Gallery, London—*The Virgin and Child with Saints* by Filippino Lippi (d. 1504). The floral ground pattern is somewhat formalised as a whole; but in the right hand corner is an individual study whose leaves, phyllotaxis, and characteristic floret reveal an unmistakable Labiate—perhaps a Hemp Nettle.

That this form of communication was limited in scope may be inferred by a comparison of these floral studies with the illustrations in the contemporary incunables (e.g. No. 489) which, though lively and not lacking in artistic merit, are for the most part botanically negligible. To account for this discrepancy—one to which insufficient attention has been given in many works on renaissance science—one must bear in mind that printers then as now had on the whole to meet an existing demand. The demand here as elsewhere was for 'standard lines' which had already given evidence of possessing a wide appeal, though in relatively small numbers, in manuscript form. Now before the *Fasciculus Medicinae* (1491) an illustration of any kind was exceptional in a medical work—physicians were clearly not in the habit of using their eyes,

---

[1] N. Pevsner, *The Leaves of Southwell*, King Penguin Books, London, 1945, pp. 36 f.

[2] Of special interest is the inclusion of a number of fallen blossoms in the beautifully informal study of *Aquilegia* in the Portinari triptych (Uffizi, Florence) formerly attributed to van der Goes (d. 1482).

and would perhaps have been insulted if asked to: the incunable herbals were apparently not for them. Yet seeing that many of these herbals were in Latin it is difficult to guess for whom they *were* intended. A similar question which has hardly received a satisfactory answer is why the herbals of this period which were written in German should have been illustrated in a more refined and naturalistic manner than the others.

A mode of communication of *proto*-scientific knowledge whose influence has been variously estimated is the guild and craft lore passed on mainly by word of mouth among the adepts. In so far as the communication was solely verbal no estimate can be much more than guesswork; but where it seems that the lore has gradually been codified and committed to writing something rather more precise may be attempted. In this field *proto*-chemistry is perhaps the outstanding case, in which there is good reason to believe that craft knowledge had reached a high level of precision and control before 'theory' had shaken itself free of magic and pseudo-knowledge, such as the doctrine of signs. One of the most valuable documents for study of this sort is the *Feuerwerkbuch von 1420* which has recently been edited with a valuable commentary by Wilhelm Hassenstein (Muenchen 1941). To this must be added the compendia of information on mining and smelting (*Bergwerk*) and on assay (*Probierkunst*), with a manuscript tradition based probably on a long oral one. Of all of these something will be said in a later chapter.

CHAPTER V

THE SYSTEM OF THE SCIENCES
IN THE SIXTEENTH CENTURY

IN the preceding chapters an attempt has been made to appreciate in some measure the state of 'culture' in which the sciences developed during the sixteenth century. I use the term 'developed' in the biological sense of 'structural change', which carries with it no implication of ordered progress but often includes temporary retrogression, as in the pupal stage of holometabolous insects. Here relatively rigid structures become more fluid as a preparation for the emergence of new organs which will release the creature from its earthbound or aquatic life and give it wings to soar into a new element. It may be that we shall come to look upon the 'renaissance' as such a phase in the life of science when to rationalism and empiricism, whose compresence in the Middle Ages has not always been recognised, was added imagination. If there is anything of value in this view what we have to look for is the appearance not so much of new facts, or even of new correlations, but of new ways of looking at familiar facts. Thus the remainder of this *Introduction* is in no sense a 'history of science in the sixteenth century' but at the most a search for significant changes in scientific perspective. Nevertheless, since a change can be fully appreciated only in terms of what is already accepted, a good deal of the discussion will be taken up with the state of knowledge or accepted opinion at or about the opening of the century. This method carries with it the danger of seeing only what is being looked for. Apart from the fact that this, *pace* the naïver forms of empiricism, is involved in any sort of 'seeing', whether of the eye or of the intelligence, its cruder consequences can be guarded against by looking for the opposite phenomenon, namely, resistance to change and also incomprehension.

But what were 'the sciences' in the year 1500? To this question an answer must be given which may guide our discussion but without being unintelligible to a critical mind of the time—Copernicus, for instance, who in that year had just completed his studies at Bologna. Clearly even the broader divisions of today would be inapplicable—'physiology' was almost synonymous with 'physics', and both terms meant something quite different from what they do today; chemistry, except as a craft applied to medicine and metallurgy, was virtually non-existent; and looming over all, strongly influencing such classification as there was, stood the Aristotelian dogma, insisting on the absolute distinction between the divine science of the changeless heavenly spheres and the natural philosophy of the region of growth and decay below the sphere of the moon. It can not be too strongly emphasised that despite the 'renaissance' this system of the world was the 'official' doctrine of every university in Europe [1] throughout the century. It might be thought that reference to the syllabuses of studies laid down for degrees would provide a basis for classification, but this is far from being the case. In the first place the time-honoured basis of the Faculty of Arts—trivium (Grammar, Rhetoric, Philosophy) and quadrivium (Arithmetic, Geometry, Astronomy, Music) through which the great majority of students passed whether or not they went on to the Higher Faculties—Theology, Laws (Canon and Civil), Medicine—had ceased to have any detailed application even in the fourteenth century. Moreover the emphasis on different parts of the traditional curriculum varied very much in different universities: whereas Vienna was a veritable hive of activity in mathematics and astronomy throughout a great part of the fifteenth century, recognition of these sciences seems to have become almost perfunctory at Paris.[2]

From our brief studies of such men as Alberti, Verrochio,

---

[1] The anti-Aristotelianism of Ramus at Paris was never accepted by the University as a whole.

[2] On this see Hastings Rashdall, *The Universities of Europe in the Middle Ages*, revised edn., Oxford, 1936, pp. 448 f. also No. 669. The great popularity of the *Margarita Philosophica* [No. 563) raises the question as to whether there was any attempt to return to the system of the Arts. It is possible, however, that the *Margarita* appealed mostly to the growing number of 'educated laymen', forming for them a kind of 'Home University Library'. With regard to Paris the *Praefatio* written by George Lokert, Professor at the Collège Montaigu and later at the Collège de Sorbon (1518), to his *adulescentes dilectissimi* admits the shameful neglect of the works of Albert of Saxony, Themon the Jew, and John Buridan, who had taught at Paris two centuries previously. The *Itali Veneti*, recognising their solid worth, had had two of them printed. The enterprise of this Scot shows that a critical 'scientific' spirit, if rare outside Italy at this time, was not wholly wanting (No. 405).

F

Dürer, and Münzer it is evident that a great deal of critical work in the sciences was being done outside the universities, and it is tempting—the temptation is not always resisted—to conclude that modern modes of scientific thought were originated solely by such men, while the universities continued to chant the old airs. The important element of truth in this view must not be allowed to obscure the fact that although—as we shall see—many of the most decisive factors in the creation of the 'new science' were at least developed outside the universities, their fruitful integration into general culture was the work of men whose wits had been sharpened in the apparently trivial and sterile procedure of the schools, to which also they owed the nice application of words to ideas which alone made possible the latter's wider dissemination.

The above considerations have provided us with warnings against the ordering of sixteenth-century science upon too narrow a plan. But they have not pointed to any classification lying ready to hand and generally acceptable to all the practitioners of the time. This is not surprising in a period in which settled ways of thought were breaking down: the situation is paralleled in our own times, when 'new' sciences (e.g. the much advertised 'cybernetics') are springing up, and recombinations of old sciences (e.g. 'biomolecular structure') are taking place almost daily. Nevertheless some basis of classification must be adopted so that the material to be assessed may be brought into a manageable form. This will involve some compromise; but one, it is hoped, which will not too greatly distort the picture by superimposing on the details a categorical scheme which developed only in later centuries.

It will be proper to start with the mathematical disciplines. In no subject (though many of the most ardent protagonists of these disciplines were under the impression that they were 'reviving' an art 'lost' for centuries) was the general attitude more in harmony with that of the Middle Ages, namely, of the use of mathematics as a means rather than as an end. This, except in the case of astronomy which had been cultivated largely as the 'celestial' branch of mathematics, was quite foreign to the spirit of Greece: Archimedes, the greatest mathematician of antiquity, as is well known, expressed a (possibly somewhat insincere) contempt for applications of the divine art.

The renaissance writers, even occupants of Chairs like Oronce Fine, show a lively concern with practical mathematics. The great majority of mathematical books published during this period bear witness to the concern to apply mathematical technique to problems of accounting, navigation, surveying, gunnery, battle formation, and fortifications. Perhaps greater than any of these, as Thorndike has massively demonstrated, was the demand for greater accuracy in astrological prognostication: it is probably fair to say that the majority of mathematicians maintained by princes were employed mainly for this purpose. But when every allowance has been made for all these demands it still remains true that a number of advances were made in pure mathematics, and in some few cases by men whose interest was in the subject rather than in what could be done with it. Provided that we bear in mind the comparative rarity of such works in the sixteenth century we shall do no violence to the subject by treating of them in a preliminary chapter, in which it will be convenient to deal also with advances in teaching methods and means of disseminating knowledge of the subject over a much wider area than had been the case hitherto. After a chapter on astronomy, which in the sixteenth century was almost wholly restricted to determining the 'mathematics of the heavens', we shall consider the peculiarly significant part played by those men whom Professor E. G. R. Taylor has so appropriately called the 'mathematical practitioners'.

In contrast to mathematics, which in itself was the science of the eternal relationships of form and magnitude, stood 'physics', the science concerned with the transformations of the sublunary 'elements' involved in the generation and corruption of all 'natural' objects, whether 'meteoric', living, or 'fossil'—that is, literally 'dug up'. It thus embraced what we should now call geology; and much of its content would now be regarded as part of chemistry. Since the sixteenth century witnessed a growing dissatisfaction with this conception of the growth of 'physics' further discussion is postponed to later chapters.

Though knowledge of 'physics' was generally considered a necessary part of the knowledge of 'animate' nature it was not in itself sufficient. We are apt to forget that our term 'animate nature' enshrines the recognition by Aristotle that among 'natural' bodies are many in which a 'soul' ($\psi\upsilon\chi\acute{\eta}$ = Latin *anima*) may be discerned. In plants the soul is 'nutritive' or 'vegetative' only; in animals there is added a 'sensitive', and in Man a 'rational', soul. A convenient division of our survey may thus be the System of Animate Nature embracing the study of all 'animated' bodies (except Man, knowledge of whom was the concern of Medicine) whether vegetable or animal. This is a more suitable term than 'biology' (which was not used until the nineteenth century), since although the two kingdoms were recognised as being compact of the same 'elements', there was no question of their being related by common descent. Moreover during the sixteenth century such development as there was towards a science of biology came rather from the Medical Schools than from the 'Natural Philosophy' of the Faculty of Arts. This was largely true in the case of botany and almost wholly so for anatomy. But whereas on theoretical grounds anatomy was restricted to one species (Man; but see below, p. 201) and on practical grounds was almost literally embedded in the medical curriculum, physicians anxious to improve their knowledge of drugs of vegetable origin found themselves obliged to extend their activities from the library to the field and mountain side (Nos. 99 and 175). Hence by the end of the century botany had acquired recognition as a separate discipline (No. 64); zoology was only just emerging as such. The far more rapid progress in the knowledge of plants than in that of animals is not without its moral for the appraisement of renaissance science in general.

With these considerations in mind it has seemed most suitable to make of botany the gate into the modern conception of plant biology but to study the progress of anatomy under the heading of Medicine. From a different point of view it might be urged that one of the abiding consequences of the organisation of higher education in the Middle Ages was to set Medicine as the crown upon the whole of Natural Philosophy as it had set Theology as a crown upon the whole of the Philosophy of Man. Probably the only preparation for the equivalent of 'scientific research' was the Faculty of Medicine. Scholars with such widely different interests as Copernicus, Georgius Agricola, Otto Brunfels, Vesalius, and Libavius had undergone its discipline. The course of study in this Faculty was indeed astonishingly comprehensive: it embraced a wide familiarity with Natural Philosophy (customarily acquired by previous graduation in the Faculty of Arts), astronomy, and

PLATE I

A sixteenth-century idea for amphibious assault vehicles. (Ramelli, *Le diverse et artificose Machine*, Vol. II, No. 545.)

the mathematics which was necessary for the grasp of this astronomy—all this of course in addition to a detailed textual familiarity with a selection of the masters of medicine, in particular Galen and Avicenna; though the latter fell under a cloud in most centres as the century advanced. Complaints about the overloading of latter-day medical curricula would have been heard with an understanding sympathy at least from about 1200. In this respect medieval, and through it renaissance, higher education had departed radically from that of Rome, whose ideals were otherwise largely those of these later centuries. No Roman would have dreamed of regarding medicine—whose practitioners were almost entirely Greeks—as the highwater mark of a liberal education. The combination in one man—Celsus—of an intimate knowledge of medicine with a Ciceronian style and *urbanitas* is still an unsolved mystery.

These considerations reveal another dilemma, namely the degree to which without distortion we may restrict the account of renaissance medical trends to the field which now goes by that name. In a sense Medicine embraced the whole of theoretical science (as distinct from applications to, for instance, navigation) and philosophy; it is not an accident that the most penetrating and modern-seeming discussions of the philosophy of science (Nos. 459-461) took place in the medical schools, especially that of Padua. Moreover it was mainly through an enlarged interest in drugs of mineral origin that *chemistry* gradually advanced beyond the status of a skilled craft. Some attempt will be made to evaluate the nature of this movement and the opposition it engendered, under the rubric of *pharmacology*. Though advances in the art of therapy can not be considered in this *Introduction*, so much thought which was of importance for the progress of science, both positively and negatively, was prompted by the various visitations of communicable diseases that these can not be passed by. Lastly it will be necessary to return in some sense to the point at which we started this investigation, namely in trying to come to terms with those attempts so marked in the sixteenth century, to seek out the spiritual ties between Man and the Cosmos of which he is a part, or even as was believed by many a copy.

This emphasis on the medical disciplines has the further pragmatic justification that it may help us to understand how it was that in his later years Descartes saw in a Medicine, refined and

F*

renewed indeed by the sea-breeze of Cartesian methodical doubt, the greatest hope for the regeneration of mankind—a way of redemption not lightly to be ignored in our present anguish.

Just as no space has been set aside for the treatment of the therapeutic art of medicine as such so there will be found no chapters on technology. Nevertheless in most of the divisions of the subject adopted there will appear in varying degree allusions to technological advances in so far as they shed light on the relationship between theory and practice—sufficient it is hoped to give a not altogether inadequate idea of the technological climate in which science was then advancing.

In the following chapters, then, I shall in respect of each somewhat arbitrary division of the field, attempt to estimate the state of knowledge about the year 1500, to point out some of the major figures who emerged during the sixteenth century, and to assess the general trends which appear to me to characterise that century. The first of these aims is the most difficult to achieve; since a balance was being sought between three pressures—the greatly increased concern with the learning and attitudes of classical antiquity, the unconscious conditioning by the legacy from the recent past—probate of which most of those then living consciously renounced—and the impact of new ideas and discoveries. An equilibrium between these pressures was established only gradually; a further, though not altogether independent, cause of the delay was the existence, during at least the earlier part of the period, of two parallel streams of communication—the duplicated manuscript and the printed book.

Since this attempt by no means aims at a comprehensive history of sixteenth-century science, the omission of any particular name or discovery must not be taken as necessarily implying the author's ignorance or even as a value-judgment. Prefixed as this *Introduction* is to a Bibliography of no inconsiderable size, its principal aim is to present prolegomena to the more minute study of the works themselves and to those far more numerous works which, though finding no place in the collection which is the subject of this study, must form the basis of any attempt to cast further light on the fascinating problem of the origins of modern science.

CHAPTER VI

THE MATHEMATICAL DISCIPLINES

BEFORE the close of the fifteenth century well over two hundred mathematical books had been printed in Italy alone; of these the great majority were arithmetical as distinct from geometrical. It is necessary to put the matter in this somewhat vague manner, since the division of mathematics into departments was on lines somewhat different from those of today. Geometry consisted of the fifteen books of 'Euclid' (Books I-XIII are attributed to Euclid of Alexandria, *c.* 300 B.C., Book XIV to Hypsikles, *c.* 150 B.C.; Book XV is probably a composite work [1]), together with a number of commentaries thereon; the greater part of the works of Archimedes (see No. 38); the *Conics* of Apollonios; the 'Spherics' of Theodosios of Tripoli (II-I), and the *Geometria Speculativa* of Thomas Bradwardine. Of these only the *Elements* of Euclid, with the commentary of Campanus of Novara, were *printed* before 1500. Trigonometry as a separate discipline did not exist; though Menelaos of Alexandria (*c.* 100 A.D.) had disengaged the study of spherical triangles from astronomy. The first book devoted wholly to the solution of triangles had been announced as a 'forthcoming attraction' in the trade list of Regiomontanus (see p. 110): it was first printed in 1533 (No. 557). During all the period with which we are concerned *arithmetica* was distinguished from *logistica, ars supputandi,* etc. The former was derived from the *Arithmetica* of Boethius, which was based on a similar work by Nichomachos of Gyrasa (*c.* 100 A.D.), itself a compilation of the theory of numbers developed by Euclid. It was useless for computation and almost strangled at birth by the cumbersome terminology used to classify the kinds of numbers (all of course positive cardinals); nevertheless it was the mainstay of academic arithmetic until late in the sixteenth century, and

---

[1] G. Loria, *Histoire des Sciences Mathématiques dans l'Antiquité Hellénique*, Paris, 1929, pp. 86-7; in the sixteenth century Books XIV-XV were both commonly attributed to Hypsikles.

kept at least half alive interest in those subtle relationships between the cardinals from which so much fruitful mathematics later followed. Contrasted with this academic discipline was the *Ars logistica* (No. 690) based on the 'Arabic' (Hindu) numerals whose symbolic form and place-value permitted rapid operation on slate or paper, such as those who were tied to the Roman numerals could do only on an abacus. It is for this reason that the first comprehensive work on the subject by Leonardo Fibonacci (of Pisa—1202) was miscalled the *Liber Abaci*. Actually the work went far beyond anything that could normally be done on an abacus, including the famous multiplicative series and a good deal of algebra. This proved its undoing; since, being too 'progressive' for the universities and too difficult for the merchants, for whom it was primarily intended, it was never printed until 1854. Its influence, however, was not lost, since the first comprehensive work on calculation in general, Pacioli's [1] *Summa de Arithmetica*, etc. (1494), draws heavily on it. Before this work, whose text was in Italian, there had appeared simpler ones also written in the vernacular: the 'Treviso' (the first *printed* arithmetic—1484); Widman's ... *Rechnung auf alle kauffmanschafft* (1489); and Francesch Sanct Climents's *Suma de la art de arismetica* (Catalan, 1482). By contrast no comparable work was *printed* in French before Estienne de la Roche's *Larismethique* (1520), or in English before Robert Recorde's *Grounde of Artes* (1542). The former had without acknowledgment made use of an unpublished manuscript of his more brilliant master, Nicolas Chuquet (see Sarton *Six Wings*, p. 27); the latter had been anticipated by Tunstall's *Ars Supputandi* (1522) (No. 690), which although written in Latin was intended for the counting-house rather than the university.

The two lines of development—*Arithmetica* and *Logistica*—were to some extent bridged during the sixteenth century by the growth of the 'Latin' [2] schools, in which boys were taught part of the elements of the arts which in earlier times were studied at the university. The growing recognition of the importance of mathematics for soldiers, sailors, and administrators brought mathe-

---

[1] Pacioli is also known as Paciuolo, Luca de Borgo, etc.

[2] The corresponding type of school in England was known as a 'Grammar School', but it was a common complaint until well into the seventeenth century that no mathematics was taught in them. (Cf. Taylor, *The Mathematical Practitioners of Tudor and Stewart England*, p. 5.)

matics into the curriculum at an earlier stage than that of the *quadrivium*. It will make for brevity if we first consider the achievement of the sixteenth century in respect of arithmetic in this restricted sense. Outstanding in this class on the continent was the *Arithmeticae practicae methodus facilis* written by Gemma Frisius about 1536 (No. 293). Rather more elaborate was Tartaglia's *La Prima Parte del general trattato di Numeri e Misuri* (1556) (Vol. II, *Appendix*), Cardano's *Practica arithmeticae generalis* (1539), and Stifel's *Arithmetica integra* (1544). In England Recorde's *Grounde of Artes*, though more elementary in scope and treatment, held its own until the seventeenth century.

It is of course impossible to give even an outline of the progress in arithmetic during the sixteenth century. For, although from the nature of the subject there was nothing 'new' to be learnt once the 'Arabic' numerals had been firmly established, yet it should be borne in mind that our 'four rules' of operation and the comparatively few modes of setting out the working were arrived at only as a result of a long and confused search. The number of rules is to a certain extent conventional: duplation, for instance, the first step towards multiplication, was often treated separately. That 'progress' was far from being straightforward may be illustrated by the fact that the most common method of long division was introduced in almost its present pattern as early as 1460, but was not widely used until well into the seventeenth century. Two reasons for this are advanced by Smith (II, 136), namely, that the 'galley' method almost universal in the sixteenth century, used fewer figures and was more compact—a great virtue before the days of cheap paper. The 'galley' method attains this compactness by not writing the series of partial products: the progressive reduction to the final remainder is brought about partly by cancellation, for which reason it was often called the 'scratch' method. Its origin is hinted at by Maximus Planudes (Smith, II, 137): '. . . on the sand table it is easy to erase numbers with the fingers and to write others in their places.'

The only fundamental 'advance' which took place in the sixteenth century was the extension of the scale of notation to include the place value, as well as the actual numbers, in fractions of the unit. The idea was implicit in the sexagesimal place notation combined with a decimal notation for the construction of the numbers of angular measure; thus in minutes and seconds the denominator (60) is understood in each case. The unification to a completely decimal scale is commonly attributed to Simon Stevin (No. 657). That this involves a considerable simplification is shown by Smith (II, 235 ff.). We can do no more here than to note that Pellos, the author of a very rare 'arithmetic' (1492), *used* the 'point' for division by multiples of ten, but, having no idea as to its meaning, converted the decimal fractions, so obtained as remainders, into the 'vulgar' form. At the end of the century came the invention of logarithms and construction of tables to replace Stevin's clumsy notation by one permitting the full advantage to be gained from the generalised denomination. The conservatism of the English is shown on the one hand by Newton's use of vulgar fractions in the *Opticks* a century later, and, at a humbler level, the reversion to Roman numerals in the accounts of the Parish of Hartland for some years after 1613 (I. L. Gregory, *Hartland Church Accounts*, Frome, 1950).

We have already seen the non-correspondence of the words 'arithmetic' and '*arithmetica*'; we now have to turn to a similar source of confusion. The difficulty facing the student inexperienced in renaissance mathematics may be illustrated by the title of the leading English work of the sixteenth century—Recorde's *Whetstone of Witte which is the seconde parte of Arithmetike containyng the extraction of Rootes, the Cossike practise, with the rule of Equation and the woorkes of Surde Nombers* (1557, No. 555). This was effectively the only English, and one of the best European, textbooks on *algebra* in the sixteenth century. The absence of the word *algebra* was in fact typical: hardly any work concerned with what is now comprehended under that name used the word *algebra* in the title, which in the vernaculars more commonly included some adaptation of the Italian *cosa* and in Latin the expression *Ars magna*. Frequently a sub-title or introductory 'explanation' was provided in which the authors unconsciously vie with each other in the absurdity of their derivations of the word 'algebra'. A brief glance at the previous history of the subject is necessary to explain both the confusion and the assumption, expressed or implied, that 'algebra' is the 'Greater' or 'occult' part of arithmetic.

Though many of Euclid's problems provide geometrical solutions of algebraical formulae it is generally agreed that this

department of mathematics derives from the Arithmetic of Diophantos. Its introduction into Western Europe, however, was
almost certainly by means of translations of the work of Abu
Abdallah Mohammed ibn Musa al-Khowarismi (i.e. 'of Khiva')
who was employed in the library of the Caliph al-Mamun during
the period 813-33. This work, which probably owes a great deal
to the earlier Hindu mathematicians, bears the title 'ilm al-jabr
wa'l muqabalah': the origin of 'algebra' is evident. Unfortunately
though the title means (art of) 'restoration and opposition' it
got mixed up with the reference to the author's birth-place—
al-Khowarismi—and also the Latinised form of the Arabic
proper name Jabir—'Geber'. The original translator, Robert
of Chester (*c.* 1140), correctly entitled the work *Liber restaurationis
et oppositionis*, and Leonardo Fibonacci correctly transliterates
the Arabic form, but Ioannes de Sacrobosco as early as about
1230 started the subsequent muddle by calling his arithmetic
Algorismus vulgaris since it was based on an 'arithmetic' written by
'al-Khowarismi'. Hence the term 'algorism' and 'algorithm'
commonly came to mean a treatment of arithmetic after the
Arabic fashion as distinct from the 'classical' Boethian. Today
the set of equations by which may be established the fundamental
theorem of arithmetic is sometimes known as the Euclidean
algorithm! But worse was to follow. By 1524 Riese brought out a
book *Die Coss*—'by that celebrated Arabic master, Algebra'; in
1537 appeared the first English printed arithmetic '. . . after the
true cast of arismetyke or awgrym in whole numbers and also
in broken'; and in the text of *The Whetstone of Witte* the same
author, Robert Recorde, refers to 'the rule of equation, commonly
called Algeber's Rule'. All this grew out of the misinterpretation of
'al-Khowarismi'. The name 'Cossike practise' (Recorde) or
simply 'Coss' (Riese) involves no confusion, but reveals a special
form of terminology. This is simply a vernacular adaptation of the
Italian *cosa* (= thing) employed by the early Italian algebraists
as the equivalent of *res*, which had been in use at least from the
thirteenth century to indicate the lowest power of the 'unknown'
(thing). With this terminology the second power was called
'census' or 'quadratus'. An alternative system was that (e.g. of
Robert of Chester) in which the first power was regarded as the
'root', the second power thus becoming the equivalent of the *res*
(called by Robert 'substantia'). It is important to discover in any

particular sixteenth-century writer which system he is employing.[1] It must of course be clearly understood that the generalised concept of 'power' or 'exponent' came only gradually. Algebra grew out of geometry, hence the third 'power' was called *cubus*, the fourth often *quadrati quadratum*, the fifth *sursolidus*, and so on. The possibility of operations on dimensions is indeed *implicit* even in Diophantos; but the geometrical association (extrapolated as in *sursolidus*) lasts even as late as Viète.[2] It was one of the less publicised virtues of Descartes's *Géometrie* to include a passage which for the first time put the matter in a clear light: 'Par a² ou b³ ou semblables je ne conçoy ordinairement que des lignes tous simples encore que, pour me servir des noms usités en l'Algébre je les nomme des quarrés ou des cubes etc.' (*Oeuvres*, ed. Adam and Tanner, Vol. VI, p. 371).

With the question of terminology is linked that of notation. Nesselmann in 1842 claimed that algebra had passed through three stages: the rhetorical, in which all statements were written in ordinary language; the syncopated, in which the terms were abbreviated; and the symbolic, where every part of an expression was characterised by an *ad hoc* symbol. Though to regard the *history* of the subject in this light involves a selection amounting to a serious distortion of the facts, as a *classification* of notations the scheme provides a useful, though far from clear-cut, basis. Thus the earliest (thirteenth-century) manuscript of Diophantos shows a completely symbolised form except for the sign of equality, where an abbreviated word is used. On the other hand, in the sixteenth century, whereas Cardano used a syncopated form:

$$\text{cub. } p \text{: 6 pos. aeq 20} \qquad (x^3 + 6x = 20)$$

Recorde, only twelve years later, would have written the same equation in a much more compact form. Nevertheless this had no advantage over the former in regard to operation, since

[1] Recorde calls the first power the 'root' and the second the 'square' (Sig. S i *v*;) but see also Sig. S ii *v* for an alternative method in which the 'root' is called 'first quantity'.

[2] Here and elsewhere in any questions of priority it may be the case that Simon Stevin has expressed similar ideas, for instance in the case of 'signed' numbers. Owing to his passionately held views on the philosophical importance of the Dutch language many of Stevin's ideas did not gain currency at the time of publication. With the publication of his *Works* by E. J. Dijksterhuis (Vol. I, Amsterdam, 1955) it should now be possible to get these matters in proper perspective.

PLATE II

of Cossike nombers.

6.ʒ.— | —.10.ʓℯ.———.8.ɋ.
4.ʒ.— | —.17.ɋ.———.7.ʓℯ.

10.— | —.3.ʓℯ.— | —.9.ɋ.

4.ʒ.ℭ.— | —.5.ʒ.— | —.6.ʓℯ.
8.ℭ.———.8.ʒ.——— 10.ʓℯ.

4.ʒ.ℭ.— | —.8.ℭ.———.3.ʒ.———.4.ʓℯ.

Maſter. Уou haue doen well : And foʒ pʒoofe of
your woʒke, you maie in this arte not onely pʒoue it,
by the contrary kynde, as you did in nôbers *Abſtraƈte*,
but alſo by the reſolution of all thoſe *Coſſike* nombers
into nôbers *Abſtraƈte*, takyng any nomber foʒ a roote
and then the *Squares* and *Cubes.* ꝛc. accoʒdingly. As here
in this table, you maie bʒiefly ſee, but moʒe largely in
the table at the eande of nombers figuralle.

A table for trialle by reſolution,
of any woorke in this arte.

ʓℯ	ʒ.	ℭ	ʒʒ.	/ʒ	ʒℭ	⁶/ʒ
2	4	8	16	32	64	128
3	9	27	81	243	729	2187
4	16	64	256	1024	4096	46384

ʒʒʒ.	ℭℭ	ʒ/ʒ.	
256	121	1024	
6561	19683	59049	
65536	262144	1048576	

And if this table in any parte, ſeme to ſhoʒte oʒ to
littlе:

Addition of signed 'cossike' numbers. Also a table to
show the symbols used for the root, square, cube, etc.
(Recorde, *Whetstone of Witte*, sig. Uv[r], Vol. II, No. 555.
Vol. I, p. 93.)

each power of the unknown is represented by a specific symbol;[1] consequently the beginner had to have recourse to a table in order to determine the correct symbol with which to represent the product or quotient. How much easier the operation would have been if the numbers had been applied immediately instead of mediately! But this implied a quite different fundamental conception, achieved only in the closing years of the century by Viète, who first employed *separate* capital vowels and consonants for the 'unknown', and arbitary constants, respectively. A closer approximation to the modern form is revealed in the *Artis analyticae praxis* of Thomas Harriot (No. 328): this form was attained by Descartes for positive integral exponents and by John Wallis with complete generality. The four stages may be illustrated by an equation of the form $ax^3 - 3bx^2 = 2c$, written according to the notation of:

Viète: B in A cubum — C in A quad. ter aequatur D bis
Harriot $b.aaa - 3.caa = 2d$
Descartes $bx^3 - 3cxx = 2d$

The question of notation is of course bound up with the sole object of renaissance algebra—the solution of equations. We now have indisputable evidence that 'solutions' of the linear equation and of special cases of the quadratic were obtained in Egypt and Babylonia in remote antiquity—*c.* 2000 B.C. From a later date came the first tabulated statements showing how a linear equation could be solved by a laborious version of the 'rule of false', that is, by guessing the required value and then, by a kind of 'practice',[2] proportionately altering the 'false' value until it fitted the given conditions. This method, progressively developed by the Arabs, by means of the principle of transposition and reduction, was used throughout the sixteenth century. There are few more illuminating examples in the history of science of the fact that familiarity with current modes of thought may place an almost insuperable barrier between the historian and the pioneer work he is trying to evaluate. Thus the long and involved arguments whereby even

[1] Note that Recorde used a different symbol (see Plate II) for 'nomber absolute' to distinguish it as 'abstract' from the 'contract' (denominate) numbers represented by other symbols. This recognition of different 'kinds' of numbers, of which he gives other examples, shows the good influence of the Boethian theory of numbers, the teaching of which still continued in the universities.

[2] This expression, still used in English arithmetic, is explained in Smith, Vol. II, pp. 493-4.

the sixteenth-century algebraists solved equations of the *form* $ax + b = 0$, despite their familiarity with the principle of transposition and reduction, appear as almost wilful perversity until it is seen that even one of outstanding manipulative ingenuity, Cardano, gave separate solutions for equations of the two types $x^3 = ax^2 + c$ and $x^3 + ax^2 = c$. If further evidence be required it is only necessary to refer to Galileo's long drawn out struggle to explain that if the velocity is proportionate to the time-lapse, then what we write as 'gt' may be substituted for any value of 'v' in any other equation in which 'v' occurs, e.g. $s = vt$. To understand this apparent wrong-headedness we have to bear in mind that not only was there, before Viète and Harriot, no notation in which these ideas could be expressed, but, even more important from the historical point of view, the ideas themselves had not been formulated. When for the sake of conciseness and clarity in our discussion we speak about 'equations of the form $ax + b = 0$', or 'of the second degree' we are inverting the whole process of discovery. The idea of a literal equation, in which the coefficients might themselves be of either sign independent of the sign preceding them, was entirely wanting before Viète. Also, such classification as there was of the numerical equations which were the sole object of study was based not on 'degree' but on the number of terms. To say then, as in one sense we certainly may, that Cardano 'solved the general cubic' is in another sense to turn the problem upside down. Cardano's separate solutions of the various kinds of equations containing a 'cubus' term; his recognition of the existence of cases irreducible by virtue of their involving the square root of a negative quantity; and his strong suspicion that all cubic equations should yield three roots—these were the stuff out of which the concept of 'the general equation of the third degree' gradually took shape, but not explicitly until Descartes stated that 'an equation has as many roots as the unknown has dimensions'.

Such was the prelude to modern algebra enacted in the sixteenth century. It remains only to add that Cardano's brilliant young associate, Ferrari, solved a problem involving the general biquadratic (quartic). When it is realised that equations of all degrees having general solutions (Abel and Ruffini in the nineteenth century showed that no general solution of the quintic and higher degrees is possible) had thus been solved by a purely geometrical approach,[1] and that the analytic method of Viète had gone a fair way towards generalising the results, this may well be accounted as one of the greatest achievements of the century.[2]

If in the history of mathematical thought the sixteenth century may be regarded as the century of algebra, in geometry it was far otherwise. In geometry *sensu strictu* there was no significant advance on the *Elements* of Euclid (*Ed.P.* 1482) the *Conics* of Apollonios (*Ed.P.* 1537) and certain works of Archimedes (*Ed.P.* 1544) before 1639 when Desargues published his little-noticed work, in which was firmly laid the foundation of projective geometry. In the field of geometry more than in any other branch of science except medicine the contribution of the 'renaissance' came nearest to the traditional view—that of restoring the contributions of the Greeks in something like their ancient purity: reference may here be made to Apollonios, Archimedes, Euclid, and Proklos in the Bibliography. Where the renaissance worker did make solid advances on anything that had been done before was in establishing trigonometry as a separate discipline.

The science of trigonometry even more than that of algebra, developed continuously out of geometry. The problem which prompted this development may well have been that of finding a measure for inaccessible distances, in particular those of the heavenly bodies. The distribution of these bodies is such that they are effectively treated as points projected on a sphere: it is immaterial whether the sphere or spheres is or is not regarded as 'real' (see below, p. 107). Trigonometrical ideas and measures were related from the start to spherical triangles and circles rather than, as is now the case, to plane triangles. In this sense trigonometry was a Greek science, since there is *implicit* in Hipparchos's solution of certain problems the relation now expressed by the equation $\tan b = \cos A \tan c$ ($C = 90°$). In

---

[1] The nature of this approach may be studied in detail in Cardano's *Ars Magna* (No. 134). A translation of the passage is given by Smith, *Source Book of Mathematics*, New York, 1929, p. 203.

[2] Although Napier's *De Arte Logistica* was almost certainly written before the close of the sixteenth century it was not published till 1839. His work on logarithms, both as regards publication and spirit, belongs definitely to the seventeenth century. It should be noted, however, that an implicitly 'logarithmic' calculation occurs in a manuscript of Pacioli; the discovery of the method is claimed for Bürgi, the self-taught technician of Landgrave Wilhelm of Hesse (see p. 120), as early as 1588.

the 'Spherics' of Menelaos [1] (I-2; his works are known only through the medium of the Arabic translations) the notion of a spherical triangle becomes *explicit*, together with the fundamental relationship which we represent by the statement that any chord in a circle is equal to twice the sine of half the angle sub-tended at the centre. It was by means of this relationship that Ptolemy constructed the tables of *chords* on which the 'trigono-metry' of the *Almagest* was based. The use of *half*-chords became *explicit* in the later Hindu writers on whose work the Arabs drew; so that when Plato of Tivoli came in the twelfth century to translate the *De Scientia Stellarum* of al-Battani he is said to have mistaken the true Arab word *jaib* (= fold, bosom) for *jiba*, which had been introduced as a mere phonetic substitute for the Sanskrit *jiva*—hence the introduction of 'sinus' (Latin = fold, bosom) into subsequent mathematical literature. [2]

The culmination of the work of the Arabs in developing trigonometry as a separate discipline, independent of astronomy, was reached with Nasr ed-Din in Persia in the thirteenth century. Unfortunately the severance of communications (consequent on the Mongol incursions) between the Middle East and the 'Latin' West prevented the scholars of the latter from profiting from the new way of looking at the subject. Hence, despite the extensive development of methods by the fourteenth century Oxford mathematicians, Bradwardine, Simon Bredon, Richard of Wal-lingford, and John Maudith, it was not until about 1464, when Regiomontanus wrote his *De Triangulis Omnimodis*, whose title indicates the change of scope, that the West 'caught up with' the East. In his epoch-making work Regiomontanus solves all kinds of problems relating to plane and spherical triangles using the 'sinus rectus' and 'sinus versus', but not the tangent; in the *Tabulae Directionum*, which though published earlier (1490) were written later than the *De Triangulis Omnimodis* there is a Tabula Fecunda which is in effect a table of tangents. [3] The earlier work was *printed* only in 1533, by which time Werner (see p. 112) had written but not published his *De Triangulis maximorum circulorum*

---

[1] Loria, *op. cit.* pp. 176 f.

[2] F. Cajori, *A History of Elementary Mathematics*, New York, 1897, p. 124.

[3] Previously the tangent function had generally been known as the 'umbra', that is, the 'shadow' of the gnomon. Since the latter was the unit of measure, Bradwardine distinguished between the *umbra recta* (cotangent) and *umbra versa* (tangent).

and Apian was just about to publish his *Instrumentum Sinuum* (No. 35). Also it is known that Copernicus had at least sketched out the material which was ultimately published as *De Lateribus et Angulis Triangulorum*. It is impossible to say to what extent these works may have been inspired by knowledge of the more comprehensive work of Regiomontanus, but it is unlikely that Copernicus had put his material in order before Rheticus brought the work of Regiomontanus to his notice; even then he failed to avoid the trap of the 'ambiguous case' noted in the earlier work. More important than any of these successors of Regiomontanus was the *Canon doctrinae Triangulorum* published by Rheticus in 1551 (No. 568) though even there the names of the functions *perpendiculum* (sine), *basis* (cosine), and *hypotenusa* (secant/cosecant) obscured the fact that he had defined them in terms of ratios of sides of a right-angled triangle and not, as previously, as lengths of chords. The introduction of names for the two other fundamental ratios (tangent and secant) was effected by Fincke (No. 261) and established by Pitiscus (No. 526) who signalised the emergence of a new mathematical discipline in giving it the name by which it has ever since been known.

If Rheticus may be regarded as having commenced the 'arithmetisation' of trigonometry it was Viète who completed it. The importance of the freeing of trigonometry from its geometrical origins lies in the enormously enlarged scope it confers upon the investigator, and the increase in ease and rapidity of manipulation whereby new relationships may be discovered. This is illustrated in the extension of purely algebraic methods to the trigonometrical relations by Viète. He must have been somewhat handicapped by his failure to pass from the symbolic product to the concept of the 'power'. It is indeed a strange thing that despite the generalisation of the exponent symbol by Wallis, and the high approximation to a purely analytic structure in his own work and that of his contemporaries, trigonometry did not attain complete symbolic expression until the time of Euler.

Of the applications of trigonometry something will be said under the heads of practical mathematics and astronomy; but it may be well at this stage to remind the reader that it was with the aim of facilitating trigonometrical computation that one of the greatest inventions in pure mathematics—'the Wonderful Canon of Logarithms'—was made by John Napier.

It would be misleading to close this sketch of the development of 'geometry' in the broad sense without qualifying the statement already made concerning the absence of advance beyond the Greeks. While this is literally true, reference to the Bibliography (e.g. No. 557) will show that though concern with spherical geometry was dominant, the unsolved problems of classical geometry were not wholly ignored. As an example of this we may glance at the ever popular one misleadingly described as 'squaring the circle with ruler and compasses'. The perennial interest of this problem, which, regarded merely from the practical point of view, consists in the construction of a square equal in area to a given circle, depends on the fact that this is implicitly equivalent to the construction of a line segment equal in length to the circumference of the circle. But as E. W. Hobson [1] points out, such a problem becomes definite only when the means available for the construction are specified. The reference to 'ruler and compasses' is merely a rather crude expression of the postulational scheme for the determination of points in relation to other points arbitrarily given, such as is implied in the axioms of Euclidean geometry. The possibility or otherwise of the solution of the problem is thus intimately bound up with the logical foundations of that geometry. Needless to say, the 'solutions' effected by Nicholas of Cues and Oronce Fine (displayed in the form of 'determining' what we—since Euler—call 'π' as a rational fraction) were illusory, as was demonstrated by Regiomontanus for the former and Buteo (No. 114) for the latter. On the other hand the mathematician Christmann favourably reviewed Aristotle's 'proof' of the impossibility of the construction: this work is not mentioned by Hobson or Smith.

In this brief sketch an attempt has been made to abstract from the mathematical disciplines of the sixteenth century sufficient data to enable an appreciation to be made not only of the progress in 'pure' mathematics but of the conditions in which the struggle was carried on. In both algebra and trigonometry this progress has been seen to culminate in Viète: Bell (*The Development of Mathematics*, New York, 1945) goes so far as to claim that there was not another algebraist of the first rank till the eighteenth century. But of that great man only that has been said which may justify his being regarded as the outstanding mathematician of

[1] *Squaring the Circle*, Cambridge, 1913, p. 6.

the century. Although the University of Aberdeen possesses no work of his published in the sixteenth century there are two copies of those edited and published by his pupil and friend, Alexander Anderson. These volumes are of more than merely local interest for Alexander, son of an Aberdeen merchant, was a brother (or more likely half-brother) of David Anderson, whose daughter, Janet, noted for her mathematical ability, married John Gregory, thus almost certainly endowing her descendants with the mathematical gifts, amounting in her son James to outstanding genius, which many of them possessed. This is a singular case of the danger of ignoring the maternal origins of great families; for these scions of Andersonian mathematical stock are known to the generality of historians merely as the 'Academic Gregories'. Two of the works of Alexander Anderson, including his edition of Viète's *De aequationum recognitione et emendatione tractatus duo*, belonged at one time to the Gregory family and William Johnston respectively. The latter fact is of interest in showing that although, as we know from a different source, even in 1631 William Johnston's lectures contained no reference to algebra (a similar state of affairs is known to have been the case at Cambridge not many years earlier) the interests of university teachers should not be regarded as limited to the scope of their lectures.

This abstract of the progress of mathematical thought has been made at the risk of doing violence to the development of mathematical culture in the sixteenth century. Important as is the former, the latter is perhaps the more characteristic; but it is so closely bound up with astronomy, astrology, navigation and surveying, that it seems more appropriate to treat of it, and of the physical instruments by which its influence was spread, in the chapters devoted to those subjects.

CHAPTER VII

ON THE HEAVENS

'O F the means of prediction through astronomy, O Syrus, two are the most important and valid. One, which is first both in order and effectiveness, is that whereby we apprehend the aspects (σχηματισμους) of the movements of sun, moon, and stars in relation to each other and to the earth, as they occur from time to time; the second is that in which, by means of the natural character of these aspects (φυσικῆς τῶν σχηματισμῶν) themselves we investigate the changes which they bring about in that which they surround.' [1] These words express what might be described as the mode of astronomical thought during the period with which we are concerned. The *data* of astronomy were the apparent motions of the heavenly bodies. The primary purpose of every astronomer was to discover or invent a rational system whereby these phenomena could be accounted for, and their past and future states determined. But it would be difficult to name an astronomer guiltless of any ulterior motive. A knowledge of their motions was necessary and sufficient for the solution of two pressing problems of the period: the correction of the calendar and the fixing of position at sea. But the additional knowledge of their 'natural character' was also necessary (though not perhaps sufficient) to determine their influence on the 'sublunary World' and its most important inhabitant, Man.[2] Concerning this part of astronomy, which has a formal correspondence to our astrophysics (see below, chapter xv), historians of science until comparatively recently have either maintained a discreet silence, or having admitted its existence as an unfortunate and inexplicable

---

[1] Claudius Ptolemy, Μαθηματικης Τετραβιβλου συνταξεως (usually referred to by the Latin catchword *Quadripartitum*), trans. by F. E. Robbins, Loeb edn., London, 1948, p. 3.

[2] The fundamental *observation* at the *time* (hence 'horoscope') of birth was the 'ascendent', that is, the degree of the ecliptic 'rising' on the eastern horizon, from which all the planetary and other influences could be calculated according to the 'theory' in vogue.

aberration, have been at some pains to separate the astronomical sheep from the astrological goats. Even that monument of historical integrity, Georges Sarton, at one time described the *Tetrabiblos*, without qualification, as supposititious. The evidence for this view is very slight, and for the opposite very strong: it is at least doubtful whether the genuineness of the work would ever have been questioned except in the pious hope of 'whitewashing' the memory of one of the greatest scientific astronomers. But if the Aristotelian world-view be accepted—as for nearly two thousand years it was, at least in respect of its 'scientific' aspects —there is nothing in the least 'unscientific' in supposing an influence of the heavenly bodies on earthly events.[1] What was reprehensible was not the belief that a science of astrology was possible, but the purely formal character that it too readily assumed, whereby from highly imaginative *à priori* assumptions deductions of great precision and complexity were drawn without any methodical attempt at verification. The general principle of astrology has in fact been shown to be entirely independent of the Aristotelian cosmology; for the scientific investigation of the last two centuries has revealed the unsuspected influence of solar radiation on animal and plant metabolism, of the lunar cycle on behaviour rhythms, of sun spots on magnetic storms, and most astonishing of all, of *cosmic* radiation of undetermined origin, whose effects may yet be shown to surpass in variety and profundity, though doubtless with far less precipitancy, the 'influences' of the most sanguine astrologers. That astrology was prosecuted uncritically and applied to evil purposes was recognised by some-one somewhere in almost every age. The Christian Church was almost continuously opposed to 'judicial' astrology, in which the character of a man was supposed to be foretold from the celestial configurations at the time of his birth, or, as some said, at his conception. But the opposition to this was on grounds of dogma, not on account of its scientific inadequacy. On the other hand it must be emphasised that there was no sort of correlation between the achievement of a man as a scientific astronomer and his attitude towards astrology. No man was held by his contemporaries as having given astronomy a greater impetus at the beginning of our period than Regiomontanus; but his contributions to astrology were held by most in equal esteem: to his deep concern

[1] Τετραβιβλος, pp. 5-13.

with this aspect of the heavens his books bear ample testimony (e.g. No. 559). His near contemporary, Giovanni Pico della Mirandola, who made no contribution, either critical or constructive, to astronomy itself, was the severest and most influential opponent of astrology. It is the absence of any such correlation which made possible the ignoring of astrology in the earlier 'histories' of science: it had always been possible, as in the case of Ptolemy, to keep the two aspects of a man's work in watertight compartments. But though one may without distortion ignore astrology altogether in recounting the technical progress in astronomy, it must never be forgotten that the stimulus for such progress was often the urge to give added precision to those data upon which the casting of the 'horoscope' or 'nativity' depended. To ignore this fact is to run the risk of drawing from the mere progress of astronomical science seriously unhistorical inferences as to the contemporary climate of opinion.

The assessment of astronomical progress in our period is facilitated by regarding it as being divided into three principal movements. These may perhaps be referred to as the humanist-critical revival by Peurbach and Regiomontanus, the cosmological revolution of Copernicus, and the shift of emphasis from speculation to observational technique initiated by Tycho Brahe. Such a view must not be regarded as implying any 'periodisation'. Owing to the complex structure of the learned world in the Renaissance any kind of methodical 'progress' was apt to be thrown out of gear by 'pressure groups'—in particular the rival Churches. Also there was much overlapping.

Though the last word on the importance and novelty of the work of Peurbach and Regiomontanus has yet to be said—and the task has been made more difficult owing to the fact that the scholar who commands the greatest knowledge of the period has allowed nationalistic fervour to cloud his judgment—there is little doubt that a great and wide-ranging stimulus spread out from Vienna in the late fifteenth century. About 1383 Henry of Langenstein ('de Hassia') departed from Paris to take a leading part in the work of the university then being re-founded by Duke Albert III.[1] A concise survey of the teachers of astronomy is

---

[1] Rashdall, *The Universities of Europe in the Middle Ages*, Vol. II, No. 1, pp. 232 f. in the 1895 edn. The required books for the Bachelor's license indicate a mathematical tradition based on recent studies (e.g. Bradwardine).

given by Georg Tanstetter in his preface to the *Tabula Eclypsium* of Peurbach (No. 669). He is at great pains to establish the importance of this tradition of teaching, but a little further on he makes the completely inconsistent statement that Peurbach and Regiomontanus 'magnificently restored the most noble discipline of astronomy, almost blotted out from the memory of men'. This habit of gross exaggeration characteristic of 'humanism' and intoned as a kind of antiphon in the most inappropriate contexts has induced a recent tendency [1] to *underestimate* the importance of these two men. Before we try to assess this importance it will be necessary to review in some detail the state of astronomical knowledge at the time when Peurbach wrote his *Theoricae Novae Planetarum* (about 1460; first printed Nürnberg, 1473/4).

It is probably safe to sssume that every student of astronomy at that time [2] (and for a century thereafter) was introduced to the subject by way of the *Tractatus de Sphaera* written by Ioannes de Sacrobosco (John of Holywood) probably about 1230. The demand for this work, of which together with the commentaries thereon there must have been innumerable manuscripts, is attested by the fact that it was first printed in 1472, and by 1500 had run through over thirty editions. Written in an eminently clear style it provided a 'sound introduction' to the generally accepted world-view—the 'sphere' being the whole universe as seen from the spherical earth.

Concerning the background of the dance of the heavenly bodies there was for nearly two thousand years little dispute. The whole sphere of the world rotated round the earth, its geometrical centre, in the period known as a 'day'. The earthy body at the centre was surrounded by spheres of water (more or less), air, and fire, which reached up to the sphere of the moon. This 'sublunary' region was the scene of continuous 'generation and decay' but the outer confines, much larger in extent, were composed of 'ether', suffering no change of any kind except uniform circular motion. Now from Babylonian times it had been recognised that

---

[1] Thorndike ever ready (and often with justice) to have a dig at 'the so-called renaissance' quotes this statement, but seems to have overlooked the fact that Tanstetter has *in the same* place spoken of John of Gmünden in terms of high praise (*Hist.* V, 32) For John of Gmünden see J. Mundy, *Isis*, **34**, 198.

[2] Required reading at Vienna, according to a statute of 1389 (Thorndike, *The Sphere of Sacrobosco*, Chicago, 1949, pp. 42-4.) also for Copernicus at Cracow in 1491 (J. Rudnicki, *Nicholas Copernicus*, London, 1943, p. 3).

certain prominent luminaries appear to move in a manner departing in varying degrees from uniform circular motion about the centre of the earth; later even the stars displayed a slight motion relative to certain points on the sphere fixed by reference to the axis of rotation. These movements, except those of the sun, which caused the seasons and unequal times of day and night in the various climes into which the earth's surface was thereby divided, were too 'difficult' for a systematic introduction like Sacrobosco's. He was content to give a superficial account of the solution proposed by Claudius Ptolemy (II–2) largely in the version (and including some of the errors) of the Arabic astronomer, al-Fargani (IX–1). Before 1496 anyone who wanted to make any original contribution to astronomical theory had to read Ptolemy's *Almagest*. If he read Arabic (which was extremely unlikely) he could use the Arabic version prepared under the supervision of the great scholar Honain ibn Ishaq in the ninth century. The Arabic text was translated into Latin by Gerard of Cremona in 1179.[1] A Latin version from the *Greek* was available in South Italy from about 1164 [2]—why it never entered the main stream is an unsolved mystery. There was, however, an alternative to reading Ptolemy, which was to read one of the original works written in Arabic between the ninth and thirteenth centuries, some of which were available in Latin translations from before the middle of the twelfth century.

The difference between the *Almagest* and the original works of the Arabs was based on a fundamental distinction of philosophy, believed to have been established [3] by Poseidonios (B.C. I–1) or his pupil Geminus. This was to the effect that whereas the astronomer's sole concern is with the elaboration of a general hypothesis from which the positions of the heavenly bodies at particular times can be deduced, the natural philosopher will not rest content until he has satisfied himself that these hypotheses are at least not inconsistent with the nature of things deduced from the observed sequence of cause and effect. The first recorded hypothesis of the former kind was that of Eudoxos (B.C. V–2) in

[1] In Toledo, reconquered by Alfonso VI in 1085. The 'school of translation' grew up under the leadership of Archbishop Raimundo, 1126-51. Mieli, *La Science Arabe*, p. 232.

[2] See above, p. 10.

[3] Quoted with provenance in M. R. Cohen and I. E. Drabkin *Source Book in Greek Science*, New York, 1948, p. 90.

response to the physical hypotheses of Plato (uniform geocentric motion) which showed how, by imagining each body to be carried round on a sphere, whose axis of rotation was itself fixed in a second sphere rotating concentrically with the first but different from the first with respect to its axis and the magnitude and direction of angular velocity, the 'appearances could be saved'.[1] Aristotle took over this system, improved in respect of accuracy by Kalippos by the addition of further spheres to the three or four already used for some bodies by Eudoxos, but turned it into a *physical* system by the incorporation of reacting spheres between the successive sets, so that the whole cosmos might be driven by a single encompassing *primum mobile*—the 'eighth' sphere supporting the fixed stars and surrounding the seven sets of spheres corresponding to the seven known planets. In the *Almagest* Ptolemy, while explicitly working within the general concepts of the Aristotelian physics, rejected this homocentric system as incapable of representing the 'appearances', which as a result of the superlatively refined observation of Hipparchos (B.C. II) were by then much more accurately known. The principal obstacle which had arisen was the discovery by Hipparchos of the fact that the sun does not traverse the successive quarters of its apparent annual path through the stars (the *ecliptic*) in equal times. Hipparchos 'saved the appearances' in this case by postulating uniform angular velocity on a circle whose centre was excentric to the earth. The irregular (looped) circles of the planets had previously been 'saved' (as reported by Hipparchos) by supposing them to move at a uniform rate on a circle (*epicycle*) whose centre moved at a uniform rate on another circle (*deferent*) centred at or near the earth. This postulation of a moving point at which no visible body was situated was the first crack in the 'physical' machine. When Hipparchos further discovered that he could 'save the appearances' just as well by means of uniform motion about a movable excentric, all semblance of a 'physical' theory was lost. Being now completely unrestricted, as he himself admitted, by any 'physical' demands, Ptolemy was able to deal with a new problem by means of a new geometrical device. The problem arose out of the fact that though a combination of epicycles or movable excentrics could account for the irregularity

[1] The expression σοζειν τα φαινομενα, or *servare apparentias*, is of constant occurrence down to the seventeenth century, cf. Milton, *Paradise Lost*, VIII, 82.

of the planetary *paths* with respect to the earth, it failed to represent the varying velocity of the point moving on the deferent. This difficulty was resolved by finding a point (*equant*) with respect to which the angular velocity was constant but which was not involved in the construction of the locus. It will be recognised that all this geometrical and kinematic complexity [1] was an unavoidable consequence of the demand that the earth should remain the reference body, understandable in respect of a *physical* theory, but unintelligible where such manifest artificialities as the equant had been introduced. Such is the inertia of even the most powerful intellects.

The growth of Arabian astronomy displays a more or less increasing reaction to the physically unsupported system of Ptolemy. The first well articulated system, whose basis was also that of Peurbach's *Theoricae novae*, was that of Ibn-al-Haitham (al-Hazen), who returned to the homocentric system with such modification as would permit of a varying distance of each planet from the earth. This was a prime necessity, since the original homocentric system was inconsistent with the physical fact of variation in the apparent size and brightness easily observed in the planets other than the sun and moon. The modification proposed was that whereas every planetary orb must rotate in such a manner as to touch, but not interfere with, the orb of the planet next 'above' and next 'below', it could contain an excentric deferent sphere surrounded by two concentric surfaces, in the space between which there rolled a sphere bearing the planet itself. Reference to, for example, Erasmus Reinhold's edition of the *Theoricae novae* will reveal Peurbach's use of this system, with the added device of the Ptolemaic equant. Duhem (*Système du Monde*, Vol. II, p. 124) claims that Ibn-al-Haitham's system was lifted bodily from a work *Hypotheses Planetarum*, ascribed to Ptolemy, though only part of it has ever been discovered in a Greek MS. Such an estimate should be treated with caution since it was a cardinal principle with Duhem that no Arab writer was capable of an original idea (*Op. cit.* p. 118 but cf. Mieli, *La Science Arabe*, p. 107). What may be regarded as established is that the principle

---

[1] For a rather fuller account of the genesis of the Ptolemaic system see my *Growth of Scientific Ideas*, Edinburgh, 1950, Ch. IV; for a more detailed description of the system itself see J. L. E. Dreyer, *History of the Planetary Systems*, Cambridge, 1906, new edn., Dover Publications, 1953, called 'History of Astronomy', Ch. IX.

of the 'nesting' of the planetary spheres without mutual interference is set forth in the earliest work on the 'Sphere', that of the Neoplatonist Proklos (VI–1).

The Arab systems most influential in the West were those of al-Fargani (d. 861) and al-Battani (d. 929) both of whom worked at the observatory erected under the patronage of the Abbasid Caliphate at Baghdad from 829 and far surpassing any observatory erected in Europe before the sixteenth century, though itself surpassed by the Mongol observatories of Meragha (XIII) and Samarkand (XV–1). The works of al-Fargani and al-Battani were translated into Latin in the twelfth century, and by virtue of the systematic tables and the more 'physical' character of their theory were probably used more than the *Almagest*. Most interesting of all the Arabic systems from the point of view of the subsequent history of astronomy was that of al-Bitruji, recently made available in the Latin text and English paraphrase of F. J. Carmody (Berkeley, California, 1952) on which the following highly condensed account is based. al-Bitruji's work, *De Motibus Celorum*, was completed in Arabic sometime later than 1185 and made available in Latin by Michael Scot. The work shows him to have been familiar with the *Almagest* and with several of the earlier Arabic commentaries thereon. Nothing less than a consistently physical system would however satisfy him. The devices of excentric and epicycle are unnatural, therefore impossible *in rerum natura*. How then is the *apparent* variation of angular velocity to be 'saved'? By spiral motion, compounded of the naturally 'perfect' circular motions by the rotation of the poles of one sphere about those of another. The 'energy' necessary to drive the machine is supplied by the ninth [1] sphere and is transmitted throughout the world, decreasing in strength with increasing distance from its origin, to become zero at the wholly inert central earth. This system was rejected by Grosseteste, Roger Bacon and Albertus Magnus among the medievals, and has been discussed by Duhem (with the usual implication that in any case it was only 'rehashed' Greek [2]) and Dreyer among the moderns. In the form in which it was presented it was falsified in every particular by the subsequent

---

[1] For a discussion of the extra-planetary spheres, see below, p. 114.

[2] Certain superficial resemblances between the systems of Averroes and al-Bitruji Carmody believes to have been due to their use of a common source—the unpublished speculations of Ibn-Tufayl (d. 1183).

discoveries in mechanics and astronomy. It was without any direct influence. Why then should it be referred to here? In so far as this *Introduction* includes any attempt at interpretation it is that the Renaissance provided the conditions for a philosophical transvaluation. In astronomy this transvaluation was mediated by Copernicus (and indirectly by Nicholas of Cues) but was effected only by Kepler, whose *Astronomia nova* was sub-titled αἰτιολογετος *seu Physica coelestis.* . . . The transvaluation could never have been effected within the Ptolemaic conceptual framework. Al-Bitruji's system, though formally completely sterile, was the most radical attempt at physical re-thinking; it is for that reason that it has been given space in this account.

If there is any substance in the contention just set out it might appear somewhat inconsistent to claim for Peurbach that his 'recovery' of the *Almagest* was an essential preliminary to the 'new astronomy'. It is not at all obvious why any 'recovery' should have been necessary in respect of a text which had then been available for three centuries. It was not merely a question of the contemporary enthusiasm for preparing new texts from the original Greek, since Peurbach died before a Greek manuscript could be obtained. Apart from new tables, Peurbach's principal works were the *Theoricae novae* and the *Epitome* of the Almagest, the responsibility for whose completion the dying author bequeathed to his devoted pupil, Regiomontanus (No. 558). What was the purpose of these works, in neither of which was any novelty except of treatment? The answer seems to be involved in that qualifying phrase. No one had done for the whole Ptolemaic system of the heavenly bodies what Sacrobosco had done, at a much more elementary level, for the earth and such part of the heavenly appearances as were directly involved in the familiar terrestrial affairs such as chronology. The *Sphaera* would have been of little use to a navigator and none at all to an astrologer. Now when Peurbach took up his burden of teaching and research, both these skills were very much in demand. At the time of Peurbach's birth (1423) Prince Henry's African ventures (see below, Ch. viii) were well under way; and for evidence of astrological activity one may read, with astonishment merging into despair, the awful catalogue assembled by Thorndike in the volume of his *History* devoted to the fifteenth century. As evidence *post factum* hardly sufficient notice seems to have been taken of the fact that though there were

more than thirty incunable editions of the *Sphaera* there was no
edition of the *Almagest* until 1515. Admitting the stimulus to
Peurbach to revive the study of Ptolemy it may still be questioned
whether an independent beginning would not have advanced
astronomy more quickly. Perhaps it would; but the question is
really only academic. The dilemma was rather whether to tread
the popular path and go on teaching one or other of the Arabic
'deviations' or to get back to the solid ground of Ptolemaic
phenomenalism, with the minimum of concession to Aristotelian
natural philosophy. Such a course would not in itself ever lead
to a really 'new' astronomy, but a remark of Rheticus lends some
substance to the view that it was the 'return to Ptolemy' which
gave Copernicus the means to 'prove' his speculation, which
would otherwise have gone the same way as that of his contemporary Calcagnini (Dreyer, *op. cit.* p. 292). When Rheticus
says that Ptolemy and the other ancient writers 'have been until
now excluded from the schools' and 'have lain ignored in obscurity' he is indulging in the customary renaissance exaggeration;
but there seems to have been more than an element of truth in the
statement. The situation may be gauged from the *Praefatio* [1]
written by Erasmus Reinhold to his text and commentary on
Peurbach's *Theoricae novae* (*Ed.P.* 1553, No. 513a) where he says
that the latter was written by Peurbach because he could find
no work suitable as an introduction to the *Epitome*. From this it
appears that Rheticus may have been stating the sober truth
when he said that Ptolemy had been excluded *from the schools*;
this is indeed confirmed by the absence from the regular course
attended by Copernicus at Cracow of any reference to Ptolemy
other than to his *Quadripartitum*—a purely astrological work.
It is known however that he was much influenced by the teaching
of A. de Brudzewo (whose commentary on Peurbach's *Theoricae
novae* was the first to be printed—1495) though apparently this
must have come about outside the lecture room. The lack of
interest in Ptolemy, apart from a few advanced thinkers like
Brudzewo, is further demonstrated by the fact that no more
commentaries on Peurbach appeared before 1508 (F. Capuanus)
after which editions by various authors were numerous. What was

[1] This provides an exceedingly clear picture of the problem of astronomical method
and education as it appeared to one of its most progressive exponents in the middle of
the sixteenth century.

the cause of this lag? We can perhaps form a better idea of the problem after a glance at Peurbach's more famous pupil, Ioannes Mueller, who from his birth at Königsberg in Franconia is better known as Regiomontanus.

Most of the strands of his life-history that are significant for our purpose are already in our hands: what we have now to do is to look a little more closely at his publishing activities at Nürnberg about 1475, comparing them with the general run of mathematical and astronomical printing at that time. The sources for this task are Zinner's [1] bibliography of astronomical books printed in Germany and Klebs's study of scientific incunables— especially the 'trade list' printed by Regiomontanus himself and reproduced in Tanstetter's work already referred to (No. 669). From Zinner's list there emerges a picture whose background consists of innumerable 'calendars', 'tables of full and new moon', and prognostications. The only other 'modern' works were Peurbach's *Theoricae novae*, and Regiomontanus's *Ephemerides*, *Tabulae Directionum, Disputationes contra Cremonensia in planetarum theoricas deliramenta*. This brief list of works printed before 1476 might alone justify the claim that Regiomontanus was the first to publish works of contemporary scientific research. But of even more significance were some of the works whose publication was in hand or promised. Outstanding were of course his *Epitome* of the *Almagest* and his *De Triangulis omnimodis*; but there were several other original works on Ptolemy's instruments, one on the squaring of the circle, and one on the motion of the Eighth Sphere. Nor is it only in relation to original works that his claim should be considered. Among the promised works were the *Perspectiva* of Witelo, the whole of the then known works of Archimedes, the *Conics* of Apollonios (1537—see No. 36), the 'Spherics' of Theodosios (1518) (see above, p. 87), the mechanical inventions of Heron (1575). The dates in parentheses are those of the first printing of the works; thus from the past he selected with unerring judgment many of those which were to be the foundation of the future. Also in respect of these he recognised, as no other contemporary astronomer seems to have done, the importance of the opportunity provided by the greatly increased flow of Greek scholars into Italy, together with texts of an authenticity never before approached.

[1] Detailed ref. in Supplementary Bibliography.

What has been said so far is concerned mostly with the contribution, actual or potential, of Regiomontanus to theoretical astronomy, including that part of mathematics of special relevance thereto. But among the monotonous list of 'calendars', etc., to which reference has already been made were many based by him (though, in many cases, printed by other houses after his death) on his own observations in the only European building which could with any propriety be called an 'observatory'. Both the observatory and the printing press were made possible by the patronage of his young associate, Bernhard Walther in Nürnberg. Here were to be found the embryo of an astronomical clock, the 'torquetum' and other instruments which will be referred to later (p. 119). Probably the stimulus for this attempt at greater accuracy and more methodical observation was astrological, but the resulting solar tables were the basis of navigational aids then coming into increasing use (see below, p. 134). That his contemporaries held them in high esteem is also evidenced by his call to Rome by Sixtus IV for the purpose of giving technical advice on the projected reform of the calendar— the journey from which, when only in his fortieth year, he never returned.

And yet this promise—for it must be admitted that it was little more than a promise—saw no fulfilment for half a century. Regiomontanus died in 1476. The first step towards the 'new' astronomy was taken only in or about 1509, when Copernicus circulated a few manuscript copies of his *Commentariolus*, in which the coming revolution was clearly envisaged, but which was already very rare before the end of the sixteenth century and disappeared completely for three centuries.[1] Moreover it was in Italy, not in Nürnberg, as pupil and assistant to Domenico Novara, that Copernicus's thoughts were turned to astronomy. The work of Regiomontanus was indeed brought to his notice, but it was the former's trigonometrical methods rather than his observations or theory which Copernicus was later to use with such skill. What was the reason for this? Thorndike has been at some pains to document the hiatus, but mainly for the purpose of demonstrating the exaggeration of the whole Regiomontane cult. Yet this can not be the whole story. The Nürnberg of Dürer, Martin Behaim, Pirckheimer, Münzer, and the Schedels may

[1] E. Rosen, *Three Copernican Treatises*, New York, 1939.

have been rather bookish, but it was not *dead*. The proximate cause for the failure to follow up the lead given by Regiomontanus seems to have been the clam-like behaviour of Walther, who, apart from the gift of three of the Master's books to Münzer, refused to allow any use to be made of the materials he had gathered. More, it seems, needs to be learnt about Nürnberg in the last two decades of the fifteenth century.

If Copernicus had died at the same age as Regiomontanus probably nothing would have been heard of him until, centuries later, as actually happened, some historian had lighted upon one of the few surviving copies of the *Commentariolus*. The date of this work can not be established with certainty, but Copernicus must have been about thirty-six at the time of its distribution. Not a word more on any astronomical subject reached beyond the circle of his immediate acquaintance before 1524, when he wrote to his friend Bernard Wapowski a detailed criticism of a work by Johann Werner on the *Motion of the Eighth Sphere*. Copies of this reached a few scholars in manuscript after which there was again complete silence for more than ten years. Complete silence, except for rumours; for as early as 1530 the text of his masterpiece was sufficiently advanced for his patron, Bishop Tiedemann Gise, to urge him to publish it. By 1533 Clement VII had received notice of it; and in 1536 Copernicus received a further request for publication from Cardinal Schonberg of Capua. These details, and those that are to follow, cast a curious light on the relation between scientific thought and the leaders of the Christian Churches during the first part of the sixteenth century. For, whereas the entreaties of his own bishop had failed, the devoted assistance of the young Lutheran professor, Georgius Rheticus, succeeded in overcoming the hesitation and doubts of Copernicus, and the *De Revolutionibus Orbium Coelestium* was given to the world, and to the author on his death-bed, in 1543. There was, however, no question of superior insight or toleration on the part of the Wittenberg circle, since the attempts of Rheticus to have the work printed there were met with coldness if not open hostility. He had, however, tested the general feeling by printing an open letter to Iohann Schöner called *Narratio Prima*. This, as Rosen points out, was more guarded in its reference to the motion of the earth than Copernicus had been thirty odd years previously in the *Commentariolus*: the absence of any hostile comment on the

PLATE III

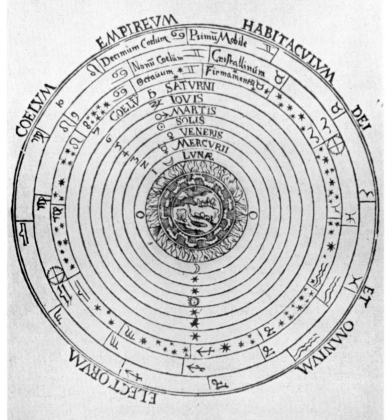

The 'final' system of eleven celestial spheres surrounding the sublunary sphere of the elements. (P. Apianus, *Cosmographia*, fo. 3ʳ, Vol. II, No. 33. Vol. I, p. 115.)

Narratio Prima may have been the main factor in gaining Copernicus's permission for the publication of his own work.

To appreciate the significance of this work for the development
of scientific thought in the Renaissance would require a book to
itself. All that can be attempted here is to indicate some of what
appear to be the most important facts and to refer the reader to
the Supplementary Bibliography.

It is in no disparagement of the laborious re-examination of the
data and of the geometrical mastery in the exposition of the
proposed system to emphasise that the work of Copernicus is
no more than a compromise between the old and the new, and is
furthermore marked by fundamental inconsistencies. Thus,
whereas all the equants are dispensed with, many of the epicycles
together with excentrics are retained. In modern terms, only those
devices which were necessary to compound the previously unrecognised motion of the earth with those of the remaining bodies
could be rejected, those due to the dogmas of *uniform* and *circular*
velocities being still unavoidable. Again, although the sun,
'sitting on the royal throne, steers the revolving family of stars'
(i.e. planets) it is nowhere suggested that the sun is in the planes
of the planetary orbits; worse still, it was not the point of reference
for these orbits, for which the centre of the earth's orbit was
chosen. There was therefore no question of the sun's exercising
any *mechanical* influence on the planets. The system was in no way
concerned with the question, but by his approving reference to
those who called the sun the 'light of the world' or even the 'soul'
and 'ruler' one may infer that he was not indifferent to it, but,
perhaps as a result of his early years in Italy, at least sympathetic
to the Neoplatonist belief in the radiation of cosmic power similar
to the propagation of light (see below, p. 162). The persistence of
ancient prejudices in regard to the behaviour of moving bodies
provided him with a needless problem—the explanation of the
fact that the celestial pole does not make an annual revolution.
This 'pole', in Copernicus's system, ceases to be the pole of the
heavens, since the heavens no longer move; it is merely the centre
of the daily circles described by every luminary, explained by
him as appearances due to the daily rotation of the earth. But to
account for the retrogradations of the planets he had of course
postulated an annual motion in translation of the earth about a
point excentric to the sun. Now motion of a spherical body on a

H

circle was conceived in no other way than that (as Dreyer puts it) of the bob of a conical pendulum. It was thus inconceivable that the axis of the earth should not itself describe an annual circle in the heavens: the fact that it doesn't has to be 'explained' by postulating a contrary motion.

The remaining problem which Copernicus had to solve was also an entirely imaginary one, based this time not on ancient theoretical prejudices but on the absence at that time and for all time past of any systematic study of error and of inconsistency in the measurements of reputable observers. This problem arose out of the observation by Hipparchos that the celestial pole does in fact describe a circle—expressed by him as a 'displacement of the solstitial and equinoctial signs'—but in a period of the order of 25,000 years. Ptolemy regarded this motion not so much as a motion of the equinoxes (the points of intersection of the equator and ecliptic) as of a motion of the whole sphere of the fixed stars—the eighth sphere in the Aristotelian cosmology. To account for this motion a ninth sphere had to be postulated marked by no visible points. Unfortunately Ptolemy was not content to adopt Hipparchos's value but redetermined the precession for himself as 1° in 100 years. By a further misfortune he thought he had found confirmation for this figure in a statement of Hipparchos in his work *On the Length of the Year* that allowance must be made for a displacement of 'not less than 1/100° in a year'. This assumption makes the complete cycle one of 36,000 years—far less near the truth than the original estimate. To this misunderstanding of the facts there was later added by Theon of Alexandria and Proklos an absurd tradition that the angular distances of the stars measured from the vernal equinox *oscillated* between two extreme values. Thus the stage was set for a controversy which lasted as long as that concerning the centre of the world, occupying men's minds to an almost equal degree. The story is long and complex; no more can be attempted here than to provide a background against which the numerous renaissance works 'On the Eighth Sphere' can be assessed. The *locus classicus* (never printed) is the work of the Jewish astronomer Tabit ben Korra, (830-901), by which time sufficient observations of a fairly high standard of accuracy had been made, which showed that the longitudes of the stars differed seriously from those calculated by Ptolemy's rule. Instead of recording the fact and leaving it to posterity to make a further comparison, Thabit constructed a mathematical model to account for the (imaginary) oscillation mentioned by Theon and Proklos. In this model the ninth sphere (*primum mobile*) produced the diurnal rotation, in which the whole cosmos shared, while the eighth sphere (of the fixed stars), which in the original system of Ptolemy turned once in 36,000 years in the contrary sense, was linked to the ninth in such a manner as to produce a periodic advance and recession ('trepidation') in the points of intersection of the equator and the movable ecliptic located in the eighth sphere. This triumph of misplaced ingenuity was put forward as a hypothesis, and (as Dreyer emphasises) was accepted, if at all, by many later Arabian astronomers with even more reserve. Unfortunately by the time the Alphonsine Tables were drawn up (1252) the discrepancy was too great to be accounted for by Thabit's theory, so the original *complete* revolution of the stars, postulated by Ptolemy, but now increased to 49,000 years, was restored *in addition to* trepidation. A tenth sphere now took on the function of *primum mobile*, the ninth provided the precessional motion, and the eighth the trepidation. This system is the one most commonly seen in sixteenth-century representations of the world, sometimes with an added 'theological' sphere as the 'abode of the blessed', the hierarchies of which, according to the scheme of the *pseudo*-Dionysios, may also be portrayed.

To return to Copernicus. It was not the least of the advantages of his system that the diurnal rotation of the *earth* removed the necessity for postulating the fantastic angular velocities required by the apparent motions of the fixed stars. The 'tenth' sphere thus became superfluous. But the fine visual imagery of Copernicus carried him further. If the apparent revolution of the stars could be transferred to the terrestrial rotation, the rotation of the axis of the *eighth* sphere (whether the stars were 'on' this or diffusely scattered in depth is one of the questions about which he seemed unable to make up his mind) could likewise be transferred to a motion of the earth's *axis*. This was done and the problem of the 'motion of the eighth sphere' lost its point, though not for some time its disputants. The ninth sphere as such likewise disappeared, but not unfortunately its function; for it was here that Copernicus showed his weakness as an astronomer. Though there is evidence to show that the whole course of his intellectual life was shaped by the discrepancy between an accepted celestial measurement and one of his own in Italy, he never seems to have grasped the idea that all measurements involve error, that skill in devising and handling instruments bears no necessary relation to mathematical imagination, and that in astronomy, in particular, a serious error in one observation may affect innumerable subsequent ones. Hence he introduced a great deal of unnecessary complication into the motion of the earth's axis in order to account for the non-existent trepidation.

Such then, in very crude outline, was the greatest systematic revolution in scientific thought since Ptolemy's systematisation of Greek astronomy. What was its impact on the learned world of the latter half of the sixteenth century? Fundamentally, almost none. Though the majority of contemporary astronomers joined in the chorus of praise of the author's ingenuity and mathematical skill, and rather fewer were glad to make use of the Prutenic Tables which Reinhold drew up on the basis of the new theory, it was generally agreed, as Copernicus himself had anticipated in his dedication to Paul III, that the hypothesis was too 'absurd' to be taken as a serious basis for further research. That the lack of any serious or widespread consideration of the new views was not due to overt theological opposition we have already seen (above p. 112). Rather, it was the very natural failure of human beings, whether scientists or not, to throw aside views by which for near two thousand years, as the Greeks said, 'cosmos was created out of chaos'. But there were also more creditable reasons, which, since they raise wide issues of methodology, will be referred to later (below, p. 125).

The earliest support for the Copernican system came from Reinerus Gemma (Frisius, No. 293) in the form of a letter written in the last year of his life (1556) to Ioannes Stadius and incorporated by the latter in his *Ephemerides novae* (No. 654). It is, as Thorndike observes, characteristic of the period that this first support should appear in a book whose purpose was mainly astrological. No comparable support of the *system*, as distinct from the use of the Prutenic Tables based on it, appeared until Thomas Digges welcomed it as an advance on 'the monstrous system of celestial globes invented by the ancients', but with proper scientific caution called for further observations whereby it might be tested in detail. This was in his *Alae seu scalae mathematicae* (1573); in the *Perfit Description of the Coelestiall Globes* which followed his revision of his father's *Prognostication everlasting* (No. 196) he set forth what was perhaps the most reasoned and favourable report before Kepler. Other claims have been staked out by historians for John Dee, John Feild, Robert Recorde, all Englishmen—and, more doubtfully, Jean Pena.

But at the most these men admitted but a partial acceptance or open-mindedness absent from most of their contemporaries. And what is most significant is the positive opposition by the most able astronomers of the times, Christopher Clavius, 'technical adviser' to Gregory XIII on the new calendar, and above all, Tycho Brahe. To a consideration of this outstanding figure in renaissance science we must now turn.

In few historical figures are the power and limitations of the human mind more clearly revealed than in Tycho Brahe. Born in 1546 of noble lineage he had the independence of mind, despite his family's opposition, to follow for himself the profession of astronomy, rather than as would then have been more proper to hire someone to do it for him. Though opposed to the contemporary Aristotelianism he rejected the Copernican system partly on the ground of its 'physical absurdity'. Realising that astronomy could become a science, comparable in rigour and precision to geometry, only on the basis of critically evaluated observations, he yet devoted the greater part of the inaugural lecture of his famous course at the University of Copenhagen in 1574 to a detailed defence of astrological prediction; and this, for a great part of his life, went with a sustained interest in alchemy, to which he devoted long periods of experiment. While capable of almost rhapsodical praise of the Creator as manifested in the serene beauty of the heavenly bodies, he sank to pusillanimous bickering with supposed plagiarists of his theories. Most pathetic of all was his legacy to Kepler of the massive array of observations on the planet Mars, wherewith the latter was enjoined to establish beyond doubt the 'truth' of Tycho's hypothesis, but which was ultimately in the latter's hands to be the means of banishing for ever the misleading assumptions on which the whole of astronomy had until that time been built. Tycho's beloved system, for whose parentage he was willing to insult friends and search the private belongings of a guest, had no lasting influence on astronomical theory, being geometrically equivalent to that of Copernicus.

H*

On the other hand his technique of observation revolutionised not only astronomy but the whole of physics; and his firm foundation for the determination of relative cosmic distances sapped the foundations of the Aristotelian cosmology in a way that the mere speculation and geometrical conventions of Copernicus could never have done. His abiding contribution to human knowledge lay in establishing observational astronomy on a scale never before approached in Europe, and with an insight into the theory of measurement never previously attained at all. To appreciate this it is necessary to take a quick glance over what had gone before.

Since the foundation of all astronomical knowledge is the measurement of angles, observations can be made with an ordinary pair of compasses opened out till the legs point to two chosen luminaries, and then applied to a graduated circle. With such a device Tycho, at the age of sixteen, made his first recorded observation. Since at least the time of Hipparchos however specially designed instruments have been used. These in the main have been variants of two principal forms, the armillary ('spherical astrolabe') and plane astrolabe: the term 'astrolabe' has been fairly consistently applied only to the latter. The armillary is composed of a number of spherical rings (*armillae*) on one of which the movable sights are carried. In the astrolabe a light bar (alidade) pivoted at the centre carries sights which move round a graduated circle; the instrument is 'set' by being carried on a small ring so that all angles are referred to the horizon. This completes one face. On the reverse is a calculating device consisting of a plane-projection of part of the celestial sphere, over which can be fitted any one of a series of 'retia': these are open-work discs showing the appropriate positions of standard stars on the projection, each of the set of discs being adjusted to a particular latitude. The first indubitable record of this device is in a work of Ioannes Philoponos (VI–1), but although Ptolemy wrote a work (*Planisphaerium*, No 752) on what was finally called 'stereographic projection', it has been urged by some authors that his reference to an ἀστρολάβον [1] has to do only with the zodiacal armillary, which was almost certainly used by Hipparchos. The astrolabe entered Western Europe not later than the twelfth century, by which time the Arabs, from whom it was obtained, had brought

[1] For a critical review of the whole question see D. J. Price in *Hist. Tech.*, Vol. III, pp. 603 f.

it to a very high degree of precision and artistic beauty. Although extensively and effectively used in the Middle Ages it was popularised in 1513 by the printing of a finely illustrated compendium by Ioannes Stoeffler (No. 658). The host of printed books which followed give no indication of advance in precision—which was hardly possible in a manual instrument—but the *Astrolabum catholicum* (No. 295) of Reinerus Gemma, by using the vernal equinox as the centre of projection, showed how a single instrument might be available for all latitudes. The same author, in his *Annulus Astronomicus* (No. 747) drew attention to a principle of even greater importance as regards astronomy; for though the instrument he described was too small to give readings of any high degree of precision, it enabled angular measures to be read direct from the celestial equator instead of from the horizon:[1] this principle was first applied to mounted armillaries by Tycho Brahe and is the basis of the equatorial mounting of most modern telescopes. Two other instruments of the greatest importance in Tycho's observatory were the sextant and the mural quadrant. Of neither of these was he the inventor, though the former had for so long fallen out of use that he appears to have re-introduced it independently.

Though mechanical clocks [2] had been used in his Nürnberg observatory by Walther the accuracy attained by Tycho would have been impossible had he relied exclusively on the unregulated mechanism which alone was available until Huygens introduced the pendulum-controlled escapement after 1658. The most accurate device at Tycho's disposal was the clepsydra dating from almost the earliest scientific records of the Greeks, but with mercury replacing the more usual water. But even this was not good enough except as a ready check, and Tycho's usual practice was to measure time in the most direct manner possible, namely by the determination of altitude or azimuth of the sun or standard stars, a method first employed in the West by Peurbach in 1457.

So much for the basic instruments themselves; but no advance in their design would of itself have effectuated the precision Tycho attained. The taking of a reading is primarily the noting of a

---

[1] An alternative method of transforming co-ordinates from one system to another without calculation was the use of the elaborate instrument known as the *torquetum* introduced in the thirteenth century (Price, *loc. cit.* p. 592).

[2] For a brief account of the history of chronometry in general, see below, p. 137.

coincidence between a visible object and a line on a scale; but before the seventeenth century the limit of division of a scale was much below the power of the eye to estimate a sub-division. An indirect method of extending the fineness of graduation was suggested by Pedro Nuñez by means of a set of divided concentric arcs; this was of no more than theoretical interest owing to the very trouble—lack of machines—which it was intended to obviate. The much simpler principle of transversals between two graduated lines—whether straight, or concentric arcs—is attributed by Thomas Digges to Richard Chancellor in the case of the cross-staff (see below, p. 146) but was first applied to arcs of astronomical instruments by Tycho. To refinement of reading Tycho added improvement in sighting, by means of the avoidance of, or allowance for, distortion of the axis in the large instruments, and atmospheric refraction. Here the permanent mounting of his instruments was an important factor.

Thus far we have, however superficially, attained some insight into the mechanics of Tycho's pre-eminence in renaissance astronomy. Why had it not been achieved at an earlier date? One most potent reason must surely be that western astronomers and their patrons, despite remarkable individual virtuosity in observation, had never before 'studied to make it' in Thomas Sprat's famous description of the aims of the Royal Society, 'not only an enterprise of one season or of some lucky opportunity; but a business of time; a steady, a lasting, a popular, an uninterrupted work'. At least one worker before Tycho had realised that astronomical research had reached the stage when further progress along traditional lines (the later invention of the telescope opened up literally new worlds to the 'amateur') would demand resources beyond those of the ordinary citizen.[1] This was William IV, Landgrave of Hesse, who about 1560 made extensions to his castle at Kassel and provided for an 'established' (*planmässig*) mathematical assistant.[2] Thus came into being the first fully

---

[1] Cf. Galluci's dedication of his *Theatrum Mundi* to Sixtus V, where he expresses the hope that 'adduceris ut instrumenta necessaria fabricanda & loca convenientia praeparanda, quibus id rite fieri possit procurare velis. Hoc non possunt privati homines; licet huius tantae rei studiosissimi sint, nisi principum auxilium accedat' (No. 288).

[2] B. Sticker, 'Landgraf William IV und die Anfänge der modernen astronomischen Meszkunst' in *Sudhoffs Archiv*, 40 (1956), 20. Also the same author's 'Die wissenschaftlichen Bestrebungen des Landgrafen William IV', *Zeit. des Vereins für Hessische Geschichte und Landeskunde*, 67 (1956).

authenticated permanent observatory in Europe—a century before those at Paris and Greenwich. Important as were the systematic records of the Landgraf and his assistants, of far greater moment for the progress of astronomy was his urgent insistence to King Frederick II of Denmark in 1576 to endow the young Tycho Brahe with the means of promoting astronomy at the highest level of efficiency. Acting on this advice the king placed at Tycho's absolute disposal the island of Hven and a sum sufficient to build a house and observatory. With the magnificence of this gesture compares ill the miserable pittance with which about a century later Charles II induced the single-minded John Flamsteed to become Astronomer-Royal.

On the island of Hven was built Uraniborg, the first European observatory on a scale sufficient to provide accommodation for a large 'research school' of young men, who later went out to careers in different parts of Europe. Its reputation was such as to bring to its hospitable doors distinguished visitors like James VI of Scots, who in 1590 was delighted to find there the portrait of George Buchanan, the author of a Latin epic on the *Sphere* and formerly His Majesty's tutor. James's presence in Denmark was due to the recent solemnisation of his marriage to the Princess Anne, previously celebrated by procuration, the king being represented by the Earl Marischal George Keith, founder of Marischal College, Aberdeen, in the following decade. Among the numerous names of learned men inscribed in the *Meteorological Journal* kept at Hven is that of Duncan Liddell, under the date 24 June 1584.

Uraniborg, it will be recalled, was founded in 1576—a year which fell between the dates of the two astronomical demonstrations for which Tycho is best known. It is necessary to call them 'demonstrations', since the phenomena themselves—the 'New Star' of 1572[1] and the comet of 1577—were observed by astronomers all over Europe. In neither case was the first observation made by Tycho, but in both cases it was the superiority of his measurements and the as yet rare cast of mind, which regards as sacred not only facts but also *necessary* inferences from the facts, which marked the beginning of a new epoch in astronomy. Since, however, it is easy to oversimplify this break with tradition it will be necessary to examine the matter in some detail. Though

[1] Now known to have been a 'supernova' whose radiation has probably been detected. See R. H. Brown and C. Hazard, *Nature*, **170**, (1952), 364.

separated in time by five years and by the foundation of Uraniborg, the two demonstrations were in a sense complementary and so may to some extent be studied together.

It is characteristic of this typical 'man of the Renaissance' that it was on returning home from a long day's work in his laboratory, in which for two years and to the complete exclusion of astronomy he had been wooing alchemy, that he was struck by the appearance of a new star in Cassiopeia '. . . a miracle indeed, either the greatest of all that have occurred in the whole range of nature since the beginning of the world, or one certainly that is to be classed with those attested by the Holy Oracles, the staying of the sun in its course in answer to the prayer of Joshua, and the darkening of the sun's face at the time of the Crucifixion. For all the philosophers agree, and facts clearly prove it to be the case, that in the etherial region of the celestial world no change in the way either of generation or of corruption takes place.' [1] This account of the observation, quoted from the exceedingly rare work in which it was published in the following year, does not at first seem to give much promise of the dawn of a new era in methodology: authority—'all the philosophers agree'—precedes the evidence of the senses—'facts clearly prove it to be the case'; and the 'Holy Oracles' are accepted as relevant to matter of fact. Tycho was 'so astonished at the sight' of the appearance of a new star that he was not 'ashamed to doubt the trustworthiness' of his own eyes. Many of his contemporaries were; others harmonised the undoubted phenomenon with unquestionable dogma by writing of the former as a tailless comet or one whose tail was invisible owing to its motion in the line of sight. This compromise was made possible by Aristotle's by no means dogmatic view that comets were fiery exhalations carried up from the outermost elements into the ether—hence must be situated little beyond the sphere of the moon. But the inadequacy of this compromise is at once apparent when the results of studies of comets then recently published are taken into account.

From time immemorial comets had very naturally been regarded as portents, and though the Aristotelian account of their

[1] *De Nova et nullius aevi memoria prius visa Stella iam pridem anno a nato Christo* 1572 *mense Novembra primum conspecta contemplatio mathematica* . . . Copenhagae, 1573. A reprint was issued in 1901 (Hauniae). The passage quoted is from the translation in H. Shapley and H. E. Howarth, *Source Book in Astronomy*, New York, 1929, p. 13.

actual genesis was very generally accepted throughout the Middle Ages, the cause of any particular appearance was most commonly regarded as *praeter naturam*. Well attested observations occur for most centuries, but it was in 1540 (but see *Isis* **20,** 443-4) that a striking regularity in the behaviour of comets was established by systematic observation and calculation. In that year Peter Apian, in his sumptuously produced work, *Astronomicum Caesareum*, drew attention to two regularities of comets, namely, that their magnitude (luminosity) *increases* as they approach the sun, contrary to the opinion frequently expressed, and that their tails are always directed away from the *sun* and not from the earth as the Aristotelian physics required. It is the latter observation that is of the greatest historical importance, since he was not content to make a merely qualitative observation of the direction of the tail at the time of sunset, but demonstrated by calculation of the sun's position that the latter lies on the longitudinal axis of the tail. This at once suggests an intimate connection between the sun and comets, which further implies that the latter are unlikely to be merely 'terrestrial' exhalations. Unfortunately the matter was not settled quite as easily as this, since there was still hope that by appeal to the laws of optics comets might be shown to be rather of the nature of optical illusions, related to the direction of the sun's *rays*.[1] A further difficulty was that the relation 'proved' by Apian was not true of all comets—doubt on this score was expressed by Grosseteste and the exceptions confirmed by Conrad Dasypodius.[2] Nevertheless the exceptions are very rare, and by no means so striking as to make it in the least likely that a comet's tail would be continuously turned away from the *earth*.

The only way to settle the question of the new phenomenon beyond a doubt was to determine its position in the physical hierarchy of the spheres.[3] This Tycho had at once started to do with a recently constructed sextant: his description of the use of this instrument provides an admirable example of his critical appreciation of measurement already alluded to. Having measured the angular distances of the star from the three brightest members of the constellation Cassiopeia he was able by means of the spherical trigonometry of Regiomontanus to calculate its celestial

[1] Cf. Cardano, *De Varietate Rerum*, referred to by Thorndike, *Hist.* V. 570.
[2] See also *Isis* **19,** 19f and **36,** 268.
[3] See Dreyer, *Life of Tycho Brahe*, Edinburgh, 1890, p. 158.

latitude and longitude. These co-ordinates remained constant throughout the star's sixteen months' life, which would not of course have been the case if it had been a comet, or in any way attached to one of the planetary 'spheres'. To get some idea of the distance of the star from the earth Tycho with a different instrument measured the parallax. This quantity is the apparent shift in the position of a celestial object whose distance from the observer is not such that in comparison with it the radius of the earth may be neglected. If any body which neither rises nor sets (as is the case with Cassiopeia in Northern latitudes) is viewed at upper and lower culminations it will show a maximum displacement as compared with a body whose distance is 'infinite' compared with the diameter of the earth. Whereas the moon gave a value well within the limits of observation employed by Tycho, no displacement whatever could be detected in the case of the new star; whence, since it could not be in any of the planetary spheres, it must have its place in the 'eighth sphere'.

When Tycho wrote the tract *De Nova Stella* he refrained from speculating on the genesis of the star, but devoted several pages to discussion of the astrological implication of its appearance—a fact that is not usually alluded to in histories of science, but which shows that, though Tycho's inferences were modest and cautious in comparison with those of many of his contemporaries, he was then in no doubt whatever that such inferences ought to be drawn. It was to combat the astronomical nonsense and astrological irresponsibilities to which the appearance of the new star had given rise that he was induced against his principles as a nobleman to permit the publication of his tract.

At the time when Tycho entered on his work at Hven he was then already an established authority on astronomical matters; he was the equal of his contemporaries in the handling of the mathematical tools forged by Regiomontanus, and surpassed them in the appreciation of the primacy of observation and of the necessity for a critique of the methods employed. On the other hand he was enthusiastic for alchemy, regarded astrology as a science with its own integrity to maintain, and despite his demonstration of a major anomaly in the system, he was in regard to the spheres, though in little else, a thoroughgoing Aristotelian. Above all he was convinced that nothing but a 'steady, a lasting, an uninterrupted work' of observation could remedy the deficiencies of even the Prutenic Tables, which were already seriously in error.

The work on the new star had, as we have seen, involved the problem of the status of comets. By great good fortune the appearance of the star was followed within five years by the appearance of an exceptionally large comet: by this time Tycho was sufficiently established at Hven to bring a fairly powerful battery of instruments into action. The results were sufficiently accurate and consistent to show that this comet had no appreciable diurnal parallax, and consequently, though its position among the stars varied continuously, it must inhabit a region at least six times as far from the earth as does the moon. But since its size and position had changed progressively, its path must have intersected the 'spheres' of some at least of the planets. It was this conclusion, coupled with the 'generation and corruption' of a body (the 'new star') in 'heaven itself', which gave to Tycho's demonstrations a physical significance far beyond that of the Copernican 'revolution'. The Aristotelian cosmology was henceforward an untenable mass of contradictions. The fact that it continued to be taught in every university after the wide dissemination of Tycho's book was due doubtless in part to the intellectual inertia of such corporate bodies, partly to the fact that the demonstration depended upon what was for that time an abstruse mathematical argument based on a vast array of data derived from only two distinct phenomena. The parallel with the general theory of relativity is clearly remarkably close, and the acceptance of the latter, even allowing for such general philosophical reservations as are proper to any scientific theory, was not so whole-hearted and immediate as to warrant too scathing a verdict on our colleagues of the sixteenth and early seventeenth centuries.

Tycho himself fully realised the implications of his demonstrations, and with this freedom which had been denied to Copernicus proceeded to sketch a new world system. The legend above the figure representing it in the work of 1588 (No. 94a), carries with it many lessons for the historian. It reads as follows: 'Nova mundani systematis hypotyposis . . . qua tum vetus illa Ptolemaica redundantia & inconcinnitas, tum etiam recens Copernicana in motu terrae physica absurditas, excluduntur . . .' Of the 'redundancy' of the Ptolemaic system it is hardly necessary to speak: it removal was the chief spur to Copernicus. But, so Tycho thought, this had been achieved only by introducing a 'physical absurdity', namely, the attribution of motion to the 'sluggish' earth. Here was a case indeed of the common spectacle of a great reformer being unable to throw off completely the unconscious trammels of the modes of thought he is seeking to discard. There was no reason—other than the Aristotelian dogma—why the earth should be any more 'sluggish' than the thousands of bodies which in the Tychonic system were compelled to hurtle round it at fantastic speeds—fantastic, since to him the radii of the circles described by the stars were so great that no *diurnal* parallax was to be expected to come within the limits of observation conferred by his admirable instruments. Of other 'physical absurdities' he must have had in mind the 'crystalline' spheres whose motions traditionally imparted theirs to the planets; but to the question as to whether Copernicus really believed in the existence of these no certain answer has yet been given though the evidence slightly favours an affirmative one. Tycho's conviction of their non-existence, deduced from the partial construction of an orbit for the comet of 1577, also enabled him to use the geoheliocentric device in which the orbit of Mars round the sun *intersected* that of the sun round the earth. Incidentally with the rejection of the spheres, as a result of his careful redetermination of precession, went also that of 'trepidation' and of the dual precessional motion.

The other reason for Tycho's rejection of the Copernican system reveals the dangers of a too rigorously deductive system and the importance of a free interchange of knowledge between the various departments of science. Analagous to the diurnal (geocentric) parallax due to the rotation of the earth is the *annual* parallax which would be a necessary consequence of an annual revolution round the sun. Tycho argued that such a parallax should be observable in every one of the stars; but since no such apparent movement was detected no such movement of the earth could have taken place. Superficially this appears to be an ideal methodological form: the falsification of one of two alternative hypotheses. Had Tycho, the pioneer of the critique of measurement, failed here to distinguish between 'detected' and 'detectable' within the limits of existing instrumental precision? The error in fact was not as crude as it may at first appear, being mainly due to the imperfection of the human eye, whose response to intensity of illumination gives an impression of relative *size*, with the result that first magnitude stars, at least, were regarded as subtending a measurable angle at the eye. Now from the absence of any detectable parallax Tycho quite properly inferred that these stars must be at immense distances from the earth. But any body so far distant and having such an apparent size as the unaided eye endows it with could of necessity have such an unimaginably large diameter as Tycho refused to contemplate: hence he rightly rejected the only factor not susceptible of direct observation, namely, the orbital motion of the earth.

As the years passed Tycho's intellectual stature grew: the succession of comets was observed with instruments of increasing accuracy, from which there resulted data, never published by him, yet of sufficient precision to enable nineteenth-century astronomers to calculate their orbits. Also he showed himself increasingly sceptical of the claims of judicial astrology, and especially of the value to be attached to 'nativities'; but his belief in the influence of the stars on the mind and well-being of man never left him; Paracelsus he described as one of Germany's greatest men. On the other hand his self-esteem grew proportionately. He became over-bearing towards his tenants, negligent of his prebend, and petty in the extreme towards academic critics. The most important of these critics was Bär Reymer whom he accused of filching the so-called 'Tychonic System' when on a visit to Hven. It has been impossible to settle this question decisively; but since the device of placing the sun at the centre of the orbits of Mercury and Venus is as old as Herakleides, it was anybody's *idea* to extend it to the superior planets. Moreover Bär's proposal agreed with that of Herakleides, in giving a diurnal rotation to the earth, a 'saving of the appearances' which only Tycho's prejudice prevented him from making use of. Less important, though of domestic interest, was Tycho's ponderously elaborate reply (1595) to John Craig's attack on his work on the place of comets. Craig's attack had its interest in relation to the history of the period, in that it throws into bold relief the beginnings of that degree of specialisation which made it an act of presumptuous folly for a man of Craig's scholarly attainments to enter into a controversy on a subject which had been removed by the work of Tycho into a realm in which mere scholarship was an irrelevance. It was this failure on the part of the scholars to read the signs of the times which fanned the flames of revolt against the current 'Aristotelianism'. With Craig's *protégé*, Duncan Liddel, Tycho also fell foul in later years, on the basis of a mere rumour that Liddel while teaching for the first time in Germany, so it is said, the three great systems of the world— Ptolemaic, Copernican, and Tychonic—was not above hinting that the last was his own independent creation. Even if the rumour were true—which Liddel indignantly denied—the claim which it bruited, as possibly in the case of Reymers, might have been true also.

An attempt has been made in this brief sketch to indicate the kind of problems the astronomers of the Renaissance were engaged in and especially to emphasise the dominant world-view from which they were able in varying degrees to release themselves. As the century drew to a close a young man, pupil of Maestlin (No. 418) and later colleague of the aging Tycho Brahe, published an ingenious piece of whimsy which showed the displacement of Aristotelian cosmology by Neoplatonic formalism. But Ioannes Kepler's *Mysterium Cosmographicum* (1595) gave an almost entirely misleading idea of this young man's future.[1] Out of the 'steady, lasting, uninterrupted' observations made by Tycho on the planet Mars, the precise degree of reliability of which Kepler knew to one minute of arc, he created the New Astronomy in which at last was rejected every vestige of the cramping hypotheses which the New Learning had embraced from the Old.

---

[1] It contained, however, an able defence of the Copernican system and greatly improved on the latter by taking the sun, and not the centre of the earth's orbit, as the reference point for the planetary motions.

Plate IV

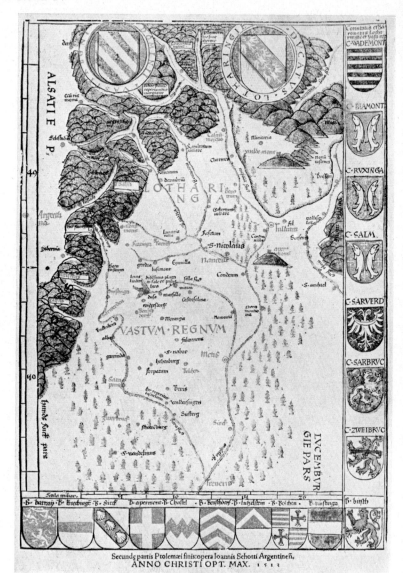

Part of Alsace, Lorraine, and Luxemburg shown in a 'new' topographical map included in the 1513 (Strassburg) edition of Ptolemy's *Cosmographia*. This is probably the earliest example of three-colour (black, red, and brown) printing of a map. (Vol. II, No. 543 c; also R. A. Skelton, *Geog. Mag.* **32**(1960), 544; and Vol. I, p. 144.)

CHAPTER VIII

MATHEMATICAL PRACTITIONERS—MAPS, CHARTS AND SURVEYS

O F all the events traditionally associated with the Renaissance none has been more generally acclaimed than the discovery of America. In the words of the first *Cambridge Modern History* 'Among the landmarks which divide the Middle Ages from modern times the most conspicuous is the discovery of America by the Genoese captain Cristoforo Colombo in 1492'. On the consequences for the growth of scientific knowledge it is unnecessary to insist: certainly in the realm of natural history and medicine they can be measured by the appearance within little more than half a century of fairly critical works describing plants previously unknown. More important, perhaps, was the shock of recognition that, in Francis Bacon's words, 'Truth is the daughter not of authority but of time'. So much is fact; but it is tempting to regard the long-planned and boldly executed feat of seamanship which brought about this enlargement of the bounds of possible knowledge as having been prompted by the 'freeing of men's minds from ecclesiastical domination' and made possible by the 'new astronomy' of Peurbach and Regiomontanus. Unfortunately the historian of science seeking an answer to this question among the works of scholars who have devoted themselves to a minute study of the enterprise of Columbus quickly finds himself in a bog of conflicting claims. The traditional view is based on the assumption, never even hinted at by Columbus himself, but first given currency in a biography attributed to his son Ferdinand and first printed in 1571, and repeated in 1575 in *Historia de las Indias* written between 1527 and 1563 by Bartolome de Las Casas, who is known to have had access to Ferdinand's manuscripts. The correspondence of which Ferdinand gives an Italian version, Las Casas a Spanish, is alleged to have passed between Christopher Columbus and a certain 'Paolo Fisico' as a consequence of the former's having seen a letter of the said Paolo

Fisico, dated Florence, 25 June 1474, to Fernao Martins, Canon of Lisbon Cathedral, concerning the possibility of reaching the Indies by a shorter route. The technical information contained in these letters, and the map which was alleged to have accompanied that to the Canon, coming from the celebrated Paolo Toscanelli (for no one doubted that he was the author) was generally supposed to have given theoretical support and detailed amplification to Christopher's 'hunch' that the coast of the 'Indies' would be reached by a much shorter sea-passage westwards from the Iberian coast than by sailing round Africa. The feature in the alleged correspondence upon which Columbus would have seized was the statement that 'Quinsay' (Hangchow) lay at 5,000 nautical miles from the Canaries, 'Cipangu' (Japan) at only 3,000. The former estimate would be arrived at by deducting from 360° the eastward extension of Asia and multiplying the difference by the number of nautical miles in a degree at the appropriate latitude. Now whereas Ptolemy had estimated the eastern extension of Asia as 180° Toscanelli had evidently added about 30°. Of the existence of 'Cipangu' Ptolemy had of course no notion: it had, however, been described in the most glowing terms by Marco Polo, and is shown lying to the east of 'Quinsay' in the famous terrestrial globe which Martin Behaim completed in 1492. Thus for three centuries the matter rested. Then in 1871 a Latin 'original' of Toscanelli's letter to Martins was discovered by Harisse at Seville; no trace of the map or of the 'correspondence' with Columbus has ever been found.

The historian of science in the Renaissance who, seeking to learn more about Paolo Toscanelli, turns to the works of the recent writers on Columbus and his enterprise must be prepared for a dusty answer—or rather several dusty answers, since no two of the six I have consulted agree. Duff (*The Truth about Columbus*, London, 1936) merely paraphrases the correspondence and dismisses it as 'doubtful' and in any case irrelevant since Columbus was not seeking the Indies; Vignaud (*Toscanelli and Columbus*, London 1902) 'proved' that it was forged—probably by Christopher's brother, Bartholomew; S. E. Morison and S. Madariaga (in otherwise scholarly and balanced works) fail to agree either on the authenticity of the correspondence or on the character of Toscanelli. One example, from the latest and most authoritative, must suffice. Morison (*Christopher Columbus—*

Admiral of the Ocean Sea, London, 1942, p. 33) describes Toscanelli as a 'Florentine physician and humanist. . . . Physicians in the fifteenth century were apt to be good mathematicians and astronomers since the stars helped their medicine to "take"; and from astronomy it was a short jump to geography and estimating the size of the globe. That happened to be Toscanelli's hobby.' In *Christopher Columbus Mariner*, p. 46, this has become '. . . a learned physician in Florence, Paolo Toscanelli, who dabbled in astronomy and mathematics', presumably 'adapted' by Penrose (*Travel and Discovery in the Renaissance*, Cambridge, Mass., 1952, p. 78) as 'Toscanelli was a celebrated Florentine scholar, whose profession was medicine and whose hobby was geography'. This ingenious but unnecessary 'explanation' of why 'Paolo fisico' (syn. 'Paulus physicus'; Madariaga provides a variant source of confusion by taking 'physicus' to mean 'physicist'—a highly improbable assumption for the fifteenth century) should be considered competent to advise on cosmography could have been avoided by ten minutes spent in referring to the *Enciclopedia Italiana*, art. *Paolo del Pozzo* (1937). Here a brief assessment by a late contemporary, Pico della Mirandola, disposes of any question of 'dabbling': 'Paolo Fiorentino, certamente dotto in medicina, ma principamente in matematica in greco e in latino. . . .' In the same place we may learn that to Toscanelli were dedicated books by Nicholas of Cues, Leon Battista Alberti, and Regiomontanus; that he studied mathematics with Brunelleschi (Vasari's 'gli' is ambiguous as to who was teacher, who pupil); and that a manuscript is extant containing his original and systematic observations on the appearance of Halley's comet. That cosmography was not just a 'hobby' or, as Madariaga avers, taken up in his old age, is hardly consistent with the fact that Gemistos Plethon testified to having been shown a map of Scandinavia (presumably the Clavus map—see below, p. 143) by him at the Council of Florence in 1539—when Toscanelli was only forty-two (A. Diller, *Isis*, **27** 441).

That there was probably no one then living *outside Portugal* (see below, p. 133) more competent to advise on cosmographical problems seems a reasonable inference from these reports. The fact that he was hopelessly wrong in his estimate is all the more significant. But all this would be irrelevant if Vignaud's 'demonstration' of the forging of the correspondence were to be accepted.

Forcefully and meticulously as his case was presented, it became less convincing when he used it as part of a highly contrived theory that Columbus's objective was not the 'Indies' but undiscovered islands in the western Atlantic; it became untenable in its original form when evidence was obtained of a meeting between Martins (of whose existence Vignaud doubted) and Toscanelli. But to say, as does Penrose (*op. cit.* p. 78) that the correspondence is 'now generally accepted as genuine' is an over-statement. Morison indeed accepts it *in toto*; but Madariaga and the authors of the articles *Paolo del Pozzo* (1937) and *Colombo* (1931) in the *Enciclopedia Italiana*, though admitting the probable authenticity of the original letter to Martins, regard those alleged to have been written to Columbus as fabricated—by Columbus himself, according to Madariaga.

This quagmire of confusion through which we have had to pass is however only part of the journey: to determine the degree to which the discovery of America was prompted and achieved by the aid of the 'New Learning' we have to see what use Columbus made of the information in the letter to Martins, the Latin copy of which (the real 'original' has never been found) was in his hand or, as Vignaud believed, in that of Bartholomew's. All the evidence, reviewed by Morison, (*Admiral of the Ocean Sea*, pp. 24 f.) goes to show that he made no *systematic* use of it at all. Columbus's aim was to reduce the inferred sea-passage westward to the Indies to a minimum: to this end he selected from each authority he could lay his hands on—Pierre D'Ailly (*c.* 1410, but copied from Roger Bacon), Enio Silvio Piccolomini (*c.* 1440), Marco Polo (1298), and the book of Esdras (!)—whatever suited his purpose, whether it was in respect of the eastward extension of Asia or in the linear measure of a degree of longitude—ignoring, particularly in the case of Piccolomini, those opinions which did not. The only conclusion for which there is any firm evidence is the possibility—at most probability—that Columbus's sight of the original letter to Martins gave theoretical support to his own vision of the nearness of land to the west. Madariaga believes that he copied this secret document in haste, and could certainly never have used it as evidence in Portugal. Morison's picturesque claim that the letter and chart were 'always his exhibits A and B' was founded on no better authority than Ferdinand's *Life*: in rightly stressing the value of this document he fails to add that on the last occasion

(1492) when these 'exhibits' could have been produced by his father Ferdinand was only seven years old.

The second claim—namely that the discovery of America was made possible by the 'new' astronomy—may be disposed of much more summarily. Here Morison's work is outstanding; for, in a series of voyages in sailing ships reproducing sufficiently closely the conditions of Columbus's own, he and a number of colleagues (the Harvard Columbus Expedition, 1939-40) followed the sea-tracks of Columbus across the Atlantic and in the Caribbean. The results demonstrated the uncanny seamanship—and luck—of Columbus in the use of winds, and his complete reliance on dead-reckoning with compass and line. His *Journal*, the general authenticity of which Morison was able to confirm in detail, reveals that on his first voyage he had no instrument for celestial observation except a sea astrolabe, which he was unable to use. Though he had a copy of Regiomontanus's *Almanach*, which stood him in good stead for his famous hoax on the natives (*Admiral of the Ocean Sea*, p. 654), he twice showed himself incapable of using it to find a longitude.

So America was discovered, not by the aid of the 'New Science', but by the old virtues of courage, faith, and consummate seamanship. Columbus's landfall was 1,000 nautical miles further west than he had calculated it would be. And it was not Japan that he had reached but Watling's Island (named by him 'San Salvador') in the Bahamas. Japan, towards which he continued his voyage a couple of days later, was still 6,000 miles further on! He had almost literally 'bumped into' America on the way.

Is then the whole tradition of the relation between the mathematical revival and the great voyages of discovery based on nothing but forged documents and wishful thinking? By no means. The researches in the early years of the present century of Portuguese historians, though not always free from nationalistic bias, have confirmed in greater detail what had long been suspected in general, that the art of coastal navigation gradually assumed a more scientific basis as the problems raised by oceanic travel became more pressing, and have established 'the pre-eminence of the Portuguese mathematicians from the time of Prince Henry the Navigator in respect of the application of their science to the problems of navigation'.[1] Prince Henry himself was

[1] E. G. R. Taylor, *Tudor Geography*, London, 1930, p. 83.

I*

in fact no navigator but, by making the study of Navigation 'a steddy, a lasting, a popular, an uninterrupted work' [1] he was much more. The actual achievements of the navigators trained in his ' school' are difficult if not impossible to estimate, owing to the increasingly dense 'iron curtain' which was drawn over Portuguese exploits as the competition of the rival kingdoms of Spain became more marked; but there is no doubt that Madeira (1419), the Azores (1435), and the Islands of Cape Verde (1456) were sighted in his lifetime by the Venetian, Alvise da Cadamosto, then in his service;[2] moreover these represent outward voyages of up to about 1,500 miles and (in the case of the Azores) a considerable thrust into the ocean. Nevertheless in no case does the problem of position-finding involve any calculation: the southernmost point reached being still far enough north of the equator for the polar latitude to be observed direct, by means of the astrolabe, or more likely the simple quadrant. After 1471, when the equator was first passed, this direct observation was no longer possible: the alternative was the determination of the noon altitude of the sun, from which, the solar longitude and declination being known from tables, the latitude could be easily calculated—provided one knew the appropriate rule for the known circumstances. Thus the mathematicians' job was to put into the hands of the navigator a calendar of solar declinations and longitudes for every day of the year and a *Regimento* [3] explaining how to use them for the particular purpose: this was all the more necessary since solar tables were often (e.g. the *Tabulae Directionum* of Regiomontanus) primarily intended for astrologers. The earliest printed *Regimento* is one discovered in Munich in 1890, which from internal evidence probably dated from about 1509—about

---

[1] See p. 120 above.

[2] These dates are taken from J. Bensaude, *Histoire de la Science Nautique Portuguaise*, Vol. 1, Munich, 1914, p. 1. Dr. A. Cortesao (*The Nautical Chart of 1454*, Coimbra, 1954, p. 98) claims that 'it is an incontrovertible fact that the Madeira and the Azores isles were discovered before the fifteenth century high seas navigation was developed by the Portuguese because they are represented in fourteenth-century maps'. See, however, S. E. Morison's review, *Speculum*, 30 (1955), 461—in which the evidence for the alleged discovery is severely criticised. Somewhat different dates from those quoted are given in the recent British Museum catalogue *Prince Henry the Navigator and Portuguese Maritime Enterprise*, 1960.

[3] This *Regimento do Sol* must not be confused with the much simpler 'Regiment of the North Star' to determine the direction of true north by observing the pole star which might be as much as $3\frac{1}{2}°$ distant therefrom. (see *Hist. Tech.* 3, 545.)

ten years earlier than the one found at Evora in a volume containing the famous letter of Hieronymus Münzer to John II of Portugal accompanying the Portuguese translation of the *Sphere of Sacrobosco*. The letter is dated 1493, but it is not known when or why it was first published; in it Münzer seems to be acting as the agent of the Emperor Maximilian urging John II to launch an expedition *westward* to 'Cathay'. Since the letter arrived after the return of Columbus and the consequent abandonment to Spain of the western route,[1] it could have had no effective value. Nevertheless John II received Münzer with every show of cordiality in the following year; similarly Martin Behaim, who is named in the letter as a suitable pilot for the expedition, had been appointed by John II to the mathematical *Junta* some years before. So there was evidently some degree of co-operation between the Portuguese mathematicians and those of Nürnberg citizens who were in some measure the heirs of Regiomontanus's enthusiasm in that city. Bensaude made out a good case for believing that the chief intermediary may have been the Nürnberg humanist, Conrad Peutinger, closely associated with Maximilian I and married to one of the Welser family, who were among the first Augsburg merchants to associate themselves with the Portuguese spice fleets (Bensaude, *op. cit.* pp. 18 ff.).

Prince Henry had died in 1460; the earliest extant *Regimento* can hardly have been much earlier than 1509. But in 1488 Diaz doubled the Cape of Good Hope—not trans-oceanic sailing indeed, but evidence of a knowledge of position-finding in the southern Hemisphere, since they were out of sight of land for long periods.[2] Ten years later the Indian Ocean had been crossed by Vasco da Gama, and in 1521 Ferdinand Magellan (Magellaes), a Portuguese in Spanish employment, had crossed the Pacific: a part of his heroic crew, leaving their captain in a grave in the Philippines, completed the circuit of the globe. There can be no doubt then that in the interval the fixing of latitude in the southern Hemisphere had been mastered and readily applied.

[1] This was established by the Treaty of Tordesillas (1494) in which the North-South demarcation line legalised in a series of bulls (especially *inter caetera*) by Alexander VI was moved 270 leagues further west.

[2] Admiral Morison believes that actual *navigation* was at this time almost entirely by dead reckoning, the astrolabe being used only after landing, in order to determine the latitude of each position newly reached. The BM exhibition catalogue cited above states that tables and rules had been reduced to a manual by about 1480.

Most of the documentary evidence has disappeared, but references to the use of a *Regimento* are to be found here and there in the manuscripts relating to various voyages: in particular the matter is dealt with in much greater detail by Duarte Pacheco in his *Esmeralda de Situ Orbis* (which may have been written as early as 1505) than in the Munich book. It is very probable that from 1492, when Abraham Zacuto was brought from the Chair of Mathematics at Salamanca to be personal adviser to John II on astronomical questions, the distribution of solar tables in manuscript was given a considerable impetus: the famous *Almanach Perpetuum* (No. 742) by Zacuto was first printed at Leiria in 1496. From internal evidence Bensaude demonstrated that among the manuscript tables which have survived none gave any indication of having been derived from the Regiomontane tables, while a large proportion—though Zacuto's name is not specifically mentioned— show strong affinities with those of the *Almanach Perpetuum*.

In relation to this mathematical problem of position-finding on the sphere all that has been said is concerned with *latitude* for the good and sufficient reason that no means of deriving longitude directly from celestial observations existed. The only method was that of dead-reckoning deduced from the ship's log and the point of departure. This method being at the mercy of every shift of wind, and particularly variation of current and leeway, made the results very unreliable. A further complication was introduced by the observation of the inconstancy of magnetic declination (unfortunately always called 'variation' in navigation) with position. For a long time this variation of the declination was looked upon hopefully [1] as a potential aid rather than as a source of error, owing to the fact that in some oceanic areas the variation is related fairly regularly to longitude. Near the time of Rotz's work (about 1530) the only fundamental method of determining the longitude, namely by the comparison of local *times*, was described by Reinerus Gemma (Frisius). The local time at the point required could of course be determined by the astrolabe: the difficulty was to 'transport', by an accurate clock, the local time of the point of known longitude. An 'accurate clock' was a thing entirely unknown in 1530 and for more than a century

---

[1] As for instance by Jean Rotz of Dieppe and Sebastian Cabot (Taylor, *Tudor Geography*, p. 66), and even as late as Edward Wright in 1599 (Taylor, *Mathematical Practitioners*. Cambridge, 1954, p. 336).

thereafter. Since the problem of chronometry—highly important in itself—has this special relevance to navigation it may be as well to give a brief sketch of its progress at this stage of our *Introduction*, since the matter is one concerning which there is still widespread confusion.

In a recent description [1] of an eleventh-century Chinese manuscript there has, it is believed, been demonstrated a connecting link between the fluid-driven clocks of the Hellenistic Age and the weight-driven mechanism which (as may be inferred from contemporary references) had become almost a commonplace in Western Europe in the late thirteenth century. The oldest extant *description* is (probably) the autograph manuscript of Giovanni de' Dondi concerning his planetarium clock [2] (1348-64) which embodied epicycles and excentrics. The great tower clock which still stands in the *Piazza dei Signori* at Padua was constructed in 1437 on the basis of the original design of Giovanni de' Dondi. An even earlier (though much restored) example of the same type as the original astronomical design stood, until destroyed in the last war, in the St. Marienkirche at Lübeck.[3] Possibly the oldest astronomical clock with a striking train still extant is that of Salisbury cathedral in which only the escapement has been replaced by a later anchor type. For travellers, whether on land or sea, 'watches' were in use probably from the time of the dissemination of the tract on the astrolabe by Hermannus Contractus in the eleventh century.[4] These were essentially cylindrical 'dials', but towards the end of the fifteenth century a spring-driven mechanism controlled by the ingenious 'fusee' was made available. These were probably first made in Italy but attained European fame through the skill of the Nürnberg instrument makers. Such contrivances were of course useless for the periods involved in sea navigation, and no appreciable

[1] Needham, Wang Ling, and Price, *Nature*, **177**, (1956), 600-2. See also Supplementary Bibliography.

[2] It is interesting to see that the medieval reawakening of interest in such devices was concerned as in Hellenistic times rather with models displaying the apparent celestial motions—the ultimate standard of all time measurement—than with the abstracted element of 'time' itself. For a full description see H. A. Lloyd, *Giovanni de Dondi's Horological Masterpiece*, 1364. Privately printed by the author, Hookwood, Oxted, Surrey. See also Supplementary Bibliography.

[3] F. Warncke, *Die Astronomische Uhr . . .*, Lübeck, 1924.

[4] L. Thorndike, 'The Horloge of Travelers', *Isis*, **13**, 51, also E. Zinner, *Isis*, **14**, 385.

improvement in time-keeping could be looked for until Huygen's correction of Galileo's approximate law of the isochronous pendulum. Even this was quite impracticable for navigation owing to the motion of the ship. An effective marine chronometer was first constructed by John Harrison in 1763. Before this the only means of fixing longitude was by observations on the moon, which involved a knowledge of astronomy beyond that of any but an exceptional navigator.

In addition to the problems of position-finding was that of course-setting from map or chart. For some time before the rediscovery of the text of Ptolemy's *Geography* navigators had employed the so-called 'portolan' charts on open sea voyages for which the descriptive coastal 'rutters' (from French 'routiers') were of no avail. The origin of these charts is unknown: involving as they do the use of a compass reading to about $\frac{1}{2}°$ they might have been in use any time after the famous tract on the magnet written by Pierre de Maricourt in 1269—or even earlier.[1] The course from one point to another is read off (in the absence of parallel rulers) by finding a convenient intersection of 'rays' from two of the 'wind roses' passing through or near the points. The National Maritime Museum at Greenwich possesses a large and representative collection of these charts from which their evolution may be gauged. The earliest specimens show that directions were indicated not by degrees but by the eight or more 'winds'; and this custom was retained until long after the use of the compass had been combined with the sexagesimal measure used from the earliest times in astronomy. In setting a course on the direction found it was assumed that this could be made good by maintaining a bearing constant with respect to the meridian throughout the voyage (apart from corrections necessitated by prevailing winds). Since the spherical surface of the earth causes convergence of the meridians, this is only approximately true except for parallel (90°) and meridian (0°) courses: the maintenance of a constant bearing on any other course will lead to a helical track on the surface of the globe. The need for allowing for this distortion in map-making was attributed to Marinos of Tyre by Ptolemy, whose *Planisphaerium* was translated from the Arabic by Hermann of Carinthia (No. 752) in the twelfth century but the converse

---

[1] The compass was in use by the Normans in South Italy in the eleventh century. The oldest extant portolan chart is the Carta Pisana (Bibl. Nat.), *c.* 1300.

relationship does not appear to have been made explicit until the *Tratado da Sphera* (1537—Latin version in 1546: see No. 481. There is a facsimile of the *Ed. P.* in Bensaude *Histoire de la Science Nautique Portugaise*, Vol. V, Munich, 1915) by Pedro Nuñez, perhaps the greatest of the Portuguese navigational theorists. Here for the first time is introduced the term 'rhumb' which is still employed for any line making a constant angle with the meridians. This name was replaced by 'loxodrome' in the work of Snell in 1624, but the older term is still more commonly found. The portolans had by then to a large extent been replaced by 'Cartes plates' (English, 'plats'), which being graduated could give measure of distance; but since straight lines still represented rhumbs this was accurate only for a certain latitude. The greatest of many contributions which Nuñez made to the effective application of mathematics to navigation was to show the approximate relation of the rhumbs to the 'straight lines' of the spherical surface, which from the point of view of Euclidean space are 'great circles'. Of these great circles the meridians were, at that time of 'wind' sailing, by far the most important, although in his book Nuñez has a section on 'Great-circle Sailing'. The advantage of reduced distance achieved by following the great circle between two points on the sphere was not to become a real issue until much later.

Though Nuñez had shown the relationship between the constant-bearing course and the consequent track, the application of this knowledge to the calculation of distances from a chart came from a cultivator of the complementary field of cosmography— Gerard de Cremer (Gerhardus Mercator) whose pre-eminence in sixteenth-century cartography matches that of Nuñez in navigation. Up to the time (1569) of his *Nova et aucta orbis terrae descriptio ad usum navigantium emendate accommodata* ('A new and enlarged description of the earth accurately adapted for the use of navigators') Mercator had been engaged in the making of instruments (for which he was employed by the Emperor Charles V), the drafting of new maps (e.g. of Palestine), and the construction of a terrestrial globe. This globe (1541) was one of the first 'maps' to include the helical rhumbs of Nuñez. In the *Nova descriptio* however he introduced the projection by which he ultimately achieved the distinction of being known to every schoolboy; though not every schoolboy understands what 'Mercator's projection' involves, and in this he does not differ from most of Mercator's contemporaries—even the more instructed. The purpose of this (cylindrical) projection, though this is not explicitly stated by Mercator, was to make all rhumbs ('directiones') straight lines. This is achieved by representing the meridians (which converge to the poles of the sphere) as parallel straight lines on the map. The result of this increase of the East-West intervals—especially in higher latitudes where the increase is naturally greatest—would be to alter the shape of the land masses. To maintain isomorphism (though this again is not explicit) Mercator says: 'Gradus latitudinum versus utrumque polum paulatim auximus pro incremento parallelorum supra rationem quam habent ad aequinoctialem' ('I have gradually increased the degrees of latitude towards each of the two poles in relation to the increase in the parallels above the proportion which they have at the equator'). In other words, the distances between successive unit parallels increase gradually from the equator to the poles. It was not the first time a cylindrical projection had been used, not even one with compensation; before Ptolemy, Marinos of Tyre had used a larger, but *constant*, scale for latitude than for longitude. An even closer approximation was achieved by Martin Fernandez de Enciso (*Suma de Geographia*) and Pirckheimer (No. 543(d)). But the great importance of this invention for navigational charts rather than for topographical maps (in which isomorphism is thereby bought at the price of a misrepresentation of the relative *sizes* of the land masses) was hardly realised before the seventeenth century. Mercator's great work, it will have been observed, was written in Latin: he represented therefore that highly important class of men of science, the craftsmen-scholars, whose enlargement during the sixteenth century may well have been one of the most critical factors in the scientific renaissance. Though primarily a craftsman he had learnt mathematics from Reinerus Gemma at Louvain; but while he was in the highest rank of craftsmen he had not quite the mathematical insight to express his empirical procedure in symbolic terms. It is perhaps not without significance that it was in England, where at this time the greatest progress in scientific pursuits was being made among men, disciplined by the universities in the arts of communication and demonstration, who had nevertheless freed themselves from the sterilising influence of the 'Aristotelian' authoritarianism of those static bodies, that the 'art of navigation' was made at the same time both rigorous and adaptable to the needs of practical men. But even there the work was not achieved without a struggle. If any one man may be singled out as 'the only begetter' of this new kind of republic of learning it was, so Professor Taylor believes, John Dee. From her pages his figure stands out as one not unfairly to be described as an English (or strictly, Welsh) Cardano. Not quite of the intellectual stature of Cardano, he nevertheless had the almost universal interests of this late 'renaissance man', and at least in his earlier years, what Cardano lacked, the ability to 'get on' with all and sundry. Though for a time closely in touch with the Elizabethan court, he numbered among his closest friends Pedro Nuñez, Oronce Fine, and Mercator (No. 543(f)). His 'tract' on the importance of mathematics in everyday affairs (No. 235(g)) has become a classic; he had perhaps the finest 'scientific' library in England. But, like Cardano, and so many other great minds of his time, he became deeply embroiled in judicial astrology, alchemy, and, as the mob which wrecked his library and laboratory averred, magic. Like Cardano, he was a 'failure'; but it is probably no wild extrapolation which sees in the circle of young and vigorous minds of which Dee was the centre, the first flickerings of that fire which ultimately burned bright and fairly steadily in the Royal Society. Among these young men were Thomas Digges and Thomas Harriot, who at some time in their lives busied themselves with the theoretical basis of the problem for which Mercator provided only approximate rules—the relation between latitude and longitude on a Mercator chart. Neither however published anything [1] on the subject, the former perhaps through an early breakdown in health, the latter, it may be, owing to his employment by the Earl of Northumberland. Thus it came about that the first table of meridional parts, whereby the scale of latitude carresponding to each degree of longitude could be read off, was published by Edward Wright in his *Certaine Errors in Navigation* (1599). The formula for the proportion $\log_e \cot \frac{1}{2}(90 - \theta)$ was, however, discovered by chance from a later examination of Napier's tables (which Wright translated); and the first proof (not based on the calculus) was given by James Gregory.

---

[1] See, however, a reference to the 'Errors in the Arte of Navigation commonly practised' in the 'Addition' to Leonard Digges's *General Prognostication*.

Although the fundamental theory of surveying and mapping differs little from that of charting there are considerable changes of emphasis—such indeed as to make the one process almost the inverse of the other. In a sea voyage direction is all-important, distance secondary; position-finding perhaps a matter of life and death on a waste of waters without distinguishing feature. The surveyor on the other hand can make use of well distributed focal points, but his measurements of distance—often demanding considerable accuracy when the value of the fertile lands of a large estate are involved—can not be even roughly achieved (except in featureless plains) by time and speed calculations as at sea. Similar considerations apply to map-making, where the demands of military operations and of the administration of large provinces are concerned.

So far as the evidence goes, map-making, except as an aesthetic exercise (e.g. the Hereford *Mappa Mundi*—XIII) or route-sequence, (e.g. the so-called Peutinger Table—IV A.D.), practically died out after Ptolemy. It was revived in the Byzantine Empire not later than (XIII-2) when Maximos Planudes constructed maps from the astronomical co-ordinates which alone were provided in the extant manuscripts of Ptolemy's *Geography*. In 1409 Jacopo Angelio completed the Latin translation begun by Emanuel Chrysoloras and thus gave the impetus for the cultivation of the art of cartography in the west. Recent research has revealed the great complexity of this development. Many men of varied talents and experience were involved. Greater knowledge— as of the Northern lands and the West coast of Africa—went hand in hand with inexplicable blunders—such as the misrepresention of the mouths of the Rhine and Maas in the map prepared by Hieronymus Münzer for Hartmann Schedel in 1493. But the search for wider horizons and greater accuracy of portrayal went on: the ignoring of the growth of a *world-concept* by Thorndike and others has led to a picture of fifteenth-century stagnation just as one-sided as that of the exaggerated idea of progress which they sought to refute.[1]

---

[1] It was only after this chapter was written that I was able to read Dr. Dana E. Durand's great work *The Vienna-Klosterneuburg Map Corpus of the Fifteenth Century* (Leiden, 1952). This work strengthens in a remarkable way the evidence for the above statement. Dr. Durand sees in the co-operation between university teachers, monasteries, and great ecclesiastical visitors such as Nicholas of Cues, a critical phase of the

In 1427 Cardinal Fillastre embellished his manuscript of the *Geography* with a set of maps which later included a copy of one of the Northern lands prepared by the Dane, Claudius Clavus: but the mojt influential of the early cartographers was Nicholaus Germanus, whose manuacript was used for the famous Ulm editions (No. 543). These included five 'cartae modernae' based on new measurements or representing regions of which Ptolemy had no knowledge. Within fifteen years of its 'discovery' a map showing America was printed, and such maps became thereafter a regular feature of the new editions of Ptolemy. In 1492 Martin Behaim completed for the Senate of Nürnbeig the first terrestrial globe, incorporating information based on the voyage to and from the Cape of Good Hope by Bartholomew Diaz. But the device which revolutionised map-making was the introduction in 1533 of triangulation by Reinerus Gemma (No. 33). Thereafter, given an accurately measured base-line, it was possible to map any region as a separate entity. But if different regions were to be compared, and a uniform system of reference to be employed, it was essential to determine the relation between the unit of length on the ground and the unit of angular measure of the spherical surface of the earth: in other words it was the problem of measuring the arc subtending one degree at the earth's centre—the possible variation of this ratio with latitude had not of course been envisaged. The measurement had already been carried out in antiquity by Erotosthenes and others, and was of course the basis of Ptolemy's graticule; further attempts were made at the command of the Caliph, al-Mamun; but one of the outstanding scientific achievements of the sixteenth century was the measurement carried out almost unaided by the great Physician, Jean Fernel, in 1528, and described by him in his *Cosmotheoria* (No. 247). The remaining principal problem of cartography—projection—has already been alluded to in respect of the rhumb line charts. Numerous styles of projection are to

renaissance transition, in which new knowledge and higher standards of mathematical precision were slowly 'built in' to traditional scholarship. He makes out a powerful case for believing that the great advances in cartographical technique introduced by Nicholas Germanus were made possible by what he learned at Klosterneuburg; and that the first 'modern' regional map (of which two somewhat different 'copies' are all that remain) traditionally attributed to Nicholas of Cues embodies 'material from two works of the Vienna corpus'. Striking also is the demonstrated influence of the construction of star maps on the application of a graticule to terrestrial maps.

be found among sixteenth-century maps. With the engraving and production of maps we are not here concerned, but it is of interest to note that the practice of collecting the individual maps of various regions under one cover was started by Ortelius in 1564 (the earliest edition in the University of Aberdeen is that of 1574) in his *Theatrum Orbis Terrarum,* the term 'Atlas' being first used by Mercator in 1585. In the earlier maps the cartographer made no attempt to reveal his ignorance or indifference—a chart of *c.* 1540 in the Greenwich Museum gives a much more accurate outline of the island of Cuba than of Scotland, which is still shown as separated from England! Men of the stamp of Ortelius and Mercator however enlisted local assistance: Humfrey Lluwyd contributed the map of Wales to Ortelius's *Theatrum;* and one of the University of Aberdeen's most treasured possessions is the copy of his *Theatrum Orbis Terrarum* (1644 edn.) inscribed by John, son of William Blaeu, to Gordon of Straloch, one of the first pupils at Marischal College, who had been largely responsible for the survey upon which Bleau's map of Scotland was based.

Books on improved methods of local surveying appeared in all the vernaculars in the sixteenth century: they were called *Feldmessen* in German; in England the term 'surveyor' replaced the earlier 'landmeater'. Instruments for the purpose are shown in use in Muenster's *Rudimenta Mathematica* (No. 469) but the absence of devices for measuring horizontal angles has been remarked.[1] The plane-table appeared in a crude form in 1555 (No. 272) the 'theodelite' is first mentioned by name in Digges's *Pantometria,* 1571 (No. 194) though all the essentials of this instrument seem to have been present in the dioptra described by Heron of Alexandria.[2] It has never been satisfactorily explained why this universal instrument was not reintroduced until after the lapse of fifteen hundred years: it would be interesting to know whether the Greek specimens really worked with a degree of accuracy comparable to that of the astrolabe.

One final enterprise of the mathematical practitioners was what was called the 'Art of Dialling'. That the sundial was still a popular timepiece throughout the sixteenth century is evidenced by the

---

[1] E.g. Derek J. Price, 'Medieval Land Surveying and Topographical Maps', *Geog. J.* **121** (1955), 1-10.

[2] See, e.g. M. R. Cohen and I. E. Drabkin, *Source Book in Greek Science,* New York, 1948, p. 336.

PLATE V

De re Metallica Libri VII. FINIS.

ſ 2

Assay balances, with draught-excluding case, drawer
for weights, and device for raising and lowering beam.
(Agricola, *De Re Metallica*, Vol. II, No. 8a and Vol. I,
p. 176.)

number of books published on the theory of graduating dials of all kinds. In neither the horizontal nor vertical plane-dial does the shadow of the gnomon describe equal angles in equal times on the dial face, but allowance has to be made for the latitude of the place and for the projection of the equal circular arcs of the sun's motion on the plane surface of the dial. As in books on instrument construction today the works of the sixteenth century vary in the amount of theory presented and in respect of the standard of precision which the instrument was expected to reach (cf. Nos. 77 and 242).

The problem of the development of the Mathematical Arts during the sixteenth century differs, at least in degree, from the problem we have already considered and are about to consider in respect of other departments of learning. For its chief interest lies not so much in the details of progress, as in its being the field in which pre-eminently the relations between the academic and the practical man, the scholars and the craftsmen, were first brought into prominence. The importance of calling upon the trained mathematicians for survey work is well illustrated in connection with the cutting of the New River between London and Ware. Although the constructional work was carried on only in the four and a half years ending in 1613, the existing records [1] show that it was Edward Wright who was employed as Sir Hugh Myddleton's 'Arts Man', and entries of the fees paid to him for surveys of the whole course—and for a special check on the level involving in one reach a fall of only five inches in a mile—show the nature of his duties.

We started this chapter with a cautionary tale showing the dangers of a too ready acceptance of a plausible thesis; but Columbus's triumph is almost an irrelevance. Given his fanatical faith and indomitable pertinacity he was bound to make a landfall somewhere in America. On the other hand we know too little about the actual proceedings of the Portugese attack on the problem of oceanic travel to come to any definite verdict as to the relative influence of mathematical learning and unlettered seamanship, though it is difficult to avoid the conclusion that the latter could not have triumphed unaided. When we come to the second half of the sixteenth century however, the case is so well

---

[1] Sir J. Davidson, *J. Inst. C.E.* **31-2** (1948-9).

K

documented that it may be discussed upon a solid basis of evidence. A highly significant, and perhaps even the earliest, item in the documentation was the translation into English of the very popular *Arte de Navegar* of Martin Cortes: this was carried out by Richard Eden and published in 1561 at the expense of the Muscovy Company at the instigation of Stephen Borough, who had visited the Casa de Contratación[1] at Seville. That such attempts at 'popularisation' were not welcomed on all sides is shown by the somewhat truculent manifesto 'Against the reprouvers of Astronomie and Sciences Mathematicall' with which Thomas Digges in 1575 prefaced the corrected edition of his father's *Prognostication Everlasting* (No. 196). In the epistle dedicatory he promised to expose further errors in navigation. In this, as we have seen, he was not alone.

An examination of the biographies which Professor E. G. R. Taylor has assembled in her *Mathematical Practitioners* reveals the very various origins and training of the men who played a prominent part in the removal of the 'Errors of Navigation'. Though Richard Chancellor, Stephen Borough, John Davis, and Robert Norman had no university education, Cambridge can take the credit for Dee, Briggs, Mark Ridley, Edward Wright, Thomas Hood, Gilbert, Blundeville, William Cuningham, Richard Eden; and Oxford for Cyprian Lucar and Harriot. In face of these facts any attempt to base the rapid progress in the science of navigation solely on the knowledge gained by observation in the practice of sailing must be dismissed. Indeed the influence of the university trained men must have been a great deal more potent than the above comparisons suggest; for in the case at least of John Davis and Richard Chancellor there is the strongest evidence that they owed their outstanding skill as much to their land-based teachers as to their own resource. We can not go further into this interesting question; but it may be necessary to remind the reader that these teachers and researchers though *of* the universities were for the most part not *in* them at the time that they made their contributions. At Cambridge, despite the pioneering work of Sir John Cheke in drawing attention to Greek *mathematics*, it was only as a teacher of *Greek* that he was tolerated at the university;

[1] Set up in 1503 as an administrative office to regulate all trade with the 'Indies'. Later, a school of navigation was added.

and the same remained true of his pupil John Dee. Mathematics was not recognised as a 'subject' worthy of a Chair until 1663; Isaac Barrow became first Lucasian Professor in 1664. At Oxford, though from the above comparisons the subject seems to have been held in even lower esteem, recognition came in 1619 when Sir Henry Savile founded Chairs of Geometry and Astronomy.

CHAPTER IX

THE NATURE OF THE PHYSICAL WORLD

'PHYSICS investigates and reveals (as far as the mistiness of the human mind permits) the order, qualities and motions of all bodies and kinds of beings in nature, and the causes of the generation and decay and other motions in the elements and in other bodies which arise from the intermingling of the elements.' Thus Philip Melanchthon opens his *Initia Doctrinae Physicae*—the course of lectures dictated to the students at Wittenberg about the middle of the sixteenth century. The definition is of course based on the *Physics* of Aristotle. But because Melanchthon is anxious to impress upon the eager young minds committed to his care that the contemplation of nature is a necessary and delightful part of the worship of God (and partly, one suspects, because of his weakness for astrology) the first 'book' is taken up with a general survey of the heavens, without going into such geometrical detail as would be required in the astronomy course. The second 'book' deals with 'that part of physics customarily so called', that is, the part which is concerned with *change*. For Aristotle 'change' meant permanent change—whether change of form, of substance, or of position. Above the sphere of the moon all the evidence (or what was thought to be all the evidence) points to a state of changelessness—ultimately even of position, which is expressed in the (relatively highly successful) assumption of uniform *circular* motion. Physics *sensu strictu* is thus concerned only with the 'inferior bodies', those at the centre of the world indeed but lowest in the hierarchy of values.

It may be wondered why it should be necessary to refer to the course of study at what was at this time almost a Theological College and also to revert to the Aristotelian physics. It would indeed be idle to pretend that Melanchthon and his circle—which it should be recalled included Rheticus and Reinhold—made any significant contribution to the science of physics; but what a confrontation of his teaching—and his may be taken as fairly typical of what was being taught in a dozen other centres of learning—may do is to keep constantly before our minds that this was the climate of opinion in which the majority of bright young minds grew up; and that it was an astonishingly comprehensive world view; so much so that it recognised and revealed the principle that every natural occurrence is in principle explicable in terms of other natural occurrences, with the corollary that 'physics' is one and indivisible. But not, let us hasten to add, physics. 'Physicists' not only create 'mixt' [1] bodies out of the elements, but seek also the causes why elements are able to be 'mixt' among themselves and changed into one another; that is, they search out the cause of generation and decay in nature. For bodies are not able to be changed into each other unless the subject is related in such a way that it receives the form of the other which thereby loses it. From water air could not be generated unless the matter of the water were able to receive the form of air, its previous form being lost. Otherwise air would be made out of nothing. But nature bears witness that nothing is created out of nothing. 'Therefore in order that the elements may be changed into each other there must be a common principle. . . .' This 'physics' has clearly nothing to do with physics: it is the heart and soul of *chemistry*. (It may not be very good chemistry; though the more physics explores the common principle the better chemistry it looks like becoming! But that is another story). What seems to stand out for the study of sixteenth-century science is that the separation of physics from chemistry involves an arbitrary distortion. Of course it may be argued that this was the very stuff which had to be got rid of before 'science' could really get going. If the annals of individual sciences are alone concerned this argument is almost wholly valid; but if what is being sought is the course of scientific thought in general, then such a separation is quite unhistorical. It is true that people talked about 'chemistry' as they talked about 'astronomy' and—more and more as the century wore on— 'botany'. But when this chemical talk is examined it is found to be—at least as regards its stock of ideas—largely an elaboration

[1] The quotation marks are mine. The Latin is 'mixta'; I have retained this spelling to emphasise the fact that the term includes *compound* bodies. Indeed in the eighteenth century (e.g. the chemical lectures of William Cullen of *c.* 1750) the term is used exclusively for such.

K*

and exemplification of 'physics': of which more later. The part of science for whose progress 'physics' had to be got out of the way was physics—both the 'physics' of the inferior bodies and the almost immaterial 'physics' of the heavenly bodies; and there is good reason for believing that the most important single step in this clarification was the demonstration that the physics applicable to both is in fact the same.

It has been said above that 'physics' was one and indivisible; and this has so far been exemplified by showing that it included at least the statement of the problem which later came to be regarded as the field of enquiry called 'chemistry'. But more important for the sixteenth century, as Melanchthon is at pains to emphasise and illustrate, was the fact that 'physics' was also the basis of the theory of Medicine, so much so that the book which may perhaps be regarded as the first 'modern' work on physiology was at first called the *Natural Part of Medicine* (No. 249). Moreover all those biological questions, which were not merely concerned with cataloguing species and, in the second half of the century, description of the parts of animals and plants, were questions of 'generation and decay', and as such parts of 'physics'.

Lastly, in case it might be inferred that the only science with which 'physics' had nothing to do was physics, we must recall the fact that the definition with which we started included the 'motions of all bodies'—that is, terrestrial bodies. The anomalies in this department of physics had been debated from the time of Aristotle himself, and were still being debated throughout our period. It is on this field that the battle was joined in which 'physics' suffered a major and lasting but by no means annihilating defeat. This was, as we shall see, by no means a 'palace revolution' but came mainly from a quarter remote from the lecture hall.

Thus a case might seem to have been made out for treating the whole of what remains of renaissance thought in science under one head; but this by no means follows. For, as has just been shown, it is in the enthusiasm on the periphery of the traditional courses of study that the universal fossilisation of the Physical World was first broken up. In the remainder of this chapter therefore an attempt will be made to display in a little more detail the framework of 'physics' within which the sixteenth-century thinkers necessarily worked, and to note where and when moves were made, not always consciously, to break through the framework. The carrying out of this task should provide guidance for the more specific enterprise of discovering the origin of modern science—if indeed there is such a thing to be discovered.

The fundamental characteristic of the physical world—the one which patently distinguishes this world from the heavens—is the peculiar character of the motions seen on the grand scale in wind, sea, earth and fire, whereby change, often catastrophic, is brought about. As a first approximation the Aristotelian principle, that each element seeks its 'proper' place, goes far to 'explain' the behaviour of bodies according to the proportion of each element entering into their respective compositions. Moreover it must be again emphasised that for Aristotle 'motion' is a characteristic of *all* change—the process whereby potentiality passes into actuality. Change of place is a special case, hence Galileo's announcement that one of his 'two new sciences' was concerned with 'il movimento locale'. But the inadequacy of the Aristotelian theory to account for the regularity of the tides and the flight of an arrow was noticed almost from the first, and alternative explanatory schemes proposed.

Though Galileo's *Two New Sciences* was not published till 1638, it is widely known that he had satisfied himself as to the form of the law of motion of freely falling bodies in the early years of the seventeenth century. What is less widely known is that before 1592, when he left Pisa for Padua, he wrote out a considerable tract, *Sermones de Motu Gravium*, in which he sought to replace the Aristotelian 'law' of motion—speed proportional to the ratio of moving force to resistance—by one in which speed was proportional to the *difference* of moving force and resistance. It is here that Galileo appealed to the mathematical *method* of Archimedes for the solution of a problem—speed attained under the action of an unbalanced force—with which Archimedes was in no way concerned. In the nature of the arguments he employed Galileo showed himself, though ostensibly striving to free the problem of motion from the errors of Aristotle, to share the latter's concern with the *cause* of motion: he was still far from the position of Salviati in the *Two New Sciences*, who insisted that however interesting this question might be it was wholly *irrelevant* to the law of freely falling bodies. This concern of the young Galileo could hardly be otherwise; for just as, in Whitehead's phrase,

European philosophy has been largely a series of footnotes to Plato, so concern with the problem of motion in the *physical* world had been merely a series of footnotes to the *Physics* of Aristotle. And almost literally so; since the vast majority of the medieval and renaissance contributions to the solution of the problem had started as 'commentaries' on the *Physics*: the 'commentary' being not merely an editorial gloss or amplification but an expression of the fact that, in the absence of *experiment*, the starting-point in all research would most naturally be the text of the master-mind who had first determined the nature and scope of the problem.

Galileo's ultimate solution of the problem of local motion made possible the foundation of physics in complete independence of 'physics'. Since this marks the 'beginning' of 'modern' science rather than the culmination of the previous epoch it has no place in the Renaissance as understood here. But it is no longer possible to regard this momentous step as one in which Galileo leapt with one bound out of the bog of 'medieval Aristotelianism'. The origin of this once universal, and even now not wholly unknown, view may perhaps be found in the fact that one of the most characteristic features of sixteenth-century 'physics' is the displacement of the problem of motion from the central position it had occupied in the 'natural philosophy' of the earlier centuries. It is indeed a fact that the historian of science not specially versed in the literature of the sixteenth century could probably not name a single book dealing specifically with the subject. In the Aberdeen collection there is only one short tract (No. 703); in the books on 'physics' such treatment as there is extends only to a repetition of the traditional Aristotelian qualitative rules. At one time Galileo's achievement was signalised as the triumph of 'renaissance' Platonism over 'medieval' Aristotelianism: the implausibility of such a view has, it is hoped, emerged from the general consideration of the renaissance scene undertaken in these pages. But that it is completely inconsistent with historical facts was demonstrated mainly by the researches of Alexandre Koyré (*Etudes Galiléennes*, Fascicules I, II, III, Paris, 1939).

This demonstration was based on a thorough examination of both Galileo's Pisan work already alluded to and two other late sixteenth-century books whose importance in the development of Galileo's thought had not previously been recognised. These were Francesco Bonamico's *De Motu* and J. B. Benedetti's *Diversarum Speculationum mathematicarum et physicarum liber* (Torino, 1585). The former, though printed (Florence) only in 1611, was the work of a man who had been professor of philosophy at Pisa in Galileo's student days and from whom he therefore almost certainly heard a very clear exposition of the problem of motion and the various attempts to solve it. Benedetti's is the more profound and original work, and the most valuable part of Koyré's first fascicule is his demonstration of the Archimedean approach of this author whose work must have been available to Galileo. It may nevertheless be argued that to regard Galileo's subsequent achievement as the triumph of the Archimedean method over the Aristotelian involves as great a distortion as did the previous claim for the triumph of Platonism. My own view is that the succession of claims for the 'triumph' of this, that, and the other, influence was a necessary phase in the explosion of the traditional myth of Galileo as the unaided 'creator' of modern science. The task of contemporary scholarship is rather to assess the nature and degree of all those influences, which played a part in this period when all values were to an exceptional degree subject to revaluation. But to give the reader some indication of the very complex issues involved—and it must be strongly emphasised how very superficial any such account must be—a flashback to the medieval discussions of the problem will be necessary.

The whole tradition of the problem of motion developed on lines parallel to that between 'astronomy' and 'physics' (see above, p. 104). The parallel distinction appears explicitly in al-Farabi's *Enumeration of the Sciences* (translated by Gerard of Cremona in XII-2) where the 'Science of Weights' and the 'Science of Mathematical Devices' are regarded as part of *mathematics*, as to all intents and purposes is 'astronomy' in the distinction made by Simplikios. This corresponds to the foundation of statics and hydrostatics by Archimedes on an almost postulational basis, only a minimum of appeals being made to experience in each case, and those only to cases of equilibrium. No question of motion arises; the 'proofs' are purely geometrical; the fundamental 'law of the lever' being established by the principle of symmetry. In the *corpus* of medieval writings on the 'Science of Weights', however, even the earliest contributions bear signs of the dynamical approach, which is an essential characteristic of

Aristotelian 'physics'. In the masterpiece of the *corpus*, the *Liber de Ratione Ponderis*, though concerned with formally the same problems as is the work on the lever by Archimedes, Iordanus de Nemore adopts a set of postulates which are frankly dynamical and Aristotelian: for instance 'The movement of every weight is toward the centre . . .' and 'That which is heavier descends more quickly. . . .' The upshot of these postulates is the re-foundation of *statics* on the principle of work. Iordanus however is nowhere concerned with *motion* as such. That the dominant interest of the subsequent medieval *savants* was dynamical rather than statical is shown, as E. A. Moody emphasises, (E. A. Moody and Marshall Clagett, *The Medieval Science of Weights*, Madison, Wis., 1952, pp. 19-20) by the fact that the 'physical' *Proposition One* of the *Liber de Ponderibus* (a work of unknown provenance, only the *proofs* of which Moody believes to have been provided by Iordanus) provoked continual controversy for two hundred and fifty years, while the elegantly demonstrated theorems of Iordanus, such as his inclined plane theorems and his resolution of the bent lever problem, were passed over by his fourteenth century commentators.

If any single thesis can be singled out as a fertile starting point in the searching study of the problem of motion in the medieval period a good case can be made out for the decision of St. Albert, in his elucidation of the commentaries of Avicenna and Averroes, that motion is *forma fluens* rather than *fluxus formae*.[1] The former corresponds to a real persistent entity which manifests itself in 'flux'; the latter to a 'perishing' quality similar to that envisaged by ibn Badja ('Avempace', d. 1138)[2] and Ioannes Philoponos (VI-1), which was made known to the West in a strongly critical exposition by Averroes. St. Albert's thesis may well have provided the basic concept making possible the development of the two great medieval explorations of the problem of motion: the *impetus* theory of the *cause* of motion, and the analysis of the logico-mathematical apparatus for giving precision to the functional relation between motive power and the ensuing motion. Actually the latter preceded the former; but, being carried out by Thomas

---

[1] See Anneliese Maier, *Die Vorläufer Galileis im 14 Jahrhundert*, Rome, 1949, pp. 16, 25. I am greatly indebted to this work.

[2] This *anti*-Aristotelian theory is believed by Moody to have strongly influenced Galileo in his Pisan period (*J. Hist. Ideas*, **12**, 163 and 375).

Bradwardine and his brilliant band of disciples at Merton College, Oxford, had relatively little influence on the Paris scholars except Nicole Oresme. Both these 'schools' were greatly aided by the *logica nova* which grew out of the critical studies of William of Ockham; but it is significant that neither of them were willing to go the whole way with him in asserting that for the local motion of a body 'sufficit quod continue sine quiete acquirat unum locum post alium et ita quod sine quiete sit in diversis locis successive' ('it is sufficient that it continuously and without rest attains one place after another and that thus without rest it is in different places successively')—a definition which removes all *physical* significance from the problem.

The *locus classicus* for the new attack on the problem of motion is the *De Proportionibus* [1] of Bradwardine written in 1328. This great pioneer work is mainly concerned with Aristotle's assumption that the velocity of a moved body is proportional to the proportion between the moving force and resistance of the medium. Unfortunately every term in this statement bristles with ambiguities which only an eminent physical insight can hope to clarify. Bradwardine's aim was to strip off the ambiguities by formulating his version of the relationship in the form of a mathematical expression. To this end he developed in the first chapter a calculus of proportions on the Boethean model (see above, p. 87) but rendered more adaptable to a 'functional' relationship by the use of letters instead of actual numbers denoting special cases. The strength of this method lies in the fact that by working always in terms of proportions he more easily avoided the use of ill-defined 'infinitesimals' (for that in fact is what his continued geometric proportion—which in its 'integrated' form can be expressed as $V^n = F/R$—amounts to) whose meretricious character would have been concealed in the context of Arabic arithmetic and algebra. Its weakness is apparent in the appalling cumbrousness of the purely verbal manipulation, which makes the work unintelligible to anyone not specially drilled in the method, and even to the expert leaves some problems of interpretation all but insoluble. There is no doubt, however, that the 'logarithmic' form of the proportion made possible the introduction of three novel concepts which entered into all subsequent discussion of

[1] See *Thomas of Bradwardine, His* Tractatus de Proportionibus, ed. and trans. by H. L. Crosby Jr., Madison, Wis., 1955.

the problem: the distinction between 'total' and 'momentary' velocity; the feasibility of regarding 'motion' as an entity which could be transferred from the mover to the moved; and the recognition of a class of 'intensive forms' (such as velocity, temperature, and—alas!—even moral virtues!) which, though not capable of addition (as are weight, length, etc.), undergo *measurable* 'intension' and 'remission'. Such intension and remission might be 'uniform' or 'difform' (that is, constant or variable); and, if the latter, uniformly or difformly so.

Of these novel concepts the first and third were given precision by Bradwardine's disciples John of Dumbleton, Richard of Swineshead ('Suiseth' or 'Calculator') and William Heytesbury [1] ('Hentisberus'). The first took the form of the 'Mertonian rule' (at one time ascribed to Galileo), namely, that a body characterised by a uniformly difform velocity would at a time half way between the beginning and end of its motion momentarily possess the same velocity as one moving with such *uniform* velocity as would enable it to describe the same path in the same time. This was a purely *formal* deduction from Bradwardine's theorem and was *not* applied (as it *was* by Galileo) to 'free fall'; since between such disparate categories as *time* and *space* there could be no 'real' proportion: the notion of *functional dependence* in a strictly mathematical sense was clearly lacking.

The second concept gave rise to the *impetus* theory in which Jean Buridan and his disciple, Albert of Saxony, sought to elucidate the *causal* aspect of the problem of motion. This theory, unlike Avempace's postulation of a *self-consuming* 'quality' in the movable, conceived of motion as an entity which could be 'acquired' in a measure determined by the 'quantity of matter' in the movable, just as more 'heat' could be 'acquired' by a large quantity of matter than by a small. But though the measure of the *impetus* depended on the 'quantity of matter' and the velocity, it corresponds strictly neither to momentum nor inertia (though Newton's term *vis insita* for the latter might represent a hangover). The theory nevertheless played an important part in the subsequent history of the problem since on the one hand it made possible a rational (though incorrect) analysis of 'free', and various kinds of 'forced', motion, and on the other it enabled Buridan to

---

[1] A valuable assessment of Heytesbury is now available in Curtis Wilson, *William Heytesbury*, Madison, Wis., 1956.

point out the redundancy of the Aristotelian astral intelligences to account for the (supposed uniform) motion of the planets.

There remains one further contribution from the Paris school—certainly the most striking and perhaps the most profound of all: this was the geometrical application by Nicole Oresme of the Mertonian notion of 'intensive forms'. In several extant manuscripts may be seen his diagrams in which the successive 'latitudes' of a 'form' are represented by a row of perpendiculars to a straight line representing a succession of instants. By this means he was able (as was Galileo by means of a similar *diagram*) to prove the 'Mertonian rule'. But the procedure must be interpreted with the greatest caution: the line joining the heads of the perpendiculars is no *locus* determined by functional dependence; hence to speak of him as 'anticipating' Descartes (who indeed had not himself reached an explicit idea of functionality) in the invention of analytical geometry is to misrepresent a stroke of genius remarkable in its way but certainly of less generality than that of Descartes. Moreover it was the whole 'bundle' of perpendiculars to which Oresme drew attention; for the figure constituted by them represented the 'total velocity' or distance traversed in a given time.

That all this medieval discussion was not wholly without appeal to the earlier thinkers of the Renaissance is shown by the fact that, though it was written by 'barbarians' in Latin which at times would have made Cicero turn in his grave, Ponset le Preux, in 1509, thought it worth while to print the very lengthy commentary of the Portugese scholar Alvarez Thomas, then teaching at Paris, on the work of Richard of Swineshead, whose *Liber Calculationum* had already been printed at Padua in 1477. The place of printing is significant: for whatever may have happened at Paris and—*triste dictu*—Oxford, the problem of motion was a live issue at Padua and Pavia at least from the time of Marliani (*c.* 1450) who, though lacking the analytical power of the Mertonians, brought some of the evidence to the test of experiment. The link between the Padua of Marliani and the mechanics of the earlier medieval period was probably Blasius of Parma. The vigour of this discussion may be judged from the fact that before 1500 not only the *Liber Calculationum* but also the leading 'documents' of Albert of Saxony, Nicole Oresme, William Heytesbury and Walter Burley accounted for about twenty editions at Padua,

Pavia, and Venice, but only one at Paris. This apparent apathy at Paris was however deplored by one teacher, the Scotsman, George Lokert (No. 405).

This *excursus* into the medieval history of the problem of motion was necessary on two grounds, partly to show the very thorough way in which it had been canvassed, partly as a gloss on the thesis that it was through a 'return' to Archimedes that Galileo found the solution which, unchallenged for three centuries, even now falls into place as a perfectly adequate approximation under certain restrictions which are valid in all 'normal' physical experience. Archimedes' method of abstraction and demonstration Galileo, on his own admission, did certainly use and with a mastery perhaps never previously equalled. But by itself this would not have sufficed. Abstraction can lead to a mere Will o' the Wisp unless you know what to abstract. It was the *physical* insight of Archimedes which enabled him to abstract the essential charac- teristic—pressure—on which the famous principle of hydro- statics could be deductively based. It was similarly Galileo's *physical* insight which led him through the tangled confusion of 'physical' and analytic theory, which surrounded his early efforts, to the choice of the essential functional *relata* from those which lay ready to hand. What our *excursus* was designed to show was that all the materials for the choice had been provided by his medieval forebears. That they existed is of course no proof that he was acquainted with them: the degree of his indebtedness is still a problem for historical research.

All the contributions to the discussion of the nature of motion which we have so far reviewed were in the 'scholastic' tradition in the broad sense—broad, since the Mertonians and Albert of Saxony were strongly influenced by the radical nominalism of William of Occam which was ultimately to render impossible the realisation of the scholastic ideal in the narrow sense. But before the end of the fifteenth century the problem of motion was one which princes could not afford to ignore; for it was no use spending a lot of money hauling guns from one siege to another if there was little chance of hitting the target when they went off. We have already seen how Dürer was caught up in this new movement; of much greater importance was the actual contribu- tion to the theory of projectiles made by his early contemporary, Leonardo da Vinci. This 'contribution' was, as is well known, never published; but Duhem in his *Les Origines de la Statique* (Paris, 1905) put forward powerful arguments for the view that not only did Leonardo's manuscripts have a wide circulation, which seems incontestable, but that they were put to good use by that enterprising *savant*, Girolamo Cardano, a contention for which there is only indirect though telling evidence.

In his *De Subtilitate* (No. 128) and elsewhere Cardano developed the theory of machines on the basis of the motion and constraint of a falling weight, thereby achieving an implicit recognition of the *moment* of a force and of the principle of virtual work. Though Cardano himself does not seem to have been much concerned with the technology of motion it was far otherwise with his rival, Tartaglia, who opens his great work *Quesiti et Inventioni diverse* (No. 673) with several discussions on the paths of projectiles from cannon. In the third of these he proves, from the assumption that the straightness of the path depends upon the *impetus*, that *no* part of the path of a horizontally *aimed* projectile can actually *be* horizontal. This is contrary to the contemporary view that at whatever elevation a cannon is fired the projectile will follow a rectilinear path along this axis until its *impetus* is exhausted, or nearly exhausted, when it will fall vertically as a result of its weight. Tartaglia's result embodies the principles of inertia and of the physical independence of forces, but it is deduced by him from an assumption as to the quantitative relation of force to motion— namely that force is measured by velocity instead of by accelera- tion—which had ultimately to be abandoned, implicitly by Galileo, explicitly by Newton.

This work—largely technological, since its later sections are taken up with the question of the composition and mode of action of gunpowder, etc.—was highly influential in the later sixteenth century, the three first *Colloquies* being Englished by Cyprian Lucar as an introduction to his own book on gunnery (No. 673b). The contributions of technological writers is further shown by the lucid but purely formal work of Ubaldi (No. 692). But although technological demands stimulated enquiry and brought about a closer correlation of theory and observation, there is no warrant for supposing that this was done by a separate 'class' of workers. Tartaglia often appears on the title-pages of his books in doctor's robes or in the Groves of Academe with Plato and Aristotle. In the science of mechanics, as in navigation, though

new problems were suggested and even more important new ways
of looking at old problems emerged, the progress and clarification
which ensued was, with rare exceptions, the work not of 'practical
men' unbiased by the reigning academic theory, but of 'aca-
demics' practised in the arts which only the universities could
provide, but ready, as Francis Bacon later expressed it, to 'light
their torches at any man's candle'.

That motion of some kind is involved in vision seems to have
been 'guessed' from at least the time of Demokritos. It could be
no more than a guess in the absence of any evidence that a time-
lapse occurs between the appearance of light at two different
points. This is further borne out by the existence of three different
theories about its mode of propagation: from eye to object
(Demokritos), from object to eye (Pythagoras and Ibn al-
Haitham), and a combination of action from the 'seeing eye'
and from a luminary (Plato). Though Euclid probably accepted
the theory of Plato, his concern being solely with the formation of
shadows and images the direction of motion (if any) along the
axis was of no consequence. It was his recognition that since sharp
shadows are formed in certain circumstances the 'action' can be,
indeed must be, represented by straight lines: from this, by the
application of geometry, the phenomena of reflection from plane
and (probably later) curved surfaces could be deduced. There
thus arose in optics as in the science of motion *per se* two parallel
lines of development—the 'physical' stemming mainly from the
Neoplatonists, whose theory embodied notions partly Platonic,
partly Aristotelian, and the 'mathematical', stemming from
Euclid. The separation, however, was never so sharp as in the
case of mere motion, as shown by the fact that whereas al-Farabi
(p. 153 above) regarded the 'science of aspects' (including the
theory of mirrors and 'perspective') as a branch of mathematics,
Robert Kilwardby (d. 1279), whose *De Ortu et Divisione Philosophiae*
followed al-Farabi pretty closely, raised the question as to whether
it was rightly regarded as a branch of mathematics rather than of
physics, (cf. No. 503). In the 'mathematical' tradition was the
greatest of all works of optics before Kepler—that of Ibn al-
Haitham (al-Hazen) who died about 1039 (No. 329). If this was
the *Almagest* of optics, John Peckham's *Perspectiva Communis*
played the part of the *Sphere* of Sacrobosco. The name *Perspectiva*
came to be commonly used for optical studies for the next three

PLATE VI

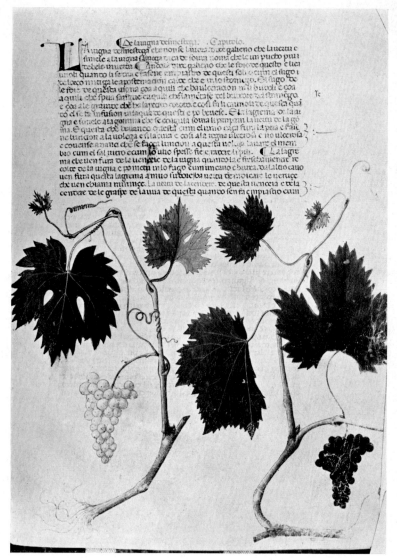

Early fifteenth-century manuscript herbal with naturalistic colour-washed drawings. (BM MS Egerton 2020.)

centuries; and it was at about this time that the painting of Cimabue, and a little later of Giotto, began to manifest the laws of linear perspective apparently lost to the West, though manuscripts of Vitruvius are known from many centuries after the eighth (Jarrow). *Perspectiva* embraced not only reflection from plane and curved mirrors, the theory of which had been taken to a very advanced stage by Ibn al-Haitham and Witelo (b.ca. 1230 —No. 329), but also refraction, concerning which no precise law was enunciated until the seventeenth century.[1] The study of refraction had been actuated first in relation to errors of observation in astronomy (see above, p. 120), later in respect of the medieval obsession with the 'physical' problem of the rainbow. Roger Bacon's writings show a fair appreciation of the mechanism of the simple biconvex magnifier, and there is documentary evidence that aids to vision were used before 1300. Why it never occurred to anyone before late in the sixteenth century to look through *two* lenses held coaxially is a mystery; and why no one recorded the fact of its first occurrence is an even greater one. The first unambiguous documentary record is still that in the archives of the States-General of the Low Countries for 1608. But there is little doubt that Leonard Digges was using some sort of telescopic contrivance (called by his son, Thomas, 'perspective glasses'—see No. 194) before his death in 1571. Claims have also been made for Recorde, Dee, William Bourne, and della Porta. Bourne also used curved mirrors, Digges a combination of mirrors and lenses. Of no one before Lipperhey is it claimed that he used coaxial lenses, nor of anyone before Galileo that he used a tube. (H. C. King, *History of the Telescope*, London, 1955, pp. 28 f.)

If the sixteenth century added nothing material to the existing knowledge of geometrical optics, in respect of the physical problem of the rainbow the outstanding work of former centuries seems to have been for a time actually lost sight of. The most distinguished work here—after allowing for Grosseteste's inspiring hints as to the means to be employed in studying it—was that of Roger Bacon, Witelo, and Theodoric of Freiberg. All three showed skill in the devising of experiments and in drawing inferences from the results in respect of the shape of the bow and the separation of the colours. Theodoric's account, though inaccurate in certain details,

---

[1] For the possibility of an unpublished discovery of the sine law by Harriot see J. Lohne, *Centaurus*, 6, 113.

L

anticipated Newton in recognising that the separation was due to the unequal refraction of the several beams reaching the eye. But none of the three succeeded in ridding himself of Aristotle's 'physics', which saw in the various natural colours the products of varying degrees of 'pure light' and 'pure darkness'. This confusion between 'physics' and physics was repeated over four centuries later when Goethe missed the whole point of Newton's beautiful demonstration that 'colours are not *qualifications of light* . . . but original and connate properties' (italic in original). The 'coloured' shadows used by Leonardo and extended by the *plein air* school of the late nineteenth century provide a misleading 'verification' of the Aristotelian theory.

In an exhaustive study of this question Crombie [1] was able to find only one specific reference during the sixteenth century to Theodoric's work: this was in Iodocus Trutfetter's (*Eysennacensis*) *Summa in totam physicam*, Erfurt, 1514. In a few other sixteenth century books there are hints of a knowledge of his demonstration, as for instance in those of the leading original writer on optics, Francesco Maurolyco; but these may have been culled from the *Questiones super quatuor libros Metheororum*, written by Themon Iudaeus and printed four times in the early years of the century (No. 405). The question whether Themon himself may have independently arrived at Theodoric's results (since he does not include the latter in his citations) Crombie leaves unanswered. These facts, together with the absence of works on optics (apart from perspective in the modern sense) during the fifteenth century, suggest that in this subject there was in the sixteenth century a rather halting 'renaissance'; but what was 're-born' was not the 'wisdom of the Ancients' but the new and in certain respects more 'scientific' discoveries of the Infidel and Barbarian.

Though it was 'scientifically' unfruitful, the Neoplatonist analogy of light as the model of all action in nature, which was given some degree of mathematical expression by Grosseteste, should not be omitted from any consideration of Renaissance thought. As a heuristic principle it may have guided Fermat in his principle of least time, as in a more general way it seems to have guided Maupertuis in the enunciation of the principle of least

---

[1] A. C. Crombie, *Robert Grosseteste and the Origins of Experimental Science*, Oxford, 1953, pp. 260-70.

action. Perhaps it is not too much to see in it a vague hint of the fundamental concept of the radiation of energy. Cardano at any rate was convinced that heat is related to motion ('Motus rursus subtilitatis causa est. . . . Subtilitas caloris causa est . . .') and this being so there is no need to look for a separate 'substance', cold ('. . . Frigidum nihil aliud esse quam quod calore caret' . . . 'Frigor solus caloris privatio est').[1] The importance of this insight, totally at variance with the "physics" dominant at that time and place, has not generally been given its full due: such clearly recognised relationships should not be put on a par with those 'anticipations' by mere guesswork.

The name of Cardano brings us to the last of those divisions of physics which find no resting place in the mansion of 'physics'— the 'magnetic virtue' and 'electric effluvium'. Knowledge of the magnet ('lodestone') itself had been well and truly laid in the letter written in 1269 by Pierre de Maricourt to his friend Siger de Foucaucourt, perhaps the finest example of the experimental method in the Middle Ages, the high commendation of which by Roger Bacon gives one a greater confidence in the latter's appreciation of experiment than any of his own efforts.   The letter tells with admirable terseness and clarity how to select a good lodestone, and the method of testing the poles by supporting it in a wooden vessel on water. It also disposes of the classical theories of 'magnetic mountains' and of the Pole Star as a source of the force controlling the orientation of the lodestone; but replaces them by the axial poles of the heavens. Though physically false (at least as a proximate cause) this was formally closer to the truth; and in the circumstances Pierre de Maricourt could hardly have done better. From the time when Columbus first recorded the reversal of the direction of the 'variation' of the compass however, it should have become clear that the axis of magnetic force is in no way related to the axis of rotation of the 'world'. When the navigations of the sixteenth century revealed the very considerable range of this variation it was evident that the poles of the magnetic axis could not be far removed, if at all, from the earth itself. This was more strongly implied by the discovery by Robert Norman in 1576 [2] that a needle magnetised *after* horizontal suspension always dips in such a way that the end which points roughly towards the

---

[1] *De Subtilitate*, Nürnberg, 1550, pp. 41, 93.
[2] The bare observation had been made by Georg Hartmann in 1544.

north also points downwards at a steep angle—the magnitude
and direction of this 'dip' were later found to depend roughly
on the latitude of the place of observation. The implication of this
was, however, drawn only some years later by William Gilbert:
it is clearly expressed in the sub-title of his great work *De Magnete
. . . et de magno magnete tellure*. The knowledge gained by observations at widely different points on the earth's surface and the co-
operation of craftsmen like Norman which Gilbert readily
acknowledged, seems here to have been crucial; for there is
hardly anything about magnets in *De Magnete* that was not already
in Pierre de Maricourt's letter, which also was acknowledged by
Gilbert. Nevertheless the power of 'physics' to suggest general
theories is shown by the fact that Avicenna had recognised that the
'propagation' of magnetism exemplifies the Aristotelian 'propagation of species', in which the lodestone modified the matter in
contact with it, which further transmitted the *species magnetica*
to its adjacent matter, and so on to the iron whose 'potency for
motion' thus tended to pass into action. Magnetism was also
considered to be an example of Sympathy-Antipathy (see p. 280
and Thorndike, *Isis*, **36,** 156). Gilbert's claim to fame must rest on
his ability to separate the proximate causation, from which physics
must start, from the speculative principles of 'physics'; this, as he
shows in his historical introduction, the other sixteenth-century
writers on magnetism had failed to do.

In regard to electricity Gilbert broke entirely new ground. For
the first time it was made clear that the attractive power of rubbed
amber had in fact nothing to do with amber as such, but was
shared by a very large number of substances for which Gilbert
for the first time introduced the term *electrics*. The *non-electrics*,
for the most part metals, are of course no different in this respect
from the *electrics*; the difference lies not in the power of being
charged, but in instantly losing the charge by conduction to earth;
this conception, however, was not arrived at until more than a
century later. Though Gilbert had demonstrated that the electric
'effluvium' is as pervasive a character of nature as light and heat,
he never used the word *electricity* nor did his discoveries weaken
his essentially Aristotelian appreciation of the physical world.
On the contrary, probably circulated in manuscript during his
lifetime and printed by the Elzevirs after his death, was a work,
De nostro Mundo Sublunari, whose title indicates that he had not

lived long enough to appreciate the implications of Tycho Brahe's discoveries (see above, p. 121); Galileo's *Nuncius Sidereus* appeared only after his death. But though he worked entirely within the circle of ideas of 'physics' his insistence on the appeal to experiment, more consistently perhaps than any other sixteenth-century thinker except Tartaglia (No. 673), showed the way to break this circle. Nor was this insistence really an appeal to experience rather than to experiment, such as had been that of most of the medieval thinkers, for Gilbert's discovery of the distinct yet pervasive character of electricity was brought about by the use of an artificial instrument devised for the purpose. This was a delicately poised metal indicator—essentially the first electroscope—which responded to electrical influences in a manner resembling the response of the compass needle to magnetic. With his mounted magnet and spherical lodestone (already used by Pierre de Maricourt) he showed how specially devised apparatus could be employed for the inductive verification of the consequences deduced from a theory (variation of dip with latitude). With his *versorium*, by artificially magnifying suspected, but unobserved, phenomena he took the first decisive step along the unbroken path to the dynamo and the cyclotron. In this case the possibility of drawing definite conclusions from negative results was all important.

So far our review of renaissance 'physics' has been mainly concerned with the question of its 'forms'—especially of the 'form' of motion—and only incidentally (since for Aristotle there is no species from which either of these two aspects is wholly absent) with matter. It is now time to recall Melanchthon's remark (p. 149 above) that 'physicists not only create mixt bodies out of the elements, but seek the causes why elements are able to be mixt among themselves'. With his usual lucidity Duhem has recreated the problem of 'mixt' bodies in terms of dropping a lump of sugar into a glass of water: 'Oublions nous . . . toute théorie chimique et analysons cette simple opération. . . . Dans ce verre y-a-t'il encore du sucre et de l'eau? Non; le sucre a été détruit, nous l'avons vu graduellement disparaître; le liquide que renferme le verre n'est plus de l'eau, c'est-à-dire cette liqueur très mobile, presque insipide, . . . mais une liqueur nouvelle, plus ou moins sirupeuse. . . . Le verre ne renferme donc plus ni l'eau ni le sucre que nous y avions mis, mais un corps nouveau, un *mixte*

L*

formé aux dépens de ces deux *éléments*.' [1] These are the facts; to them an Aristotelian would have added the following gloss: The 'elements' are no longer present in actuality, since there is no direct evidence of their presence, but only in 'potency' since they can be recovered by careful distillation. The alternative account of modern chemists, that there is nothing 'new', that the sugar and water are still 'there', is a fiction based on the 'atomic' (really 'molecular') hypothesis available since Demokritos or earlier. But it is a fiction that works. Note that the two alternative accounts apply to both homogeneous mixtures ('solutions') and chemical compounds, in the traditional sense. The modern tendency to blur the rigid distinction between these two classes shows in a certain respect, as Duhem recognised in 1902, a tendency to 'follow once again a way abandoned since the sixteenth century, the Aristotelian method'.[2] It should therefore be of more than usual interest to familiarise ourselves with that part of renaissance 'physics' which was concerned with the generation of 'mixts'. Unfortunately we are met at the outset with a difficulty of a kind almost unique and of a degree quite unparalleled in the other departments of renaissance thought. For the problem had during centuries before the beginning of our period beome the concern of 'chemists', 'alchemists', 'physicians', and a variety of technical craftsmen, such as dyers, gunpowder manufacturers, glass makers, and above all miners and metal workers. All these in addition to 'physicists' or 'natural philosophers'. Moreover, insofar as anatomy and botany became disciplines apart from medicine they were during nearly the whole of the sixteenth century largely guided (or misguided) by 'physiological' considerations, which, since the time of Galen, had been dominated by the notion of the balance of humours, itself drawing its theory from the 'formal' (hot, cold, wet, dry) aspects of the general problem of the 'mixt'. This multiplicity of interested parties would in itself have presented no serious obstacles to clear exposition had they merely applied the orthodox theory of the mixt to their several fields; but they not only developed modifications of their own, but by the overlapping of their interpretations introduced a confusion which is as yet very far from having been resolved. Thus—to take a few examples—George Ripley, Kertzenmacher, Tycho Brahe, Libavius, and Paracelsus would all have accepted the title of

---

[1] *Le Mixte et la Combinaison chimique*, Paris, 1902, pp. 1-2.   [2] *Op. cit.* Preface.

'alchemist'; but, whereas Kertzenmacher and Libavius were primarily concerned with the progress of preparative chemistry and its application to mining or medicine, both regarded the search for the Philosopher's Stone as part of this enterprise. Paracelsus and Libavius were both embroiled in violent controversies with medical schools: the former had burnt the books of Avicenna; the latter was also 'struck off the roll' for his alleged anti-Galenism, but in his own writings deplores the fact that no chemist is held in popular esteem unless 'he follows the principles and footsteps of the *utterly corrupt* Paracelsus' (*italic* mine). Again, whereas the whole basic conception of alchemy lies in the Aristotelian conception of the mutability of elements, Tycho Brahe vigorously attacked Aristotelianism in general. From another point of view, although Paracelsus gave a new and valuable stimulus to the embryo of chemistry by allying it to medicine, his *interpretation* of this relationship was shot through with Neoplatonic astral mysticism; and, though contemptuous of the gold-making alchemists by then a by-word in Europe, he nevertheless adopted their 'mercury' and 'sulphur' as first principles, adding to these 'salt'—the non-inflammable, non-volatile 'residues', to which little attention was being paid in an age obsessed by distillation and extraction. (Cf. R. P. Multhauf, *Bull. Hist. Med.* **30** (1956), 329). In his mysticism Paracelsus reflects to some extent—though he may never even have heard his name—the 'alchemy' of George Ripley. This Canon Regular of Scarborough dedicated to Edward IV a poem—*The Compound of Alchemy* (No. 577) in which, it is probably safe to say, the language alone is chemical, the object in some sense spiritual. We shall return to this work later (p. 290).

Such then is the diversity, amounting at times to fundamental opposition, which characterised the writers on 'chemistry' (also called by the followers of Paracelsus the 'Spagyric Art') and 'alchemy'—terms which may sometimes be used almost interchangeably, at others to indicate violent opposition. Little can be done here except to sketch in the background; substantiate in somewhat greater detail the internal relations which have been hinted at above; and indicate some of the reassessments that have been made latterly, on the one hand of the meaning of alchemical philosophy, and on the other of the possible origins of chemistry. Such an exposition of this second part of 'physics' is superficially parallel to that of the first; but complex and incomplete as the latter was seen to be, it must be understood that for the present undertaking there is hardly a patch of solid evidence on which a survey may be based: almost every site, on which the historian may attempt to take his stand, is likely to sink into a whirlpool of contradictions.

At least two, at times distinct, traditions of alchemy have been recognised from the earliest extant documents—those written in Greek and traceable to the region of Alexandria in the early centuries of the Christian era. Some of these writings indicate the recipes of a craft for counterfeiting metals by chemical means, with intentions probably no less honest than that of 'electroplating'. In others there are hints of an intention to deceive the purchaser. In some there is evidence from the mystical character of the language and symbolism employed that the operator was succeeding only too well in deceiving himself. Knowledge of these practices almost certainly reached Western Europe only through translations of Arabic works into which they had been woven during the previous four or five centuries. The most important of these works were those of 'Geber', ar-Razi, and Avicenna. It is highly improbable that the huge corpus of works by 'Geber' were written by one man: it was only in 1926 that an Arabic manuscript was discovered of any of them. From internal evidence it seems clear that the original work of Jabir ibn Hayan al-Sufi who worked at the court of the Caliph Haroun ar-Rashid (VIII–1) was expanded first by later Arabic writers and subsequently by Latin writers as late as the thirteenth century. The most famous of these 'composite' works, the *Summa Perfectionis*, embraces two traditions, namely, the mystical search for the Stone and a strictly empirical account of the operations—filtration, sublimation, etc.—which still enter into the routine of a chemical laboratory. The preparation of the red sulphide of mercury is accurately described, and from it the lesson is drawn that the 'mercury' and 'sulphur' used in the preparation are not to be confused with the 'philosophical' entities bearing the same names. This distinction is a commonplace of many original works of the sixteenth century (e.g. No. 577).

As a result of the researches of Ruska,[1] Kraus, Holmyard and

[1] For Ruska's theory of the origin of the work see his *Uebersetzung und Bearbeitungen*, etc., in *Quellen und Studien*, Vol. LV, Berlin, 1935. The above account is based on the

others it now appears probable that only the mystical tradition (perhaps associated with the rise of the Si-ite sect of Islam) derives from the time of Jabir ibn Hayan—whether written by him or not—the empirical chemical interpolations being of much later date. The difficulty of disentangling the various threads in the *Summa Perfectionis*, which was current in the West only from about the middle of the thirteenth century, is aggravated by the fact that what was intended to be only a mystical philosophy in a symbolic form was subsequently applied to a truly chemical process. Thus the principal object of the *Summa Perfectionis* is to teach the conversion of 'base' metals into 'noble'—silver, and especially gold. This is to be effected in the main by means of well-defined chemical operations which probably owe a great deal to sources not much earlier than the period at which the work first appeared in the West. But the theory underlying the whole procedure is that metals all consist of 'principles' of two kinds—the volatile 'sophic mercury' and the combustible 'sophic sulphur'—and that gold can be obtained by the gradual purging away of the latter present in relatively greater amount in the baser metals. But this theory as such is to be found clearly set out in the 'encyclopaedia' of the esoteric sect known as the 'Brethren of Purity' which flourished in Basra about 950. Now there is nothing in the rest of this encyclopaedia (a fairly definitive text of which has been set up) to suggest that the Brethren were intent on the manufacture of gold: the whole tenor of the work is that of an eclectic mysticism, borrowing the material from a number of eastern cults but strongly marked by a latent Aristotelianism.

At this stage it should be made clear that although the *Summa Perfectionis* and many other works of 'Geber' (e.g. those included in the *Ars Aurifera* and *Ars Alchemiae*—Nos. 314 and 316) which had a great vogue in the sixteenth and seventeenth centuries were in no sense translations of Arabic works, there did nevertheless exist among the later Arab writers an empirical tradition from which Western alchemy drew freely. The best known of these is perhaps he *Secret of Secrets* written by ar-Razi, a definitive text of which wast established by Ruska, together with a German translation and commentary. Of this work Mieli says: 'Il est très juste de dire que par son ouvrage al-Razi inaugure la chimie scientifique. Pas une

recent appreciation of the 'Jabir' question in Holmyard, *Alchemy*, Penguin Books, 1957 pp. 66-80.

trace de mysticisme ou d'allegories extrascientifiques dans ses ouvrages sur l'alchimie.'[1] But though the preparation of the material is described with the clarity and objectivity of a modern text-book, the *purpose* of this preparation is unambiguously the transmutation of base metal into gold—one allegedly successful attempt being actually recorded by ar-Razi.

It must not be supposed, however, that the 'gold makers' had everything their own way. Probably at no time did the theory of transmutation go unchallenged. One of the most effective of these challenges appeared as long ago as about 1020, when Avicenna in the section of his *al-Sifa* dealing with minerals (the Latin version of which was for many centuries attributed to Aristotle and included in the *Meteorologica*) wrote: '. . . ars debilior est quam natura, nec sequitur eam, licet multum laboret. Sciant vero artifices Alchimiae species rerum transmutari non posse. Sed similia illis facere possunt, et pingere rubeum citrino, ut videatur Aurum, et album pingere colore quo volunt, donec sit multum simile Auro vel aeri. Post quoque Plumbi immunditias abstergere. Ipsum tamen semper erit Plumbum, quamvis videatur Argentum. Sed tunc optime erunt in eo qualitates aliae ut errent homines, ut qui accipiunt Salem et Salem Arminiacum. Ceterum quod differentia specifica tollatur ingenio, non credo possibile, et non est quod complexio una in aliam convertatur, quia ista sensibilia non sunt differentia, qua permutatur species, sed sunt accidentia, et proprietates. Differentiae eorum autem non sunt cognitae, quia cum differentia sit ignota, quomodo potest sciri utrum tollatur necnon vel quomodo tolli possit' ('But art is feebler than nature and does not catch up with it, however hard it exerts itself. And the adepts of Alchemy must realise that the species of things can not be changed. Nevertheless they are able to make things which resemble these species and colour " the red " with " citron ", in order that it may appear to be gold, and colour "the white" with any colour they wish until it is very like gold or bronze. Afterwards also they can purge away the dross of lead. Yet it will always be lead though it may look like silver. In that case at the best there will be in it other qualities so that men are mistaken about it as those are who take sal-ammoniac for salt. But that a specific difference can be removed by man's ingenuity I do not believe to be possible and it is not the case that one

[1] *La Science Arabe*, pp. 132-3 and notes.

"complexion" is changed into another, since those sensible qualities are not a "differentia" whereby this species is changed but are accidents and properties. Further their *differentiae* are not known, therefore since the differentia is unknown how can it be known whether or not it is removed or how it can be removed').[1]

The empirical tradition so notable in the work of ar-Razi was continued in the medieval Latin works known as *Liber Claritatis* and *Liber de Aluminibus et Salibus*, both of which were probably based on the same Arabic source. Nor was the transmutation of metals the only concern of medieval alchemical operations: from the thirteenth century there appeared a series of works on the Fifth Essence (*Quinta Essentia*). This is not to be confused[2] with the fifth *element* of Aristotle, the $αἰθήρ$, which exists only 'above' the sphere of the moon; it is nearer to the Aristotelian $πνεῦμα$, the 'living breath' whose action confers on inert matter the powers characteristic of life. The possibility of grades of $πνεῦμα$ became of central importance in the Stoic philosophy and appears in various guises in all kinds of alchemical thought. After all, the 'sophic mercury' and 'sophic sulphur' are 'souls' relative to ordinary mercury and sulphur. But in the doctrine of the quintessence it was held that every substance owes its 'suchness' not only to the characteristic proportion of the four material elements composing it but to a *specific* essence. And its separation from the grosser matter of the substance became a task to which some alchemists were particularly dedicated. Though he was not the first to write about it, the doctrine finds its clearest exposition in the work of the Franciscan Ioannes de Rupescissa (No. 313) on whose identity[3] new light has recently been shed. The work exists in a large number of manuscripts which are reviewed by Thorndike (*Hist.* III, 355 f.) showing a considerable variation in their contents. The following account is based on the printed version of 1597 and does not appear to differ materially from Thorndike's abstract.

John says that his book is intended for 'men in religious orders' (*evangelici*) who have no money, and he hopes that by following his

[1] Avicenna, *De Congelatione et Conglutinatione Lapidum* also known simply as 'Mineralia', quoted from *Gebri Philosophi Summa Perfectionis . . .*, Venice, 1542, fos. 111-15.

[2] Though the distinction was not always made: Ioannes de Rupescissa (below), for instance, admits a 'celestial' influence on the 'essences' of terrestrial bodies.

[3] Discussed by E. F. Jacob in his Seton Memorial Lecture 'Jean de Roquetaillade' (1954), *Bull. John Rylands Lib.* **39** (1956), 75.

instructions they will be able, at small cost, not indeed to prolong life beyond the term fixed by God, but to 'keep the body free from corruption'. For this purpose physicians use extracts from the 'corruptible' elements. But just as the heavens in relation to the four elements are incorruptible, so we should seek a fifth essence which in relation to the four qualities (presumably the Galenic 'temperaments'—see below, p. 217) of the body is incorruptible— 'I shall call it by the three names ascribed to it by philosophers: *aqua ardens, anima vini seu spiritus, aqua vitae*'. His nomenclature is somewhat ambiguous for he goes on to say that everyone knows about 'aqua ardens';[1] what is to be sought is the *essence* of this 'water', to be obtained by prolonged distillation 'up and down'— presumably with a type of reflux condenser—to remove all the corruptible ingredients of the original wine. It is clear that the theory of the quintessence has received a remarkable degree of confirmation as a result of practical experience with *aqua ardens* (alcohol) obtained by the distillation of wine. The liquid so obtained has the properties one would expect of a 'spirit'—it 'flies away' (volatile) and burns away almost without residue; also it causes other substances, such as sugar, to become readily inflammable. Now what is particularly characteristic of John's work is that although there is a lot of talk about the planetary influences (in which it is noted that the moon, not the sun, causes tides), and the 'sophic' sulphur, which being invisible, differs from ordinary sulphur, nevertheless the *procedure* is wholly practical and shows a very considerable knowledge of chemical operations. Thus 'si intra aquam corrosivam factam ex vitriolo et sale petra immitas argentum vivum sublimatam absque vitriolo laniabitur totum et in atoma convertitur' ('if you put mercury sublimed without vitriol into the corrosive "water" made from vitriol and saltpetre it will be completely torn to pieces and changed into atoms'). Also his belief in the power of the quintessence to 'preserve' the living body is based on the analogy of its *observed* power to preserve from putrefaction the flesh of the dead. The 'corrosive water' is elsewhere called 'aqua fortis', and a process described which would probably involve the production

---

[1] It had in fact been distilled by the Greeks and Arabs, but its *re*-distillation, with efficient condensation, was probably a Western invention of the twelfth or thirteenth century—cf. Holmyard, *Alchemy*, 1957, pp. 50-1, and F. Sherwood Taylor, *The Idea of the Quintessence* in Singer, I.

of *aqua regia*. The 'fifth essences' of other bodies, e.g. human blood (obtained from the 'barbitonsores'), eggs, capons (the sexual affinities are to be noted) may be obtained by allowing them to putrify under certain conditions, followed by distillation, as in the case of *aqua ardens*. One other quintessence of special interest is referred to—that to be obtained by the *extraction* of gold by means of *aqua ardens*. This process of 'extraction' with or without subsequent distillation became a major concern during the sixteenth century (e.g. No. 101). The idea of the quintessence was far from being an altogether silly one: the greatly increased powers of scents and drugs obtained by alcoholic (as distinct from simple aqueous or steam) extraction and subsequent distillation would naturally give rise to the idea of a latent specific power. But its subsequent development led especially in medicine to wildly extravagant claims and numerous nauseating recipes. Theory was paramount; experimental checks in relation to the efficacy of extraction (e.g. 'aurum potabile' made from gold) almost non-existent. But the cult had a far-reaching effect on the design of apparatus: reference to Brunschwig *Distillierbuch* (No. 101) will reveal pictures of stills in all essentials—waterjacketed condensers, fractionnating columns—similar to those used today. Detailed comparison of the illustrations provided in books throughout the sixteenth century will also reveal another 'modern' characteristic—a morbid need to vary the basic pattern, often to an absurd degree of complexity, without any recognisable concrete advantage: one is painfully reminded of the succession of 'new models' of motor cars and radio receivers in successive annual exhibitions.

A question we may properly ask is whether John's alchemy is merely the application to a mystical nature-philosophy (in which the traditional view of Man as a microcosmic mode of the macrocosm clearly plays an important part) of chemical procedures developed in the world outside the religious houses for purely practical ends. The difficulty here is to be sure what those 'ends' could have been: pigments for the illumination of stone and parchment, glass-making, dyeing, certainly provide a possible answer, but the 'major chemical industries' of gunpowder and metal extraction were still to come. Moreover the fact that chemical industries could *use* the kind of processes John mentions should not too readily be regarded as evidence that their artificers *invented* them. We have already considered a parallel case in navigation (p. 145). The enthusiasm for such arts in religious houses is attested by the existence of an order of the Dominican Chapter of Rimini in 1288 forbidding the erection of such 'instruments' in the Houses of the Order.[1] It seems at least possible that the reverse may have to be considered: namely that starting with the quite illusory case of 'extracting gold' it gradually became rationalised into an 'industry' for the manufacture of scents, liqueurs (e.g. Benedictine), and flavouring essences. However this may be, there seems little doubt that during the fourteenth century the mystical side of Ioannes de Rupescissa's teaching also developed into the kind of alchemy which appears to have hardly any connection with the science of chemistry, that is with the physical world, but bids fair to be of great interest to the psychologist. In a study of *Science and the Renaissance* there would seem to be good grounds for paying no further attention to this development, but to take this course would be quite inconsistent with the view of the historiography of science on which the study has been based. Nothing is more characteristic of the Renaissance than the two-fold wave of alchemical *enthusiasm* which swept over Europe during the sixteenth and early seventeenth centuries. The omission of any consideration of this would involve as serious a distortion as the omission of any reference to that other *enthusiasm*, astrology. But to emphasise it without making some attempt, however tentative, to explain it, would be to risk a serious misunderstanding of the nature of this aspect of culture. Nevertheless, whatever opinion may be held as to its relevance to the progress of scientific thought, it belongs less to the question of the nature of the physical world than to 'anthropology', hence consideration of the matter will be deferred to the last chapter.

It may at this stage have been remarked that hardly a word has been said about the progress of thought on the chemic aspects of the world during the Renaissance itself. The fact is that an examination of the bibliographical literature, including that under review, gives the impression that the sixteenth century was remarkable more for a wide dissemination of works previously in manuscript than for any original thought. Thus from Hirsch's [2]

[1] E. S. Holmyard, *Endeavour*, **14** (1955), 117.
[2] R. Hirsch, The 'Invention of Printing and the Diffusion of Alchemical and Chemical Knowledge', *Chymia*, **3** (1950), 115.

valuable study we learn that up to 1536 by far the most popular work was the *Liber Aggregationis* by 'Albertus Magnus' which ran to about a hundred editions. No contemporary author comes anywhere near this; but the works of Cornelius Agrippa had an even greater vogue during a period of a few years. This was not due to any strikingly original ideas, since, as Thorndike points out, he had not any. The reason for their popularity suggested by Thorndike—that publication had been banned—assumes that morbid curiosity was as rampant then as now. Nearly all the remaining works of this period which came out in several editions were either 'classics' (e.g. Arnaldus de Villanova and 'Raimundus Lullius') or 'practical' handbooks on the making of wine, mining and metallurgy, minerals and precious stones, dyeing, cosmetics, etc. The only ones of a more 'theoretical' nature are Brunschwig's great *Liber de Arte Distillandi* and Brunfels's *Onomastikon*. Each of these has a medical bias, but the former displays a fairly high standard of appreciation of the 'theory' of distillation, and the terms explained in the latter give a good insight into current modes of thought. Ulstadt's *Coelum Philosophorum* itself claims only to *revive* interest in Ioannes de Rupescissa and other authors of his time. (No. 694).

What has been said above concerning the early sixteenth century should not of course be regarded as in any sense decisive: it may be that among the little known works cited by Hirsch—and of course he makes no claim to completeness—there may be some which include novel views too far in advance of contemporary thought to gain popular recognition for their authors. Moreover in this period falls almost the whole of the immense output of Paracelsus (d. 1541)—a point of which Hirsch might have been wise to remind his readers. Hardly any of it—especially the 'chemical' items—were printed until some years later, yet they were circulating in manuscript and preparing the ground for the ideological battles of the second half of the century.

In the present state of our knowledge, however, it seems that advances in the chemical aspects of 'physics' in the sixteenth century came less from attempts to increase understanding of the physical world as such than from men whose business was to improve techniques. We shall therefore conclude our discussion of this topic by an examination of the progress of technology, restricting ourselves here as elsewhere to those aspects which are clearly relevant to the scientific thought of the period. First, since it takes its rise most nearly from the traditional 'physics', we shall consider mining and metallurgy.

The literature of mining and metallurgy consisted of the recipe and assay books (*Probierbücher*), the general works with a practical bias such as G. A. Pantheo's *Voarchadumia* [1] (1530—based on two earlier works and not untinged with alchemy), Ercker's *Aula Subterranea—Beschreibung allerfürnemsten mineralischen Ertzt-unnd Berckwercks-arten* (1574) and Biringuccio's *Pirotechnie* (1540); and the comprehensive treatises, theoretical and practical, of Georgius Agricola—*De Re Metallica*, (1556), *De Natura Fossilium* (1546), and *De Ortu et Causis Subterraneorum* (1546). Already at the beginning of the fifteenth century manuscript recipe books reveal a considerable knowledge of the extraction of ores from the rocks, the smelting of the metal from the ore, the 'parting' of metals such as silver from lead by cupellation and of gold from silver by nitric acid (commonly called 'Scheidwasser'—'parting water'—in these and even later works), and of fairly accurate assay by chemical operations with chemical apparatus (including the balance) such as is depicted in *De Re Metallica*, pp. 205-7. It is difficult to assess the novelty of this knowledge since there is hardly any branch of science worse represented in medieval manuscripts. Doubtless many of the practitioners were illiterate and the methods carried forward by oral tradition: the nearest approach to the subject is the *Feuerwerkbuch* of 1420, of which something will be said hereafter.

The more comprehensive works open up wide vistas of interest which can here be only indicated. In his *De Ortu et Causis Subterraneorum* Agricola discusses at length theories of the origin of mineral deposits of all kinds. The theory, of which all later ones were little more than variants, is the brief and unfortunately obscure passage [2] at the close of the third book of Aristotle's *Meteorologica*, where he attributes the formation of metals to the solidification of a vaporous (wet) exhalation within the rocks before it has had a chance to become water. There is also a 'dry' (smoky) exhalation whose action is responsible for the production of the non-fusible 'fossils' but it is not altogether lacking from

---

[1] F. Sherwood Taylor, *Some Metallurgical processes of the early fifteenth century*, Newcomen Society, Reprint (1954).

[2] For an interesting interpretation of this passage see T. E. Eicholz, 'Aristotle's theory of metals and mines', *Classical Quarterly*, **43**, (1949), 141.

PLATE VII

DE HVMANI CORPORIS FABRICA LIBER II.   237

DE INSTRVMENTIS, QVAE SECTIONI-
bus adminiſtrandis parari poſſunt.   Caput *VII.*

ANATOMICORVM INSTRVMEN-
TORVM DELINEATIO.

Collection of dissecting instruments figured by Vesalius, *De Humani Corporis Fabrica.* (Vol. II, No. 709, and Vol. I, p. 226.)

metals. The dominance of the 'watery' exhalation in metals is presumably the best Aristotle could do to indicate that potential fluidity is the common characteristic of all metals—least in iron which must therefore contain a higher proportion of 'earthiness'. The woolliness of all this is due partly to Aristotle's misguided attempt to deduce the properties of all substances from the four primary qualities without reference to quantity, and partly to the poverty of language in regard to abstract or dispositional terms. But the appalling consequences of this are seen in Agricola's oscillations between sound observation (e.g. of the 'pestilential exhalations' into subterranean air, some of which are deadly only to birds, some to other animals, some even to man—*De Ortu* . . ., p. 34) and the rival theories not only of Aristotle, but also of the philosophers, chemists, astrologers, and even of the common herd. The subtle but fruitless controversy as to the proportions of the 'wet' and the 'dry', of the relative generative power of 'heat' and 'cold', of the justice of the comparison of male and female, was given a special turn by the chemists, whose theory in regard to the part played by 'mercury' and 'sulphur' in the actual *genesis* of metals could be given a good deal of plausibility by the fact of the frequent association of actual sulphur with metals and the partially metallic character of mercury. Agricola, who displays the conservatism of the Humanists in matters of theory, had no sympathy with this view, which probably suffered from being—with little justice—linked with the name of Paracelsus. In 1575 the issue was brought to a head in the reply of Joseph Duchesne to the attack 'contra chemistas' of Jacques Aubert in his *De Metallorum Ortu et Causis* (No. 48). An examination of the involved but forcefully and on the whole clearly written works is rewarding in the sense that only by as it were entering into the fray can the modern chemist have any adequate conception of the unreality of the dispute. For the method of these men is medieval in the worst sense: both strain every nerve to show the consistency of their beliefs with the canon of Aristotle ('philosophorum facile princeps', as even the neo-Paracelsian Duchesne calls him) by twisting the meaning of his terms to suit their several interpretations; it is thus, for all that it is the product of the 'Renaissance', almost entirely a dispute about words. It this were all, it might serve the purposes of those who are anxious to belittle the achievements of the sixteenth century; but it is not quite all. For despite

M

his attempt to get the best of both worlds Duchesne is out to justify the claims of novelty: he is rightly angered at Aubert's slighting remarks about Albertus Magnus and 'Geber'; he is on solid ground in defending the claims of the 'philosophi chemici' (presumably a more deferential title than 'chemistae') to recognise the existence of 'imperfect metals' such as arsenic and antimony which go up in smoke when heated. What a study of these exasperating tracts teaches us most surely is that, despite a growing mass of sound observation, drawn mainly from intercourse with men who were willing to dirty their hands and even risk their lives in the mines, there was no hope of a science of *chemistry* emerging until by ridding itself of the universalism of 'physics' and its ideological entanglement with medicine (see below, p. 256) it could formulate its own concepts free from the protean impalpability of the current 'principles', 'essences', and 'qualities'. No one who has not wrestled with these shadows can fully appreciate the eminent achievement of Robert Boyle in his *Sceptical Chymist*.

In *De Ortu* . . . Agricola appears mainly as the critical humanist, displaying the learning and literary grace which was to make him the most influential writer on mining and metallurgy and thereby raise these subjects from the status of 'crafts' to that of 'sciences'. In the accompanying *De Natura Fossilium* on the other hand he reveals his intimate first hand knowledge of minerals, and perhaps by virtue of his philosophical training provides the first classification of minerals with any pretensions to an empirical basis. Nearly all the physical characteristics—hardness, cleavage, fracture, colour-streak imparted to the 'touchstone', etc.—which are still in use by the mineralogist in the field, are employed. So impressive is the result—though it still leans too heavily on the often misleading character of colour—that the American Society of Geology has recently published a full translation. The method employed—the *systematic* application of empirical tests—is equally the basis of *chemical* analysis, little developed until the time of Boyle.

The only other technology for which space allows a brief account is that of 'pyrotechny' in its broadest sense. 'Fire-raising' chemical mixtures go back to the 'Greek fire' used by the Byzantine navy as early as the sixth century,[1] but it is with the

[1] See A. R. Hall in *Hist. Tech.* Vol. II, p. 374.

introduction of gunpowder into Europe in the thirteenth century that any adequate documentation starts. Of the circumstances of this introduction there is as yet no definite knowledge, probably for the same reason as has been suggested above in respect of metallurgy. The first printed book on gunpowder was published in Augsburg in 1529; called *Büchsenmeisterei* it was largely a reproduction of the *Feuerwerkbuch*, of which several manuscripts are still extant dating from about 1420. The existence of many other manuscripts of about the same age suggests that the *Feuer-werkbuch von* 1420, as it is often called, was a compilation from several sources; the long delay before any printed version appeared may have been for 'reasons of security' rather than the existence of a merely oral tradition, since one of the sections in the work stresses the importance of the master-gunner's being able to read and write. The 'theory', with an account of which the work opens, shows an appreciation of 'science' beyond mere trial and error methods: one question in particular—whether the cannon ball is driven by the fire or by the vapour (*Dunst*) which goes out from the fire—raises hopes, which however are dashed by the reasons given for the belief that the sulphur and saltpetre play an equal part, namely, because of the opposition of the 'heat' of the former and the 'cold' of the latter! The *Büchsenmeisterei* was reprinted in 1569. No. 758 (1582) is a somewhat abbreviated edition. The problems, both of powder and ballistics, set in these early works were evidently a stimulus to scientific activity both theoretical and practical, as they appear throughout the sixteenth century in numerous books whose contents may, like Biringuccio's *Pirotechnie* and Ercker's work cited above be also concerned with quite different matters. Even the scholarly Melanchthon recommends lime as the best source of charcoal—since it is the 'hottest' tree!

Looking back over the sixteenth century a modern chemist can discern little to encourage the view that the chemical aspects of the physical world were much better understood than at the beginning: the century seems to have been spent almost literally in raking over the old embers or in finding new meanings for old words. But as the century drew to a close there were signs of a new spirit stirring: the Renaissance of chemistry had been delayed in comparison with that of the sister sciences. Three years before the close there was published what is commonly described as 'the first textbook of chemistry'. Characteristically it was called *Alchymia* (No. 394 and 396), and it included sections on the Philosopher's Stone. But its author, Andreas Libavius, also put into it just what had previously been left out, without which chemistry could not change from a 'mystery' to a science: this was a collection of clearly written accounts of all the apparatus and materials commonly handled, and of the preparation of a few new substances such as the *liquor fumans Libavii* (stannic chloride). Henceforward when anyone wished to carry out experiments with specific substances he could, if he were willing, leave no one in any doubt as to what it was he had used, and what operations he had carried out. In this respect it was hardly surpassed until 1675, when Nicholas Lemery brought out his *Cours de Chimie*. The fact that here and elsewhere Libavius defended the creed of transmutation till his death does not detract from his great contribution towards positive knowledge. Priestley was to repeat the pattern in respect of Phlogiston two centuries later. But just as important as the experimental basis prepared by the alchemist, Libavius, was the attack on alchemy by a chemist (as distinct from a conservative humanist) Nicolas Guibert, delivered in his *Alchemy . . . assailed and demolished by reason and experience* (No. 321). This was in 1603; about ten years later a modest laboratory manual—*Chemistry for beginners, produced from the Fount of Nature and by manual experience* (No. 69) appeared, in which Jean Beguin announced to his pupils that 'chemistry is the art of dissolving natural "mixt" bodies and precipitating (*coagulandi*) solutions for the preparation of more pleasing, healthful, and safer medicines'. Rather a narrow aim perhaps, and in the direct Paracelsian tradition,[1] but the method is that of Libavius in which Beguin says the 'second part of the definition, which concerns the transmutation of elements, formerly greatly valued, is excluded': he will use the mercury-sulphur-salt theory for purposes of classification but not of explanation. A presage of the 'new' chemistry is the testing of distilled water with a drop or two of 'spirit of vitriol' to demonstrate the absence of lead (Beguin, *Tyrocinium chymicum*, 1625, p. 101).

[1] See below, p. 249.

CHAPTER X

THE SYSTEM OF ANIMATE NATURE

THAT in the science of living things no less than in the science of the heavens and the sublunary world of the elements there was no Royal Road from credulous dogmatism to critical understanding is well illustrated by comparing the following passages in which two outstanding naturalists of different epochs handle the problem of the generation of the Barnacle (Bernicle, or Brant) Goose.

'No one has seen the Bernicle's nest or egg, nor is this wonderful, since Bernicles without a parent's aid are said to have a spontaneous generation in this way: When after a certain time the firwood masts of a ship have rotted in the sea, then fungi, as it were, break out upon them first, in which in course of time one may discern evident forms of birds, which afterwards are clothed with feathers, and at last become alive and fly. Now lest this should seem fabulous to anyone, besides the common evidence of all the long-shore men of England, Ireland, and Scotland, that renowned historian Gyraldus . . . bears witness that the generation of the Bernicles is none other than this. But inasmuch as it seemed hardly safe to trust the vulgar, and by reason of the rarity of the thing I did not quite credit Gyraldus, . . . I took counsel of a certain man whose upright conduct, often proved by me, had justified my trust, a theologian by profession and an Irishman by birth, Octavian by name, whether he thought Gyraldus worthy of belief in this affair. Who, taking oath upon the very Gospel which he taught, answered that what Gyraldus had reported of the generation of this bird was absolutely true, and that with his own eyes he had beholden young, as yet but rudely formed, and also handled them. . . .' [1]

'There is a small species known as the barnacle goose, arrayed

---

[1] Quoted from *Avium praecipuarum, quarum apud Plinium et Aristotelem mentio est, brevis et succincta historia* by William Turner, Cologne, 1544, trans. and ed. by A. H. Evans, Cambridge, 1903, p. 27.

in motley plumage . . . of whose nesting haunts we have no certain knowledge. There is, however, a curious popular tradition that they spring from dead trees. It is said that in the far north old ships are to be found, in whose rotting hulls a worm is born that develops into the barnacle goose. This goose hangs from the dead wood by its beak until it is old and strong enough to fly. We have made prolonged research into the origin and truth of this legend and even sent special envoys to the North with orders to bring back specimens of those mythical timbers for our inspection. When we examined them we did observe shell-like formations clinging to the rotten wood but these bore no resemblance to any avian body. We therefore doubt the truth of this legend in the absence of any corroborative evidence. In our opinion this superstition arose from the fact that barnacle geese breed in such remote latitudes that men in ignorance of their real nesting places invented this explanation.' [1]

The traditional contrast of medieval science, dependent upon authority, especially ecclesiastical authority, and the 'new' science of the Renaissance, independent, critical, and based upon personal observation is, it might be thought, admirably illustrated by the above citations. Unfortunately they are, as it were, the wrong way round: for the first was written about 1540, the second about three centuries *earlier*. It is true that Frederick II was hardly a good churchman, and the contemporary description, 'stupor mundi et immutator mirabilis'—suggests that he was far from being typical of his age; but his early contemporary, St. Albert, the great Dominican and teacher of St. Thomas Aquinas, held exactly the same opinion. The legend of the generation of the Barnacle Goose goes back to a time long before Giraldus Cambrensis gave it a *pseudo*-authority, and it was to exercise the curiosity of naturalists for a century after Turner. It would be an over-simplification of the historiography of science to draw from this case broad and general conclusions about the degree of critical insight characteristic of successive centuries. More significant than the belief itself—and perhaps future historians may come to regard the case of 'flying saucers' as a parallel from this 'scientific' age—are the reasons given for holding it.

---

[1] Quoted from *De Arte venandi cum avibus* by Frederic II of Hohenstaufen, trans. and ed. by Casey A. Wood and F. Marjorie Fyfe, reprinted by Oxford University Press, London, 1955, pp. 51-2.

Turner was generally reluctant to accept any statement on mere hearsay (see below, p. 204): he weighed his authorities, but was not aware that different kinds of reports demand different kinds of *expertise*: theology would not now be regarded as an adequate preparation for field biology. Of more than local interest is the report of the first Principal of King's College, Aberdeen, Hector Boece, who was also the first historian of the Scottish nation. In his section on the 'Nature of the Claike Geese', as Bellenden translated the Latin original, Boece shows that he has no reason to doubt the report that a bird is commonly generated from a 'shell-fish': he says that he has seen it himself 'about seven years ago', and it was 'notably proved in the yeare of Grace 1490 in sight of many people beside the Castle of Petslego [Pitsligo, Aberdeenshire] whither the body of a great tree was brought by the working of the sea'. What he feels he *is* called upon to prove is that the birds are generated by the power of the *sea*, the trees in themselves being inadequate. When the tree was sawn in two there was revealed 'a great number, on the one hand of worms, some being undeveloped (*rudibus*), others having certain members already formed, and on the other of perfectly formed birds, among which some had feathers, others were bare'. The evidence that the tree played no essential part had been provided by Alexander Galloway, who, seeing a mass of *Conchae* stuck to some seaweed (*Alga marina*) opened them to find not a fish but a fowl. Boece adds that on the evidence of some specimens which Galloway brought him he felt justified in saying that the seeds capable of generating birds dwell not in the trunks or in the fruits of the trees but in the ocean itself which both Virgil and Homer not lightly called the 'Father of things'.[1] This testimony would repay detailed study: Boece was a man of upright character who had made a name for himself in Paris as a scholar above the ordinary. When he says that he saw these things we can but believe that he *did* see them; and it is perhaps significant that he makes no claim, as nearly a century later did that rather ingenuous liar, John Gerard, that he had seen the birds at every stage up to maturity. It can hardly be doubted that Boece was merely 'seeing', exemplified in nature itself, the working of the πνευμα which Aristotle

---

[1] This is a much condensed version of the account given in H. Boethius, *Historia Scotorum*, Paris, 1526, which is much fuller than Bellenden's so-called translation into the vernacular.

regarded as the power which generates living things out of the elements. If this is so, it supports the view of a recent commentator [1] on the revival of the study of living creatures during the sixteenth century, that the progress of anatomy and the achievement of accurate description of biological fact were seriously hampered in that century by physiological prejudice. Nor must it be forgotten that not even Francesco Redi, the pioneer of controlled experiment in biology, who in the seventeenth century finally disposed of the Aristotelian theory of spontaneous generation of 'worms' from putrefying matter, still held that the larvae found in galls were produced by the generative power of the *living* tree. [2]

The compelling influence of tradition and literary authority which kept alive the absurd legend of the generation of the Barnacle Goose must not be confused with the widely accepted assumption of spontaneous generation in general. For the latter, in a manner similar to the saner forms of astrology, was a plausible inference from the general system of ideas almost universally held. Aristotle himself never doubted the life-giving entry of πνευμα into the 'elements' in the right conditions, and if we look at the evidence with unprejudiced eyes we can hardly blame him for 'seeing' confirmation of a process which theory foretold. We may well extend the same charity towards sixteenth-century writers who for instance report the generation in summer of fleas (*pulices*) from drops of water (Balduinus Ronsseus,[3] No. 585) or of worms within the human body (Nos. 283 and 623). But what is so disconcerting in the naturalists of that century is their failure to distinguish between the reports (fifteen hundred years old!) of Virgil, Pliny, Ovid, and Lucian, and those of their own contemporaries, as when Baccius in his treatise on hot springs (No. 53 pp. 441 f.) refers to Pliny's views on the generation of fish and frogs in hot water and Scaliger's account of Irish (!) leaves which change into fish in water or birds on land. The widespread tendency to 'explain' the 'facts' in terms of a universally acting 'cause' had the effect of lulling the critical sense and allowing 'experience' to provide spurious confirmation. The work of

---

[1] E. Callot, *La Renaissance des Sciences de la Vie au XVIᵐᵉ Siècle*, Paris, 1951, *passim*.

[2] For an account of Redi's experiments see W. P. D. Wightman, *The Growth of Scientific Ideas*, Edinburgh, 1950, pp. 355 f.

[3] *De Humanae Vitae Primordiis* Preface.

Ronsseus again provides illustrations: 'Eels, in which difference of sex is lacking, by rubbing against projecting rocks (*scopulorum attritu*) leave behind them certain fragments (*strigmenta*) which it is certain (*certum est*) are at length transformed into eels by penetration (*influxu*) of celestial rays' And again, 'What shall I say about a certain kind of fish (*aquatilium*) which all experience teaches . . . arises from slime and decaying matter?'[1] What indeed! Let us recall that Ronsseus was not a monk scribbling away in medieval 'gloom', but a respected physician of Ghent in the Elizabethan Age. There is, however, another side to the picture in which what appears to be healthy scepticism may be a bar to the extension of knowledge. In denying the possibility of a change of sex in Man, Severin Pineau (No. 522, p. 56) was showing a critical spirit to be commended on account of its rarity in his day; but this phenomenon is now recognised as not only actual but explicable in terms of a more general theory.

Being thus warned against the expectation of finding any sudden and widespread awakening of the scientific spirit in relation to the world of living things we may now attempt to assess the circumstances in which, here a little, and there a little, such awakening may be discerned.

In contrast to what we have seen in the case of astronomy an examination of the *incunabula* fails to reveal a single new work of biological significance; and this remains approximately true when the term 'biological' is extended to include such medical studies as are concerned with anatomy and the botanical aspects of pharmacology (see below, p. 191). Of twenty-four authors considered under this rubric twelve are 'classical', eleven are medieval and had completed their work before 1400. The herbals (see below, p. 186) though 'new' in arrangement, were based closely on medieval manuscripts going back in an almost unbroken succession to about the sixth century. Nothing could point more clearly to the relative stagnation of this period than the fact that the 'latest thing' in anatomy among the printed books was that of Mondino (early fourteenth century) included in the eight editions of the *Fasciculus Medicinae* (see below, p. 209).

On the other hand the humanist revival had done its work better than on the corresponding mathematical side; for Aldus had brought out both Dioskurides, *De Materia Medica*, and

O[1]*p. cit.* pp. 3-4.

Theophrastos, *De Historia et Causis Plantarum*, in Greek before the close of the century; and for those, doubtless the vast majority, who could not read Greek, there were Latin versions of both these works. In contrast to this there was at this time no printed *text* of the *Almagest* in any language.

But the lesson from this incunabular literary history does not stop there. Though the works of Theophrastos were available in Latin by 1483 the 'scientists' do not appear to have read, or if they read them, to have understood them, for half a century thereafter: for with one exception (see below) the flood of herbals, even including the otherwise epoch-making *Herbarum Vivae Eicones* of Brunfels (1530), ignored completely the wisdom and insight into the habits of plants revealed in those incomparable books, especially the recognition of the variation of the flora according to climate and situation. Brunfels unconsciously reveals his vast inferiority to Theophrastos in his assumption that the plants described by Dioskurides for the Eastern Mediterranean region are to be exactly matched in southern Germany. The beautiful Pasque Flower (*Anemone pulsatilla*), unknown to Dioskurides and of no medicinal value, is admitted with an apology, together with some others of the same under-privileged class, under the heading 'Herbae nudae'. It is, however, a sign of grace that they were admitted at all. The exception to this stricture, already referred to, is the *Herbarius zu Teutsch* (*German Herbal*) or *Gart der Gesundheit* (Garden of Health). This was first printed in 1485 by Schöffer of Mainz, the year after his publication of the so-called 'Latin Herbarius'. The Preface (which is unsigned) makes it appear that this was the work of a wealthy and devout man who says that after causing the medical descriptions to be gathered out of the usual classics (see below, p. 237) by a ' Master learned in physic' he came to realise that 'there are many precious herbs which do not grow here in these German lands'. So he made preparations for a pilgrimage to the Holy Land, taking with him a 'painter, ready of wit and cunning and subtle of hand'. Unfortunately there is reason to believe (cf. H. Fischer, *Mittelalterliche Pflanzenkunde*, Munich, 1929: I am indebted to Dr. Arber for this information) that the Preface is an example of that device not uncommon even in the early days of printing, the publisher's 'blurb'. Nevertheless, if not factually true the form of the blurb is highly significant in showing that as early as 1485 a publisher thought it worth while to base his appeal to the reader on the inclusion of newly observed facts instead of the much more usual gambit of an ancient name and tradition. Moreover it is worth noting that two years before the work was printed Bernard von Breydenbach, a secular canon of Ulm, was one of a party of pilgrims from Jerusalem to St. Catherine's Monastery in the Sinai Desert, and that he wrote an account of the journey—or rather took what he wanted from the much more authentic account written by Felix Fabri (see above, p. 24), who made critical notes of many of the plants and animals seen on the journey. The recognition at that time of the limited geographical range of some plants reflects little credit on the progress of the medical schools during the next fifty years; for Otto Brunfels had not fully learnt this lesson in 1530 (see below, p. 190). Whatever the circumstances of its origin the *Gart der Gesundheit* was what Wilfred Blunt has described as the only botanical incunable of real importance, the supremacy of whose illustrations remained unchallenged for nearly half a century. For the historian it provides a touchstone to the quality of botanical thought. It was not that it passed unnoticed: on the contrary many herbals were based on it, including the famous *Ortus Sanitatis* (No. 589); but interesting and lively as the latter is, it shows a sad backsliding in regard to the naturalism of figures or any critical appraisal of text in comparison with the earlier work.

One further fact reveals the unenterprising character of contemporary thought about the world of living creatures. In comparison with the single Latin edition of Dioskurides and of Theophrastos there were fifteen Latin, three Italian, and one French (part) of the much inferior *Historia naturalis* of Pliny. There were, in addition, twenty-three of the encyclopaedic *De Proprietatibus Rerum* of Bartholomaeus Anglicus, divided between Latin, French, English, and Low Dutch (the Spanish being restricted to the section on metals). It is not that these were to be despised: it was altogether proper that works which had had a wide circulation in manuscript should be more widely dispersed by the new means; but the almost entire absence of any novelty of approach until nearly half way through the sixteenth century is probably still not as widely recognised as it should be. Pliny's *Natural History*, though hardly a scientific work at all, is of outstanding importance on many grounds: it was the 'Bible' of

Natural History in the widest sense throughout the whole of the Middle Ages; owing to its astonishing completeness it serves the modern historian as an almost infallible guide as to what had already been discovered or guessed by A.D. 77; and the tradition of 'knowledge' which it established continued to exert an insidious influence,[1] cramping and misleading, well into the seventeenth century. Nor was this influence restricted to a 'popular' audience as may have been more nearly true of Bartholomew's encyclopaedia; on the contrary, apart from three Italian and one French, no version appeared in a vernacular until the seventeenth century. Its appeal must therefore have been mainly to the learned, but not necessarily to those learned in natural history. Since critical commentaries appeared from 1492 onwards it was at one time the custom to represent this fact as evidence of the awakening of a scientific spirit in contrast to the medieval reliance on Pliny's statements—a reliance which Pliny himself never demanded, being always ready to admit that most of his information was second-hand. But an examination of these commentaries by Thorndike (*Hist.* Vol. IV, p. 593) and later Castiglioni (*Singer*, Vol. I, p. 569) has shown that in the case of Niccolò Leoniceno and Ermolao Barbaro the criticism was almost wholly textual and in the scholastic tradition; in that of Pandolfo Collennucio alone—which was actually directed against Leoniceno—is there much evidence of interest in the authenticity of the *facts* rather than that of the *reports* of the facts. (For Barbaro see No. 58.) Nevertheless it would be a mistake to regard these commentaries as of no importance in scientific thought. Even today men of science base the vast majority of their 'facts' upon the authority of written statements, and the relatively high order of authenticity of these facts is largely due to the unsparing criticism of the body of interested scientists. The commentaries of Barbaro and Leoniceno were at least *critical*; and, in applying the latest techniques for this purpose, were strictly speaking humanist rather than scholastic.

The last category of literary sources relating to the living world made available by the growth of printing is that of the 'useful arts' of agriculture, silviculture, hunting, fishing, equitation, and

[1] A similar instance of reliance on the Ancients for 'facts' is the slavish copying until comparatively recent times of the periods of incubation of the eggs of many species of birds. This has been admirably documented by M. M. Nice, *Centaurus*, 3, (1953-4), 311.

viticulture. In addition to the well-known classical works of Columella, Palladius, Varro, and Virgil there were the very popular work of Arnald de Villanova on wines and the outstanding *Opus Ruralium Commodorum* of Pier de' Crescenzi (1233-1321). This last work provides abundant evidence that in thirteenth-century Italy the great Latin classics on *Res Rusticae* in the widest sense were sufficiently familiar for a comprehensive, lucid, and well arranged text-book to be based mainly on the materials they provided, but with some significant additions. Of the roughly 130 manuscripts of the fourteenth and fifteenth centuries in Latin, Italian, French, and German a fifteenth-century French one is of special interest for our period since its numerous clear and detailed illustrations [1] give a sure indication of the degree of sophistication which had been reached in respect of the management of a consolidated estate in which crops of various kinds were being raised, trees planted, beasts reared, fishponds, dovecotes, and beehives maintained, and a formal garden laid out about the house. That this work was in wide demand is shown by the ten Latin, three Italian, two French, and three German, incunable editions. It contains a large section on medicinal herbs, most of which can be identified from the descriptions (an unusual feature before 1540) and also a veterinary section, which, it has been alleged, was largely copied without acknowledgment from the slightly earlier work of Iordano Ruffo (No. 595).

Such then was the literary background of the sixteenth century in respect of the study of the living world and in so far as it may be assessed from printed books. Most of the 'standard classics' were available, but were by no means always used with intelligence. Of novelty there was none. The study of animals, except in connection with the farm, was even less enlightened than that of plants: the greatest work on birds ever written before the time of Belon (p. 196) both in respect of its text and illustrations, the *De Arte Venandi cum Avibus*, was not printed at all until 1596, and there is no evidence that it was widely read in manuscript, though a few small works on hawking did appear in a total of eight editions—two English, two German, and four French.

That the evidence from printed books may if taken alone give a misleading picture of the state of affairs has already been

---

[1] Reproduced, with numerous critical articles in *Pier de' Crescenzi*, Studi e Documenti, Bologna, 1933.

shown above (pp. 78). But in addition to the conventionally 'artistic' tradition there is manuscript evidence of a high degree of naturalistic illustration at a date even earlier than that of the Italian masters already referred to. A singularly beautiful example of this is the herbal (B.M. MS., Egerton 2020), written about 1400 for Francesco Carrara the Younger, Lord of Padua 1391-1403. The Italian text, based on a *materia medica* of 'Serapion' the Younger (see below, p. 242), is medical in intention but contains descriptions of the plants referred to, and finely drawn and tinted illustrations. The Vine shown on fo. 28^r reveals a high degree of botanical sophistication incomparably superior to anything printed before 1530: latent axillary buds, leaf scars, leaves, tendrils, venation, inflorescence, fructification, roots—all are shown and tinted in shades of green, brown, and yellow. The artist is unknown; the fact that no conventional Italian painting of so early a date shows anything like this naturalism makes it not inconceivable that it may have been the work of a Flemish or Burgundian visitor, these countries, as we have seen, being well in advance of Italy in respect of naturalistic representation at this time. (Plate VI).

It has for long been the custom to regard the year 1530 as marking the beginning of a new attitude to plants. With this judgment there will be no quarrel providing certain qualifications are taken into account. We have already seen two respects in which the text of Brunfel's *Herbarum Vivae Eicones* failed to break new ground; but equally serious was his failure to attain any degree of consistency, either in nomenclature or in the criteria which he chose for the description of the various kinds. Thus on the first page of his book (I have seen only the second edition— 1532—B.M. copy belonging to Sir Joseph Banks) he gives as synonyms for the plant he calls *Plantago maior* '*Arnoglossa, Ortygia, Cynoglossa*', etc.—all in addition to such familiar names as *Breyter Wegrich*. The next 'species', *P. minor*, is indifferently called *P. lanceolata*, and so on. This multiplicity of names was not of course Brunfels's fault; but he shows himself (in a section— '*censurae*'—in Vol. II) more concerned to quote the corrections of Pliny introduced by Leoniceno, and the corrections of Leoniceno by Collenuccio, than to investigate a means of removing this nomenclatural confusion. That he may have been conscious of his inability to undertake this task is suggested by the inclusion in

Vol. II of an appendix by Fuchs of *Annotations of some herbs and simples not previously properly understood by physicians*. Fuchs, as the following sentence shows, was at any rate conscious of the need for such clarification: 'I shall show that what we call [*nostrae aetatis*] *Buglossus* is not the *Buglossus* of the Ancients, which we call *Borago*. Our *Buglossus* is the herb which the Greeks called *Cirsion*, or sometimes, on account of its great likeness to *Buglossus*, *Buglossus magna*.' Ever since the *De Materia Medica* of Dioskurides (No. 198) which, though it may have drawn heavily on the earlier work of Krateuas, is the earliest herbal of which anything like a complete text is known, the absence of any systematic description of plants has been a serious defect. For nearly two millenia between Theophrastos and Cesalpino (p. 198) Albertus alone seems to have realised that progress in knowledge of plants is dependent on a high degree of *reproducibility* of evidence. Astronomy rapidly became an exact science because each generation could enlarge and correct the observations of earlier workers on unambiguously defined objects. But as long as the same name could apply to different plants, and different names to the same plant, and in the absence of descriptive criteria as to what constitutes the 'same' and 'different', no progress in botany could take place. Moreover the influence is reciprocal: for until a systematic account of the relationships of the parts of plants can be worked out and a consistent terminology agreed to, confusion between 'kinds' is inevitable. It is one of the many unsolved mysteries of the history of science that despite the *unbroken* interest in plants as sources of medicaments so little progress was made. It may well be that though their medical application kept alive in some form an interest in plants, this restriction of interest brought about what Whitehead calls the 'Nemesis which waits upon those who deliberately avoid avenues of knowledge'. The position of Brunfels as innovator in the study of plants can not be fairly assessed without taking into account on the one hand his other activities in medicine (No. 109 f) and on the other the age-long tradition of *Materia Medica* in which he stood, and which can be but imperfectly appreciated by exclusive attention to the earlier herbals *sensu strictu*. Less violence is done to this tradition by recognising that the works in which the plants are considered against a background of their 'virtues' were, as late as 1530, only one extreme of a graded series, at the other end of which were pharmacological works in which the relationship is reversed. These can be more profitably reviewed after a consideration of the contemporary general theory of medicine to be undertaken in Ch. XI.

What justified the emphasis on 1530, then, was not so much what Brunfels did as what he allowed his illustrator to do. But for the aid given by the woodcuts made from the colour-washed pen sketches of Hans Weiditz it would be almost as difficult for the modern botanist to identify plants from Brunfels's text as from any earlier one. But these woodcuts transform an otherwise botanically useless document into one containing the type-pictures of two Linnaean species—*Cardamine pratensis* L. and *Anemone Pulsatilla* L.—ironically enough two of those which Brunfels regarded as unworthy of inclusion in the text, since only their German names were then known! But if Brunfels himself can hardly be regarded as a botanist, he had at any rate an eye for one who was. This man, Jerome Bock (Hieronymus Tragus), seems to have been the first to publish a work which, though intended to be a guide to medicinal herbs, displayed them as living organisms. This book, *New Kreutter Buch*, Strassburg, 1539 (*De Stirpium, maxime earum, quae in Germania nostra nascuntur* . . ., Strassburg, 1552), though at first unillustrated, contains a description of his refutation of Dioskurides concerning the existence of fern 'seed' (spores). The country people assured him that it could be gathered on midsummer's night, with the proper ritual to ward off the attendant dangers; and gather it he did—even without the ritual. But, as Dr. Arber points out (*op. cit.* p. 61) he remained wedded to the old beliefs to the extent that he made no attempt to discover whether it could be gathered on any other night! That he tried to learn botany from plants and not exclusively from books is also shown by his statement that he had succeeded in raising willows from the 'wool' which grows on the tree—but only of certain kinds; he hesitated to state that wool *always* takes the place of seed. It is to Brunfel's credit that had it not been for his journeying forty miles on foot, when no longer a young man, to persuade Bock to publish, this first successor to Albert's *De Vegetabilibus* might never have been printed. In the year following its publication appeared what is perhaps the most perfect of the illustrated herbals, based primarily on classical sources. Leonhart Fuchs, the author of this work (No. 276), lacked the scientific imagination

PLATE VIII

A notably fine portrait of Paracelsus. (*Paracelsus,
Astronomica et Astrologica . . . opuscula.* Vol. II, No.
84/14.)

of Bock but carried the ideal of Brunfels—the representation of the mature living plant—to the utmost perfection by achieving the closest collaboration between himself and his artists, which was so much lacking between Brunfels and Weiditz. Moreover, if not a botanist, he was on his own admission (*Praefatio*) a 'botanizer' whose delight in wild nature was enhanced by the recognition of all the flowering plants which compose so striking a part of the scene. A more elegant Latinist than Brunfels, he was nevertheless free from the latter's inhibitions about the inclusion of plants not referred to in the classical authors: thus the delineation of the culinary cabbage (*Brassicae quartum genus*) has been reproduced frequently down to the present day and in a variety of contexts.[1]

These three men are sometimes referred to as the 'German fathers of botany', and to them has more recently been added a fourth, for, though nothing of the work of Valerius Cordus was published in that wonderful decade 1530-40, notes of his lectures on Dioskurides delivered at Wittenberg during that period were edited by Conrad Gesner and published in 1549. These annotations by Cordus were again published in 1561 (No. 175) together with his *Historia Stirpium* and an account of his ill-starred journey in Italy starting in 1542 and ending fatally in 1544. That this arduous journey was undertaken for the purpose of studying the plants characteristic of a climate different from his native Germany is sufficient testimony of his outstanding importance among the founders of botany—a testimony greatly amplified by the model descriptions of the plants contained in his *Historia*. Before his death at the early age of twenty nine he had also made a signal contribution to pharmacology (see No. 174).

Since this *Introduction* aims at providing only a general view of scientific thought in the Renaissance no attempt will be made to trace the ramifications of the movement which had created the new type of herbal. As the century wore on there were published original works written by scholars in Switzerland (Gesner, 1541), France (Ruel, 1536), Italy (Mattioli, 1544), England (Turner, 1551), the Low Countries (Dodöens, 1554), Portuguese India (Garcia de Orta, Goa, 1563), Spain (Monardes, 1569)—to mention only the earliest examples compiled mainly by natives of the countries named: some of these were in the vernaculars, others in Latin; many appeared in several languages. The debt owed

[1] E.g. E. Anderson, *Plants, Man and Life*, London, 1954, pp. 38-9.

N

to the German 'founders' was not only indirect, but many of these later works were illustrated by copies of the figures in the octavo version of Fuchs's great work; some even used the original blocks.

Was it a mere coincidence that the four men thus honoured as the 'Fathers of Botany' were all Protestants? More fundamental perhaps was the fact that they were all Germans at a time of national resurgence. It was of 'plants, particularly those that grow in our Germany' that Bock wrote; and it was for the glory of the Fatherland that Brunfels persuaded him to publish it. This note of pride in the power of the national soil to produce herbs of virtue appeared about the same time in Symphorien Champier's *Hortus Gallicus pro Gallis in Gallia* (being an astute Frenchman Champier did not omit to mention that it was no less necessary for Italians, Germans and Spaniards! No. 146) and also in William Turner's *The Names of Herbes*, in whose Preface he says that he has refrained from publishing his Latin herbal until he might 'declare to the greate honoure of our countre what numbre of sovereine and strang herbes were in Englande that were not in other nations . . .'.

It will probably have been noted with some surprise that from Italy, whither Copernicus naturally turned his steps to be at the centre of the new learning, there came no original study of plants until 1544. This fact will have occasioned all the more surprise when it is recalled that throughout the fifteenth century both manuscript illustrations and naturalistic painting were in Italy far in advance of the utterly inadequate figures of the incunable herbals, and that very early in the next century appeared the incomparable flower studies of Leonardo da Vinci. The failure to anticipate Brunfels must indeed remain something of a mystery; but an important aspect of the botanical renaissance is hidden by exclusive reliance on the tale of printed books. There was in fact in Bologna a sign of this renaissance unparalleled elsewhere: this was the foundation of a Chair of Botany ('Reder of Dioscorides', Turner calls the occupant) in 1534. Moreover this first occupant of the Chair, Luca Ghini, though he published nothing, may fairly be described as the teacher of all Europe, implicitly in general, explicitly in respect of the fact that it was he and his pupils who taught botanists the use of the *herbarium*, consisting of a collection of sheets of paper to which are gummed specimens of the actual plants preserved by drying. The earliest record refers to 1551, when Ghini sent some such specimens to Mattioli, but the oldest extant herbarium is that of the former's pupil, Gherardo Cibo, who is believed to have started collecting as early as 1532. The first printed reference, somewhat surprisingly, is to the Englishman, John Falconer, a correspondent of Gesner (No. 298), who is reported by Amatus Lusitanus in his commentary on Dioskurides to have had a collection of dried plants sewn and gummed on to sheets of a book 'miro artificio'. Only one of the numerous recorded (and several extant) sixteenth-century herbaria can be referred to here: this is the collection of Felix Plater (see below, p. 235) recorded in a diary of 1554 but unknown for centuries until 1930 when Professor Walther Rytz discovered it in the Botanical Institute at Berne. Great as is the intrinsic interest of this collection of more than eight hundred plants drawn from a wide area, of perhaps even greater historical importance was Professor Rytz's discovery that scattered among the herbarium sheets were numerous superb water colour sketches of the accompanying plants, which he was able to identify as the original sketches of Hans Weiditz, from which the blocks for Brunfels's herbal were cut. Among the manuscript notes on the plants was the date '1529'. With commendable zeal the University of Berne undertook the printing of photographic reproductions in colour of a number of these lovely sketches (Aberdeen University, fo. 58).

Complementary to the herbarium is the botanic garden where comparisons can be made of living plants drawn from widely separated areas, and rare plants may be propagated. Gardens of course were not unknown to the classical writers; the herb garden of the monastery of Reichenau is described in an extant manuscript of the Abbot Walafrid Strabo; reference has already been made to a fifteenth-century picture of a garden. But the first 'botanic garden' in anything like the modern sense is probably that of Padua founded in 1542; already before the end of the century Egyptian plants were established there by Prospero Alpino, whose portrait (attributed to Leandro Bassano), bears the significant inscription 'Prof. Simplicium Hortiq. Praefectus'. In the *Coloquios* of Garcia de Orta (No. 487) published in 1563, there is a reference to 'wild herbs' being transferred to the garden of the University of Coimbra; and before the end of the century such gardens were comparatively common. Interest in 'exotic' plants started before the sixteenth century at least as early as the return of Columbus from his second voyage, when he brought back unfamiliar plants and animals. It was of course mainly to the Spanish and Portuguese physicians living in the newly discovered or colonised lands that the recognition and description of novel plants were due; but the earliest systematic work to be published on the subject seems to have been Pierre Belon's *Observations des plusieurs singularitez et choses memorables* . . . (Paris, 1553, No. 71 is the Latin translation by Charles de l'Ecluse) in which he gives an account of plants and animals seen for the first time in his travels through Greece, 'Asia', Egypt, 'Judeae', Arabia, and other lands during the years 1546-9. This is a work of disinterested natural history, and is all the more important for being so; it was followed ten years later by the first account of 'simples and drugs' written by Garcia de Orta who had been resident physician in Goa (Portuguese India) for nearly thirty years. The original work (No. 487) printed in Goa in 1563 was unillustrated; but in 1578 an illustrated version in Spanish was prepared by Christobal Acosta, a Latin translation of which was made in 1582 by de l'Ecluse, who had already produced an abbreviated Latin version of de Orta's original text in 1567: the bibliography of these works is thus complicated—see No. 3.

A few years after the appearance of de Orta's work on Portuguese India there followed the even better known account by Nicolas Monardes of the Spanish West 'Indies'. This appeared in the English version of the merchant John Frampton, whose epistle-dedicatory to Edward Dyer sheds an interesting light on the close commercial connections between England and Spain in the middle of Elizabeth's reign (Nos. 456).

Though this *embarras de richesses* must have acted as a stimulus to the study of plants, in the absence of any just ideas of classification it can not have been an altogether unmixed blessing. To the already formidable difficulties of sorting out the known plants into manageable units there was added that of a large number of forms bearing hardly any resemblance to those which were slowly being recognised as being conveniently grouped together. Although for the greater part of the sixteenth century classification, if it went beyond mere alphabetical arrangement, was mainly restricted to the medical uses of the herbs, towards the end there appeared at least four attempts to make use of the characters of the plants themselves. This is all the more interesting, since three at least of the promoters of the new methods had no explicit intention of separating botany from medicine: any change they proposed must have been forced upon them by constant familiarity with the plants themselves and could have added but little to the convenience of the apothecary and physician.

The classical division by Theophrastos into trees, shrubs, undershrubs and herbs has much to commend it, and was gradually reintroduced. But it does not go far enough when thousands of species are in question. The genus was the unit, though minor modifications of each of the natural kinds might be recognised: Gesner for instance claimed to know ten 'species' of Gentian. An early example of a herbal to be based explicitly on a systematic plan was that of Jacques D'Alechamps (No. 20). This work is remarkable on two counts: first, its acceptance of a thoroughly 'natural' (but not of course in the modern sense of implying community of descent) basis as one criterion; and second its violation, in a century which prided itself on being well versed in philosophy, of the logical canons of classification by the use of other over-lapping criteria. The 'natural' criterion was that of habitat; the second, also largely 'natural', was that of 'form', which of course over-lapped the first. The inevitable intrusion of the 'virtues' of the plants provided a further source of confusion. But at least let us rejoice at the advance beyond Brunfels, signalised by the recognition of a group 'with beautiful flowers'. An almost preponderating importance was given to morphological characters by Matthias Dodöens, who refers to 'umbelliferae herbae' in his *Historia Frumentorum* (1566, No. 201 is of the 1569 edition) and illustrates 'not a few' of them in an appendix to a work of 1574 (No. 203); but that relatively gross morphology was held to over-ride detailed floral structure is shown by his inclusion of two saxifrages (pp. 494-6) among the 'Umbelliferae'. A considerable advance in precision and consistency had been made by de l'Obel, who used leaf structure as the sole criterion of his attempt to arrange plants—a method which, from the modern point of view, had the advantage (all but established by Theophrastos but ignored by de l'Obel—see No. 403) of separating mono- from di-cotyledons. Though failure to understand the relation of compound leaves to corresponding simple ones marred this new classification, it was recognised by the printer

N*

Christophe Plantin as so superior to earlier systems that he arranged his famous collection, *Icones Plantarum* (No. 528) to correspond with it. With the series of works by Gaspard Bauhin, beginning in 1596 and continuing well into the seventeenth century, we reach the embryo of the general plan of a modern 'natural' classification, based on general morphology. In the first place Bauhin realised the convenience of a binomial nomenclature, though he does not raise it, as Linnaeus was to do, to the rank of a rule admitting of no exceptions. A perusal of Bauhin's works, especially of the *Pinax theatri botanici* (1623), reveals his 'intuition', not explicitly indicated in his review of the genera, of natural affinities such as are indicated by the development of bulbs, compound flowers, and the like. His grouping together of plants possessing certain *kinds* of 'medicinal virtues' may strike the modern systematist as a serious aberration; but it should not be overlooked how closely such chemical *types* may be correlated with morphological characters. Dr. Arber has drawn attention to the striking instance of the Willows (article in *Science Medicine and History*—'Essays in honour of Charles Singer', 1953, Vol. I, p. 318); and on a different scale the essential oils of the Labiatae come to mind. Even more suggestive is the recent work on the genic determination of such characters as the genesis of anthocyanin glycosides giving rise to definite gradations of colour.[1]

The confounding of *floral* types in all these early efforts at classification must not be taken as examples of Renaissance obtuseness in the light of the facts: there were no 'facts' suggesting the superior diagnostic value of the reproductive organs. When ultimately used by Cesalpino as the basis of his classification it was in the form of an *a priori* postulate deriving from a too rigid application of Aristotelian natural philosophy. In seizing upon a *single* character—the 'seed', which in many cases he failed to distinguish from the fruit—Cesalpino achieved a system which was logically almost unexceptionable, but which as his master, Aristotle, would probably have recognised, was bought at the cost of flying in the face of 'natural affinities' such as are revealed by the 'process of becoming' in the embryos of mono- and dicotyledons. This was all the more regrettable, since the introduction to Cesalpino's system (No. 116) shows an awareness of

---

[1] J. B. S. Haldane, *Biochemistry of Genetics*, London, 1952, pp. 53 f.

the general biology of plants far in advance of most sixteenth-century herbalists. An exception to this was his late contemporary, the Czech, Adam Zaluzanzky, who in his *Methodi herbariae libri tres* (1592; No. 744 is of the 1604 edition) is the first to recognise the distinction between cryptogams and phanerogams; for though, on account of the highly organised leaves, he placed ferns among the 'higher' plants, he was aware of their quite different mode of reproduction. The difficulty of assessing the degree of scientific awareness of the men of this tantalising century is underlined by the fact that the only 'monograph' on a natural group of plants—that on the Umbelliferae by Thurneysser (No. 691)—was based on the ancient doctrine that all created things bear in their outward parts 'signs' of their inward virtues (see below, p. 300 and Vol. II Plate VII).

We may in the present context conveniently consider how the sixteenth-century naturalists envisaged the corresponding problem of ordering the kinds of animals they were familiar with. Having in mind the present very proper attitude of regarding the separation of animals and plants as dictated more by convenience of study than as a fundamental distinction in nature, the reader may have felt that the exclusive concern with plants in the preceding pages was a retrograde step. It must, however, be borne in mind that though the sixteenth-century natural philosophers accepted the Aristotelian view that animals and plants represented a more or less continuous gradation of 'perfection' of a common fundamental principle of being, in practice the study of the two stages in this gradation marked by the presence or absence of a 'sensitive soul' was prosecuted with far less concern for the mutual relationship than is generally the case today. There is little doubt that this was the consequence of the much greater pragmatic importance of botany than that of zoology: the study of plants was at first stimulated and furthered almost solely by the desire to revise and extend the *Materia Medica* of Dioskurides: it was only incidentally and under the spell of the plants themselves that the herbalists were charmed into investigating them for their intrinsic beauty and delight. It was not till 1566-84 that J. C. Scaliger made available critical Latin texts of the botanical works of Theophrastos. In the case of animals, except for Man, the Horse and the Hawk, there was no similar stimulus. During the period (1530-50) when so many of the great herbals appeared there was only one comparable work on animals—William Turner's *Avium praecipuarum quarum apud Plinium et Aristotelem menti oest . . . historia*, Cologne, 1544. The title indicates the 'literary' character of the undertaking, but the good Dean had so strong a feeling for the *subject* that as his modern translator, A. H. Evans, states 'almost every page bears witness to a personal knowledge . . . which would be distinctly creditable even to a modern ornithologist' (Intro. p. ix). This is high praise for a period (1477-1550) in which a recent bibliographer [1] was unable to find any other work of similar subject matter in English. And it was almost exclusively towards Pliny that even the continental presses had to turn for 'copy'.

Just as the 'renaissance' of botany occurred within the decade 1530-40 so a similar decade may be recognised in zoology almost exactly twenty years later. Four outstanding naturalists took part in this—Pierre Belon, Guillaume Rondelet, Conrad Gesner, and Ippolito Salviani. Though all four are remembered principally for their zoological works the first three were also botanists of the first order. To Belon's and Gesner's botanical works some reference has already been made; Rondelet published nothing on plants, but since de l'Obel was his pupil and became heir to his manuscripts it is likely that Rondelet was one of those at Montpellier for whom provision was made in an *Arret des Grands Jours* of 1550 'pour lire aux écoliers et montrer *oculairement* [italic mine] les simples'.[2] Rondelet wrote exclusively on fishes, Belon primarily on these but later also on birds and other animals. In 1551 came the first volume of Gesner's monumental *Historia Animalium*: this was on viviparous quadrupeds. The second and third, on oviparous quadrupeds and birds respectively, appeared in 1554 and 1555. For these three volumes Gesner had to rely mainly on the ancient authors and on such supplementary information as he could gather either by his own observations or by means of an incredibly extensive correspondence (see No. 304). In the fourth volume on fishes and animals living in water he included much material provided by Belon and Rondelet. He also acknowledged the assistance of the Englishmen Turner, John Parkhurst, Falconer, Edward Wotton, and John Caius.

---

[1] C. H. W. Bickle, *A Bibliography of British Zoology* (1477-1550). (Unpublished dissertation, School of Librarianship, University of London.)

[2] Hervé Haraut, *Endeavour*, **13** (1954), 97 f.

A perusal of these works reveals an indefatigable industry; the description of many new species—particularly of Mediterranean fishes; a wealth of fine illustrations—those of Belon and Gesner being generally superior to Rondelet's and surpassed in their turn by Salviani's, some of which are still regarded as definitive; and evidence of study of internal anatomy. In Belon's *Histoire de la Nature des Oyseaux* occurs the famous figure in which skeletons of a man and of a bird are shown side by side in a similar posture, most of the corresponding bones being labelled. The homologising is not accurate in every detail,[1] but is the first example of of the systematic use of the comparative method, except for Leonardo's unpublished comparison of the Horse and Man, and Frederick II's correction of the false homologies of birds and Man made by Aristotle. It is unlikely that Belon knew of either of these, since he gave Aristotle the credit for having anticipated him! On the general question of renaissance anatomy more will be said later. What one misses from these works is any advance on the principles of classification employed by Aristotle; indeed from the present standpoint there is retrogression, since morphology is generally made secondary to habitat. Gesner, though more of a compiler than any of the others, here shows more percipience than they in his distinction, following Aristotle, between oviparous (certain reptiles, such as the tortoise, and amphibia) and viviparous (mammalian) quadrupeds. The group 'Marine Fishes', forming the subject of Rondelet's chief work, bears no relation to the Aristotelian class of Fishes, since it includes even Jelly 'Fish', not to mention a number of entirely imaginary monsters (Seals?) included only on hearsay. Of course there is nothing 'unscientific' in writing a book on the fauna of a particular habitat, and Rondelet shows that he is conscious of this. The point here is that it is only in this 'natural history' that Rondelet advanced knowledge beyond that of the 'Ancients'; as a systematic zoologist he is inferior to Aristotle. Belon in this respect as elsewhere is more critical than Rondelet, and at the lowest taxonomic level created groups which Linnaeus was able

---

[1] For a detailed analysis of this see F. J. Cole, *A History of Comparative Anatomy*, London, 1949, pp. 7 f. where there is also a chronology of the use of the *method*, freely used by Harvey, and of the *term*, which appears in the text of Willis's *Cerebri Anatome* (1664) and for the first time on a title-page in N. Grew, *The Comparative Anatomy of Trunks* [of Trees], 1674.

to use as the basis of his *genera*. The most remarkable testimony to the independence of mind and acuteness of perception of Rondelet and Belon as observers is their recording of the placental dogfish previously noted by Aristotle. Apart from Nils Stensen in the seventeenth century, later zoologists were inclined to write this off as a renaissance aberration until Ioannes Mueller in the early nineteenth century re-established the facts and demonstrated the nature of the relationship between embryo and mother. (Cole, *op. cit.* p. 34).

The Aristotelian tradition of classification at the higher taxonomic levels by reference to morphological and functional similarities was transmitted in the sixteenth century by Edward Wotton. His *De Differentiis Animalium*, published within the great decade (1552), was almost entirely lacking in originality (cf. Gesner's remarks, No. 298), but set forth a system which retained the best features of the Aristotelian and applied it to the known species, including many unknown to the Ancients. In so doing he adopted a cautious attitude, especially where he had been unable to verify structural details. Of special importance in the Aristotelian tradition is the recognition of the invertebrate animals: these were largely ignored by the sixteenth-century zoologists, but Wotton included a section on insects and another on squids, crustaceans and molluscs. It is probable that Gesner would have included similar sections in his *Historia Animalium*, but it must be remembered that he died of plague in his fiftieth year even before the last volume dealing with the vertebrates had been published. His manuscript notes on insects passed into the hands of Thomas Mouffet whose *Insectorum sive minimorum animalium theatrum* (London, 1634) was largely based thereon. This neglect of invertebrates is difficult to account for seeing that one of the most brilliant of Aristotle's observations was that of the hectocotylised arm of the Cephalopods; and in the High Middle Ages the description by Albert of the life history of the butterfly [1] (though not quite as accurate as some medieval enthusiasts would seem to imply) and the remarkable series of coloured naturalistic drawings [2] of insects, spiders, molluscs, scorpions and centipedes employed in a purely decorative manner to embellish a dissertation on the Vices testify to a living interest. It may be noted that

[1] No. 15 Sig. z 8*v* 'Papiliones sunt vermes volantes. . . '.
[2] A. Crombie, 'Cybo de Hyères', *Endeavour*, **11** (1952).

the first 'scientific' monograph on insects was that of Francisco Stelluti (Rome, 1625); this was on the mouth parts and limbs of the Honey Bee and was the first memoir to be based on observations with the newly invented microscope. Observations of such minuteness could not therefore have been carried out in the sixteenth century. But the simple magnifier would have sufficed for at any rate comparable detail; yet there is no record of anyone having attempted it.

It is time we made an attempt to gather together the threads of an account which inevitably lacks the coherence of one dealing with the supposed much more orderly 'Heavens'. It would probably be generally agreed that pre-eminently in the study of plants there came the earliest signs of something like a Renaissance. The literary tradition is maintained, giving to the young science of botany a sound basis to build on, but at the same time introducing a good deal of largely irrelevant erudition swelling some of the herbals inordinately. But almost opposed to this tradition, though often enough the two characteristics are found in the same person, is the urge to 'get out of the study' and into fresh fields to discover the floral wealth and limitations of various regions and climates, and of more or less abrupt changes of conditions within a single region. The Alps came to be looked upon as the haunt not of unknown terrors but of unknown beauties, to be attained by human stamina and enterprise. Gesner (Sarton, *Appreciation of Ancient and Medieval Science during the Renaissance*, p. 107) was the pioneer of alpinism and the botany of high altitudes, but a more intensive study, if also on a more modest scale, was the pioneer effort of Calzolari (No. 175). All this came to be accompanied by a growing concern for a new systematics, aided by such contrivances as the botanic garden for acclimatisation as well as demonstration, and the herbarium of dried specimens. As the century approached its close the term 'botanist' appears in the titles of those teaching plant lore. In the universities at least it was still taught only as a part of Medicine, but one writer (Zaluzansky), rather apart from the chief centres of learning, had the temerity to claim that it is a discipline in its own right, a view which seems obvious enough when it is observed that at this time, if a part of Medicine, it was also a part of Agriculture, Forestry, and Horticulture—fields in which a knowledge of drug-yielding plants is quite irrelevant.

In the study of animals no such clear-cut 'renaissance' is to be seen. The liberation from the literary tradition came later, the number of practitioners was at all times much smaller (if we may judge by the published books or known manuscripts), and study was almost entirely confined to the vertebrates. Nevertheless, though progress was uneven it was in many respects clearly marked. Outstanding among the fields in which the growth of a spirit of enquiry is to be discovered in the sixteenth century is anatomy. But with comparatively few exceptions it was on Man that the anatomists exercised their skill and developed their critical power. For the progress of medicine this was unavoidable, since nothing was a greater source of confusion in the healing art than the fact that human physiology had been based by Galen mainly on the anatomy of the Barbary Ape, and by the School of Salerno on the Pig. Of the progress of the art of anatomy and of anatomical illustration it will be proper to treat in a later chapter. Nevertheless it is important to note a piece of evidence showing that disinterested knowledge of the structure of beasts other than Man and his companions the Horse, Hound, and Hawk, was not unknown outside the medical schools even before the great decade already referred to.

In the course of his attempts to identify the birds with which he was familiar with those named and described by Pliny and Aristotle, William Turner was compelled in the case of the *Onocratalus* to resort to dissection, which he reports as follows: 'It has a belly not like that of other birds but like that of a dog: it is also large and capacious. But lest what I have written thus far of this bird seem false to anyone, or lest I seem to have learnt the above from the reports of others rather than from sure experience: while the first pages of this book were still at press, and while I was examining it and dissecting it and taking note whether it really had a belly and a stomach such as Pliny had assigned to it, there were assisting me [Here Turner names four learned men] with certain others versed in learned arts, who can and will bear witness to the fact that I have written nothing here about this bird which I have not observed in company with all of them.' This insistence on the supporting evidence of his own experience bears a double message, namely, that not only was such dissection being resorted to but also that it had not yet (1544) become a commonplace. In his *Peroratio* Turner alludes to the expense of maintaining *vivaria* in which captured birds and beasts might be observed alive. This habit was certainly less of a novelty: it was mainly in connection with such otherwise hardly accessible animals that John Caius assisted Gesner by correspondence.[1]

It is a reflection on the dominant part that human anatomy and its study in the medical schools came to play that the man who might well be regarded as the greatest *anatomist* of the sixteenth century, Volcher Coiter, is often dismissed in a phrase (e.g. Callot, *op. cit.*) or omitted altogether (Nordenskiold). Though this neglect remains something of a mystery there is no mystery about his works. I have examined two of them:—*Externarum . . . principalium humani corporis partium tabulae* . . . (1566) and *Lectiones Gabrielis Fallopii de partibus similaribus humani corporis ex diversis exemplaribus* . . . (1575) in the British Museum, and there has been available since 1944 a comprehensive outline of his achievements in F. J. Cole's *History of Comparative Anatomy*. Coiter's neglect [2] may have been due to the fact that in topographical human anatomy his original contribution was limited to studies of the foetal skeleton, accompanied by plates of such merit as to be used (without acknowledgment) by Felix Plater (see below, p. 235), but not published under his own name till 1659. His position in the sixteenth century 'hierarchy' is especially interesting: he inherited from Vesalius through the latter's pupil Falloppio; he was related to the *anti*-Vesalians through Eustachio, and brought into touch with the whole field of vertebrate anatomy through Rondelet and Aldrovandi. In his work on the hyoid apparatus of the Woodpecker, and by his observation of the living heart in all the vertebrate classes he came nearest of all the sixteenth-century anatomists to the comparative standpoint.

In the last years of the sixteenth century there appeared the second of the two giant encyclopaedias of Natural History—Gesner's unfinished one being the other. Its author, Ulysse Aldrovandi, died in 1605, and, although he was then eighty-three, only four of the total of thirteen volumes of this colossal work had been printed (No. 19); one of these was on insects, and it is interesting to note that the first posthumous volume (1605) was entitled *De reliquis animalibus exsanguibus . . . nempe de Mollibus*

[1] C. E. Raven, *English Naturalists from Neckam to Ray*, Cambridge, 1947, pp. 138 f.
[2] The neglect has now been made good in R. Herrlinger, *Volcher Coiter*, Nürnberg, 1952.

Crustaceis, Testaceis et Zoophytis. The publication of the remaining volumes was completed only in 1667/8. They differ as much from the modern critical reference works of systematic zoology on the one hand as they do from the highly imaginative and moralising medieval 'bestiaries' and even such encyclopaedic works as Bartholomew's *De Proprietatibus Rerum* (see above, p. 187) on the other. During the seventeenth century works of much more critical character began to appear; but no general reference work of comparable scope and authority until Buffon's *Histoire Naturelle* in 1749. If the naturalists of the sixteenth century did not create the science of biology, they laid a broad and firm foundation on which it could be built; and this they achieved by an enthusiasm, a devotion, and an almost fanatical resolution in the face of untold obstacles of communication and extraneous duties, such as can hardly have been surpassed.

CHAPTER XI

THE MEDICAL DISCIPLINES—
SYSTEM AND METHOD

'SINCE for the great desire I had to see fair Padua, nursery of arts, I am arrived for fruitful Lombardy. . . .' The words are spoken by Lucentio, but the thought may well have been Shakespeare's own; for throughout the century at the end of which he wrote these words there had been a procession of Englishmen making their way to Padua, not only to see it, but to learn, and some even to teach, in that 'nursery of arts': Linacre, Edward Wotton, John Caius, and, a few years after Shakespeare had voiced the thought, the greatest of them all, William Harvey. Why did this medical school draw so many ambitious young men? The answer—or most of it—was Montanus, Vesalius, Realdus Columbus, Gabriel Fallopius, Hieronymus Fabricius, these were their teachers; but as a fellow student some of them would have had Hieronymus Fracastorius; and Harvey, Galileo. Here, if anywhere, was a place where a new birth—not merely a rebirth; for its throwing off of the cramping bookishness of the Humanist Renaissance was its most distinctive feature—of human biology can be as it were watched from our vantage point. What Salerno was until the twelfth century and Bologna and Montpellier in the thirteenth and fourteenth, Padua grew to be and to surpass in the fifteenth. Not that the lead of Bologna [1] was eclipsed; not that Montpellier, under the shock of François Rabelais (No. 342(7)) and the wide-ranging learning of Rondelet, did not achieve its own rebirth; but in every department of medicine, as it was then conceived, Padua was pre-eminent; no such lineage of teachers can be equalled elsewhere.

Since our concern is with Science and the Renaissance we must as far as possible restrict our attention here to those activities

---

[1] The claim that 'in the sciences and in medicine the Studium of Bologna was equalled, possibly, only by the Studium of Padua' is made by Gnudi and Webster, *The Life and Times of Gaspare Togliacozzi*.

of the Faculties of Medicine which are relevant to the progress of scientific understanding and the growth of scientific knowledge during the sixteenth century. I say 'as far as possible', since the determination of the relevance of these activities to our theme is perhaps one of the most difficult problems we have to face. Just as the former underestimate of the importance of medieval science was, apart from the prejudice generated and transmitted by the men of the Renaissance, largely due to ignorance of the fact that most of the really interesting ideas were hidden in works on 'philosophy', so, I believe much renaissance thought significant for the subsequent history of science is buried deep in the books on various aspects of medicine which poured from the press in our period. The fundamental importance for the philosophy of science of the disputes in the Medical School of Padua in the fifteenth century has been revealed by J. H. Randall Jr. in an article,[1] the importance of which can hardly be exaggerated; what has not, I believe, been sufficiently explored are the works devoted more closely to the theory and practice of medicine, as distinct from discussion of its method. My reasons for this judgment are partly 'empirical', based on fairly wide but admittedly superficial sampling; partly à priori, based on the fact that in any age still dominated by the teaching of Galen medicine was still a branch of 'natural philosophy', and that the Faculty of Medicine was, and for about two centuries remained, the most convenient entry into the higher study of science for a particular kind of intelligence. It is chiefly with these hopes in mind that the following pages have been written, with the object of familiarising as much as possible historians of science with this confusing territory and saving them the needless expense of time and effort unavoidable in the absence of some kind of map. As a check against the temptation to stray into facile generalisations, so plausibly made and so liable to be perpetuated in the works of scholars in neighbouring fields who must perforce rely on such assessment as will here be attempted, I shall as hitherto base this sketch on a review of the works actually current at the beginning of the sixteenth century.

A perusal of the check-list of scientific incunables already referred to (p. 110), supplemented by a recent survey of the

[1] J. H. Randall, Jnr., *The Development of Scientific Method in the School of Padua*, J. Hist. Ideas, **1**, (1940), 177.

incunables in the Wellcome Historical Medical Library, reveals a situation with a marked difference from that of other divisions of knowledge. An analysis of about 125 authors of 'medical' works shows that 6 were either Greek or Roman, 12 Arabic, and of the remainder 29 had written their books before the fifteenth century. This leaves 78 authors whose works might be regarded as 'contemporary'. Of these works 22 were authors of 'plague tracts' and 9 of tracts relating to the recently appeared 'Morbus Gallicus'. Even if the last two categories be set aside, the proportion of 'contemporary' to 'traditional' authors whose works were selected for printing before 1501 is clearly much higher than was the case for astronomy, mathematics, 'physics' or 'natural history'. Too much weight should not be attached to these figures: no useful purpose would be gained by attempting to make them more than approximate, owing to the difficulty of estimating the relevance of the contents of the books to a strictly 'medical' interpretation. Also the number of *works* of each author varies from one to eight (Ugo da Siena) and no account is taken of the fact that the enormous *Canon* of Avicenna was issued— in varying degrees of completeness—fourteen times. But there can be little doubt that there was a readier market for contemporary works in this field than in the others we have examined. This fact taken by itself might lead us to infer that at last we had lighted upon a department of science in which 'the sun of the Renaissance was dispersing the clouds of medieval obscurantism'; if so, a closer examination would quickly bring disillusionment. For in 1491 it will be recalled there appeared the first edition of the *Fasciculus Medicinae*, which went through three further Latin editions together with an Italian and three Spanish before 1501. A work of such popularity at such a critical time demands more than merely passing reference.

The contents of the various 'editions' differed so much that Singer declines to regard them as one work. I have examined only the facsimile of the Venice 1491 and the Aberdeen copy of the Venice 1500. The former, a compilation by G. de Monteferrato, contains a series of charts, with pages of commentary, demonstrating uroscopy, phlebotomy (male and female), with relevant astrological indications, conception (*De Secretis Mulierum*, with numerous quotations from 'Aristotle'), and a male figure showing the likely seats and kinds of wounds; and an anatomical

o

figure with the number of bones, teeth, and veins. In addition there is a kind of concise *Practica* (see below, p. 214) and a *Consilium* for avoidance of the plague, written by Pietro de Tausignano. The main differences in the later editions are the much greater refinement of the illustrations and the addition of the short tract on anatomy by Mondino (see below, p. 230) and of the *De Aegritudinibus Puerorum* by ar-Razi. But what is common to both editions is the fact that, apart from the plague tract, no part of the text dates from a time later than the fourteenth century— indeed the researches of Sudhoff and Singer have revealed that the greater part of it existed already in manuscript about 1400 and was being popularised as a 'textbook' by Ioannes von Kirchheim ('Ketham') by 1450. The illustrations have nearly all been matched by far older coloured drawings. It would of course be just as misleading to judge the level of medical knowledge and teaching in 1500 solely by the *Fasciculus* as to judge that of 1900 by a popular 'Family Physician'; but the fact remains that the first and most frequent editions were in Latin, and that some editions include an admirably executed drawing of an anatomy lesson which shows the medical schools of the day in a very poor light.

The *Fasciculus* was not the only medical textbook printed before 1501. On a considerably higher plane—as judged by the almost complete absence of astrology and 'visual aids' thereto—was the *Articella*, six editions of which appeared from 1476 through 1500. With the exception of 'Ioannitius' (Hunain ibn Ishaq) and of the commentary by Ali Ridwan on Galen's *Tegni*, the authors, selections from whose works were included, were all Greek or Hellenistic; later editions (e.g. No. 47), however, included numerous Arabic works and one or two medieval Latin commentaries. But there was nothing later than the early fourteenth century.

Another aspect of this question of the degree of 'enlightenment' which is traditionally associated with this period is that of the authors in chief demand. Reference has already been made to the huge output of Avicenna's *Canon*. Without attempting to estimate the quality of this work it can at least be said that the continued demand represented an unquestioning conservatism; for however original may have been Avicenna's re-examination of Galen— whose system forms the basis of the *Canon*—it was written near the beginning of the eleventh century, hence its persistence up to and far beyond 1500 (see No. 351) stamps the medical practice of the late fifteenth century as predominantly traditional. What of the Greco-Roman masters themselves who formed the basis of the medicine of Islam? There still seems to be an impression that the early sixteenth century marked the rejection of the authority of Galen. A review of the incunable and subsequent editions shows that this was far from being the case. Up to 1500, apart from a single edition (Venice, 1490) of Galen's *Opera*, the works of Hippokrates seem to have received a rather greater attention from the printers. After 1500—and especially after 1530—a steady flow of the works of Galen—including numerous 'complete' editions—continued throughout the century; the Aberdeen collection alone contains twenty-three items, including four 'complete' editions and two 'epitomes'. Moreover it should be remembered that it was mainly the works of Galen that the traditional 'star' of the English Renaissance, Thomas Linacre, translated from 1517 onwards. These are the facts; but what interpretation is to be put upon them? The central position of the works of Galen, almost unassailed until far into the sixteenth century, justifies a brief survey of his system and of the hazards which his works had to face from the second century of our era, when they were produced.

The majority of the works of Galen were translated from the Greek originals, some into Syriac, others direct into Arabic, by the outstanding scholar Hunain ibn Ishaq during the ninth century. Many of his translations are still extant: that of Galen's *On Medical Experience* has recently been published together with an English translation. Special interest attaches to this work, since the Greek original, apart from a few fragments, has never been known in the West, though its title appears in Galen's own list of his own works. The excellence of Hunain's translation—he says that he always tried to collate three Greek texts [1]—and the fact that he was himself a physician sufficiently original to compose the first systematic textbook on ophthalmology known—ensured for Galen a pre-eminence in western medicine from the time when the Islamic influence made itself felt, which was shortly before 1100, when Constantine the African began his translations of

[1] Max. Meyerhof, article in *The Legacy of Islam*, ed. Sir Thomas Arnold, Oxford, 1931, on which this account of Arabic medicine and its transmission of Greek medicine is largely based.

Arabic works into Latin at Salerno and Monte Cassino. Hunain and his numerous disciples did not altogether neglect Hippokrates and Galen's commentaries on several of his works, but the more systematic form of Galen's medicine doubtless appealed more to the Islamic mediators. The work most fully expounding his system was the *Methodus Medendi, libri ix ad Hieronem*, also known as Μεγατεχνη or in Latin, *Ars Magna*. A summary for the use of his friend, Glaukon, was usually known as the θεραπευτικα or *De Medendi Methodo, libri ii*. But most popular of all—the physicians' 'pocket book' for centuries—was the Μικροτεχνη also known rather confusingly as *Ars Medica, Ars Parva* or most commonly, owing to Arabic influence, as 'Tegni'. Although of such modest proportions this work attained great importance, not only on account of its natural popularity, but because two penetrating and detailed commentaries were written on it, one by Ali ibn Ridwan (998-1061) and, much later, one by Jacopo da Forlì; the latter was printed as early as 1475; the text was printed together with the two commentaries in 1515 (No. 287(23)); we shall consider them in some detail when we turn to the influence of Galen on medical (and scientific) method.

It is one of the ironies of the history of medicine that the ascendancy of Galen during the sixteenth century was guaranteed to a great extent by the efforts of many of the most prominent physicians to stamp out the supposed corruption of the true medicine by the Arabs and the 'utterly futile (*ineptissimum*) crowd of medical barbarians' (No. 280). If at first this scorn of the 'humanist' physicians for anything which the Arabs had touched appears inconsistent with the above assessment of the excellence of Hunain's translations, it must be remembered that knowledge of *Arabic* was probably as rare in the sixteenth century as in the twelfth: to the humanist physicians therefore the original translations of Hunain were closed; only medieval Latin versions were available, which had already passed through an Arabic stage. As Greek manuscripts accumulated and competent Greek scholars like Linacre multiplied, Latin versions became available, which provided the physicians with a Galenic system far more to their taste. Doubtless the Arab 'reforms' of Galen were not all in the line of progress; but it may be questioned whether the powerful advocacy which brought back and firmly entrenched for a century the original Galen was not at least as much the result of a

cultural bias towards the 'glory that was Greece', even though the
chief representative of the culture had been born in Asia (Per-
gamon) studied mainly in Africa (Alexandria), and achieved his
greatest triumphs in Rome. Be this as it may, it is probable that
the most adequate assessment of the progress of medical thought
in the sixteenth century may be attained by regarding it as at
first a struggle between 'orthodox' and Arabised Galenism in
which the former quickly gained the ascendancy, to be slowly
undermined during the second half of the century, not by its
previous opponent, but by forces which were the products of the
general change of outlook.

As a relatively firm base from which we may set out on our long
and difficult investigation we shall examine in some detail the
exposition of the 'art of medicine' published in a series of manuals
by Leonhart Fuchs during the middle decades of the century. The
choice of this exposition as a norm is dictated not only by the
fact that it was continually enlarged and revised, the total output
running to about ten editions, but because its author, though no
innovator in the theory or practice of medicine, proved himself by
his epoch-making medical herbal (see p. 192) to be no mere
time-server. Also he was a man of international renown, a friend
of Vesalius, and equally experienced in classical scholarship, the
human problems of dealing with an exceptionally severe outbreak
of plague, and the conduct of the teaching duties of a university
chair at Tübingen.

The book of which a brief sketch is to be given appeared first
in 1531 under the title *Compendiaria & succincta admodum in medendi
artem introductio* (an abridged and altogether concise introduction
to the healing art). How this was rapidly sold out, together with a
revised second edition, is described by Fuchs in the dedication to
Cosimo de' Medici which he prefixed to the third edition, now so
completely revised and greatly enlarged that it was virtually a new
work (No. 278) and was issued under the title *Methodus seu ratio
compendiaria cognoscendi veram solidamque medicinam ad Hippocratis &
Galeni scripta recte intelligenda mire utilis* . . . . Like most 'short
introductions' it had now swollen to 234 pages, with an additional
172 on the theory and practice of *Materia Medica* (see below,
p. 237). By 1594 under the third, and historically important, title
Institutiones Medicinae (No. 279) it reached 809. The dedication
of the second form of the work is dated 1548—five years after the
o*

publication of the *Fabrica* (see below, p. 227) of that 'best and dearest friend Andreas Vesalius'—and yet Fuchs explicitly states, what was only implied in the early editions, that it was intended to help students to a proper appreciation of the works of Hippokrates and Galen. Though this explicit reference was dropped in the later *Institutiones*, the general character of the work remained unchanged, and its popularity apparently little abated until well into the seventeenth century.

This introduction to the art of medicine bears much the same relation to the Galenic *corpus* as Peurbach's *Theoricae novae Planetarum* does to Ptolemy's *Almagest*. Though based on the system of Galen, it by no means followed slavishly the text of any of his works, whose prolixity Fuchs admitted in the textbook of the practice of medicine which he published in a more or less parallel series (Nos. 280–2). As was not uncommon in books of that period the dedicatory preface casts an important light on the conception of medical education Fuchs was trying to inculcate. It was indeed to be an education of a very comprehensive character, based on a thorough knowledge of grammar and languages—Greek as well as Latin—dialectic, geography, astronomy, and above all mathematics. The whole of philosophy is essential, for every physician (as Galen asserts) must be first a philosopher. So much for the base. The more specifically medical training must be based on *physiologia*, anatomy, dietetics, hygiene, and *materia medica*. Evidently the medical curriculum was already getting out of hand four centuries ago! The insistence on the fundamental importance of *physiologia* was not new: it is to be found in Galen's work *On the Natural Faculties*—the only complete work of Galen's in the Loeb Classical Library. But whereas in classical times—and in Gilbert's *De Magnete* of 1600—it was scarcely to be distinguished from 'physics', Fuchs explicitly defines it as dealing with the 'nature of the *human body*': the logical outcome of this was Fernel's epoch-making use of the term as the title of a *book* (No. 249). Nor was the demand for a thorough knowledge of anatomy without parallel. At the beginning of the fourteenth century Guy de Chauliac had stressed it in his opening lecture. But it was as a surgeon that he had gained renown; among physicians it was with Fuchs a sign of the times—a sign of the growing influence of Padua, of which more later. Dietetics and hygiene were of course the corner stones of Hippokratic medicine, as later they charac-

terised the attitude of that open-minded Roman, Celsus, with his
recommendation of plain living and regular exercise in the fresh
air as the best physicians. Fuchs's last point—the deplorable
ignorance shown by so many of his contemporaries of the *materia
medica*—is that of a supporter of Galen, for it was in the use of
complex mixtures of drugs of vegetable origin that the latter
departed most radically from the teaching of his hero Hippokrates.
Curiously enough it was in this department of medicine that
Fuchs had to admit that the Arabs had made considerable
progress by using plants unknown to Galen. Fuchs also required
that the physician should know the virtues of 'metals, stones, gems,
earths, and of those things which animals, the sea, and waters
yield'—a recommendation which his master might not perhaps
have viewed with unqualified approval.

So much (and a good deal more in similar vein) Fuchs wrote in
the dedication. When we turn to the text we find a very clear
account of the departments of medical theory as laid down by
Galen, who, though (according to Fuchs) he excelled in all disciplines, cultivated medicine in the highest degree, for which task
he had no doubt been raised up by God. Medicine is not a science
which is certain and based wholly on the use of reason, but an
art seeking a useful end by the application of many notions gained
by use and practice: the reader will recall that in the Dewey
system of library classification he still seeks medical works in the
section comprising the 'Useful Arts'. Moreover it is one and indivisible in essence—neither a collection of separate disciplines
nor divided into theoretical and practical parts: here came a
chance for a dig at Avicenna, who however is confuted out of the
mouth of Averroes, a later Arab. The departments of medicine
recognised by the Greeks were the φυσιολογικη, ὑγιεινη,
ἀιτιολογικη, σεμειωτικη, θεραπευτικη.[1] These he defines and
clarifies by reference to the principal works of Hippokrates and
Galen which respectively deal with them. From this it appears
that these five terms are still in use in something like their original
sense. To 'physiology' we have already referred. 'Hygiene'
corresponds to something like 'preventive medicine', being dealt
with in works having titles of the form *De Sanitate Tuenda*.
'Semiotic', the study of 'signs', was concerned with knowledge of

---

[1] The adjectival form presupposes τεχνη (φυσιολογικη etc.) = 'the (physiological)
art'.

the past, inspection of the present, and prediction of the future. Hippokrates laid the greatest stress on 'prognosis' as well as 'diagnosis': 'semiotic' included not only indications of the pulse and urine (carried to absurd lengths by the medieval physicians) but also of the heavenly portents, and referred to the—partially imaginary—'critical days' in fevers. This department accounted for the emphasis placed upon the study of astronomy in the medical curriculum—one shudders to think of the time wasted on this almost entirely fruitless labour. 'Aetiology' (which Fuchs notes was also known by the name παθολογια—see No. 278) is that which 'seeks out the causes of affections *praeter naturam* (see below, p. 225) and symptoms of diseases'.[1] The inclusion of 'symptoms' in the department (αἰτιος = cause) concerned, by definition, with causes seems to the modern critic a methodological confusion; but perhaps it is not wholly gratuitous to see in this long tradition part at least of the origin of the tendency to regard the data of morbid histology as *causes* rather than as *effects* of an underlying disharmony of functions: the modern attitude to this represents in some degree a return to Galen himself. 'Therapeutics' deals of course with the action taken by the physician: the modern preference for the term 'management' rather than 'treatment' reflects a return to Hippokrates, though to many a modern medical student 'Hippokrates' is merely a word attached to a professional commitment. Therapeutics is dealt with in works having titles of the form *De Medendi Methodo*, which are based on διαιτητικη and φαρμακευτικη, but may also involve χειρουργικη: it is a sign of the times that Fuchs not only mentions this, but to later editions of his own series of books on *Methodus Medendi* (Nos. 280–2) he added a long section on surgery. The relations between surgery and medicine form a long and highly complex story which, as part of the history of medicine, can not be treated here: the reader may, however, be warned against accepting without reserve the over-simplified and sweeping statements which are still too often met with; it now seems pretty clear that there was no continuous development, but the relationship varied widely in respect of both time and place. 'Pharmacology'—the part of therapeutics dominant among physicians owning Galen as their master,—was based on the *De Materia Medica* compiled in the

---

[1] A beginning of a more 'natural' approach to pathology is seen in Benivieni's book on the causes of diseases (1514; see No. 205).

first century A.D. by Dioskurides, an Asiatic Greek. This work may be compared with Euclid's *Elements* in respect of its continuous and unrivalled influence for about sixteen centuries. Since this sub-department of medicine greatly influenced the subsequent development of many branches of natural science it will be dealt with, like anatomy, in a separate section.

The Galenic 'physiology' is the heart of the system of medicine taught by Fuchs and embraced by the majority of sixteenth century physicians, just as the Aristotelian 'physics', to which it was closely allied, formed the basis of all thought about the nature of the sublunary world. Man's body being part of nature subject to generation and corruption is compact of the four elements with their corresponding pairs of qualities; mutual interaction is made possible by the fact that the elements are not the *ultimates* but are formed by the inherence of the qualities in 'first matter' (*materia prima, ὕλη*). According to the proportion of the various qualities there exists at all times a characteristic *temperament*; thus, spring has the temperament wet and warm and so does infancy (i.e. *pueritia*—from birth to fifteen years). The physicians of his time, Fuchs says, regard the 'perfect' temperament as an ideal hardly to be found in any individual; but in each kind of living being there is an optimum measure according to its nature; and 'health' is the state which departs as little as possible from this. The remaining 'natural' components of the living body are the four 'humours'—blood, phlegm, (*pituita*), black bile, and yellow bile. On the correct balance of these depends not only bodily health but also character—sanguine, phlegmatic, melancholic, choleric—when any particular one predominates. 'Natural' also are the 'spirits'—'natural', *sensu strictu*, present in all living things; 'vital', and 'animal'. These provide the 'reason' for actions and faculties. Among the seven 'natural' components which Fuchs lists are also the 'parts' of the body—flesh, bone, heart, hand, etc., which had been classified by Aristotle [1] as either ὁμοιομερῶν (*similares*), which when divided give parts similar to the whole, or ἀνοιομερῶν (*instrumentales* or *dissimilares*): the former correspond to a certain extent to tissues but include arteries, ligaments, nerves, etc., as such; the latter correspond more closely to organs. The inclusion of these visible and tangible parts on a level with the hypothetical elements, humours, and spirits is what chiefly

[1] *De Partibus Animalium*, 640 b, 21-2.

distinguishes Galenic physiology from that which took its rise with Harvey. The hypotheses put forward to account for the phenomena of living animals including Man were of course almost wholly erroneous, but they were not wholly *confused* as is the classification just referred to. For instance, the fundamental process of converting food into living 'parts' was said to proceed in the gut, whence the products of the 'coction' passed through the membrane of the latter into the branches of the portal vein, wherein, changed into blood and charged with the 'natural' spirits, it flowed to the liver. From the liver it was transferred to the right side of the heart. All this is broadly correct. From the right side of the heart, however, the blood might filter through the pores in the interventricular septum or, for the most part, proceed through the great 'hollow' (caval) veins to all parts of the body. A continuous ebb and flow occurred along both these routes, the blood in the left ventricle receiving 'vital' spirits from the air brought from the lungs *via* the 'venous' arteries (pulmonary veins). The arteries distributed this 'vitalised' blood to all parts of the body: that which reached the brain received from the *rête mirabile* (which in fact is absent from the human brain) the 'animal spirits' conferring the higher powers of activity characteristic of animals: this form of *pneuma* was distributed to all parts of the body through the nerves originating in the brain.

There are only two objectionable features in this 'physiology': first, it was so ingenious, comprehensive, and self-consistent that, provided you kept strictly within the context of function, it was almost impossible to prove it wrong in any particular; second, that the structural details of the organs responsible for the various functions were either unknown or ignored. It was in fact teleological in the worst sense: it merely provided a *schema* of how an all-wise Providence had ensured, barring accidents, a smoothly running machine. What is so remarkable about its founder, Galen, is the fact that in *Anatomical Procedures* (see p. 228) he shows himself not only as good an anatomist as any of the sixteenth century, but, even more surprisingly, capable of demonstrating (in his book on the *Natural Faculties*) by actual experiment the falsity of the relation alleged by a rival school to subsist between the kidneys and the bladder. Galen in fact illustrates in his own nature the importance of 'temperament'. Of a contentious 'nature' and largely devoid of self-criticism, he could display great ingenuity, both in rhetoric and practice, to demolish a rival: thus in his monograph *Against Erasistratos* he demonstrated that the arteries contain blood (imbued with 'spirits') and not merely air (the source of the vital spirit); it apparently never occurred to him to test his own theory of the flux and reflux of the blood and waste matter between right ventricle and lung which is evidently rendered impossible by the one-way control of the tricuspid valves.[1]

I have looked more closely into this relic of antiquity, accepted in all essentials throughout the sixteenth century, in order to clarify a point in the history of medicine which seems to me as a layman to have been passed over in silence by medical historians. 'Why', the lay historian ought to ask himself, 'why, in the history of *medicine*, is such stress laid on the great advances in anatomy in the sixteenth century and the demonstration of the systemic circulation of the blood in the seventeenth century, when therapeutic practice was left virtually untouched by these "advances"?' Anyone who doubts the justice of the last statement has only to read the account of the (mal-)treatment of the wretched Charles II, who in his last days earned the title of Charles the Martyr as surely as had his father—and this at the hands of the most 'progressive' physicians of the day. Poor, 'unscientific', Galen would have been horrified at such a perversion of the *Ars Medendi*! The resolution of this paradox, I suggest, is that physiology from the time of Harvey embodies a growing complex of abstractions which may become a necessary, but can never be a sufficient, condition of 'total' therapy; only after the 'general' physiology of Claude Bernard could it even begin to form a generally valid basis for therapy. The Galenic physiology, though doubtless false in abstract detail, showed a remarkable insight into the broad and truly empirical picture of *mens sana in corpore sano*— as witness our growing appreciation of the 'temperamental' indications of glandular imbalance and of 'psychosomatic' medicine, a term which, incidentally, Galen would not have understood, since he recognised no other kind of medicine. But no amount of verbal refinement, or of balancing of temperaments by compound medicines and diet, would have produced a cure

[1] Cf. Harvey, *Anatomical Disquisition on the Motion of the Heart* . . ., Everyman edn., p. 17) in relation to the mitral valves between left auricle and ventricle 'Good God, how should the mitral valves prevent regurgitation of air and not of blood?'

for the already well known disease of diabetes: for this the detailed abstractions of Bernardian physiology were necessary. And this brings us to the heart of the paradox: for until there was a means of *falsifying* the details of Galenic physiology there could be no hope of breaking out of the teleological circle. Chemistry, on an adequate level, was still a thing of the distant future; the falsification could be carried out only in respect of the *mechanical* devices to be found in the body, and to this accurate knowledge of *structure* was the key. If it be objected that in the case of the heart at least this was already available to Galen, the answer is that where positively conflicting evidence was available (as in the case of the valvular apparatus) he ignored it, and when the evidence for his teleological theory was absent (as in the interventricular 'pores') he created it—though no one who *wanted* to find passages through the highly reticulate fasciation of the septum could be blamed for 'finding' them. The process of ratiocination had to be reversed—from a deductive to an inductive form. Rather than look for anatomical details to verify an hypothesis it was necessary to construct an hypothesis on the basis of, as far as possible, impartial evidence. Impartiality in human affairs nearly always implies a high degree of autonomy: the implication here is that anatomy had to become a discipline—and a passion—detached as far as possible from 'physiology'. How this came about in the sixteenth century we shall consider later.

Meanwhile it is necessary to take note of the fact that the distinction between inductive and deductive procedure, expressed in general terms by Aristotle in his *Posterior Analytic*, had been applied by Galen, who was a logician as well as a physician, to the special problems of medicine. In the article already referred to (p. 208), J. H. Randall Jr. revealed the prominence given to this question in the medical school of Padua in the fifteenth century. The lively and informed discussion reviewed in the memoir took the form of a series of commentaries on the *Tegni* of Galen. The opening paragraphs of this work discussed the threefold 'doctrine' of medical study, comprising the methods *compositiva*, *resolutiva*, *definitiva*. These terms had been previously used in a somewhat similar sense by Cicero, but Galen had given to them a significance rather logical than rhetorical. The correspondence of the resolutive and compositive forms of statement to those discussed by Aristotle in the *Posterior Analytic* (78.a.21 f) was first pointed out in the highly influential commentary on the *Tegni* by Ali ibn Ridwan (Haly Rodoan; XI–1). Aristotle distinguished between inference by means of the recognition of relationships which 'are the case' (τι ὅτι) and that which is according to reason, that is, for which a *cause* can be assigned (διοτι). In the Latin translations of the commentary of Haly Rodoan the latter's comparison of τι ὅτι with *resolutio* and of διοτι with *compositio* is further expressed by the Latin phrases *quia* (*not* 'because', but in the more usual medieval sense approximating to 'namely that') and *propter quid* ('as a result of which') respectively. Thus *resolutio* approximates to the assertion of a cause from the deployment of the effects; *compositio* to the demonstration of what must succeed if the cause so hypothesised is operative. Thus they represent the two moments in what J. S. Mill was to call the 'inductive-deductive' method; though it must be remembered that the thought of these pioneers was still so much entangled with syllogistic form and metaphysical characters such as 'essence', 'accident', and the like, that centuries were to elapse before anything approaching Mill's clarity was attained.

The Medical School of Padua came into the picture with the famous physician Jacopo da Forli (d. 1413) whose re-working over the commentary of Haly Rodoan was printed in 1475 and five times more before 1500 (No. 287 (23) is a still later edition). Held in little less esteem was Ugo Benzi (Ugo da Siena, Hugo Senensis) whose commentary on the *Tegni* was printed in 1496. Finally Leoniceno reviewed and corrected Ugo's (uncompleted) commentary in 1505. The work of Randall already referred to provides strong evidence for the view that the preoccupation of this medical school, famous also for its *consilia* (p. 266 below), with the problem of method was due to the absence of a Faculty of Theology, which was always apt to drain off the most brilliant graduates in Arts, and also to the 'Averroistic' colour of its philosophy. Into this latter jungle of controversy, set about with the swamps of doctrinal loyalties and wastes uncharted by adequate first-hand knowledge of what Averroes really taught, I shall not venture, but merely remind the reader that when the promising critical Aristotelianism of Paris and Oxford wilted under the scorching light of Occamist nominalism the tradition, Averroist if you will, continued with undaunted vigour in the teaching of Paul of Venice, Gaitano da Thiene (Cajetanus) Augustino Nipho,

Alessandro Achillini, Pietro Pomponazzi, down to Jacomo Zabarella, the importance of whose lucid exposition of scientific method for the Galilean 'revolution' has not as yet been widely recognised. Attention has already been drawn (p. 157) to the 'local' outcrop of editions of the fourteenth-century logicians.

In such an atmosphere grew to intellectual maturity the last of the predominantly humanist (pre-Vesalian) professors of medicine at Padua, Giovanni Battista da Monte (J. B. Montanus). Such was his conviction of the importance of these questions that he could open one of his courses with the words: 'Cum in nostris hisce prelectionibus (optimi iuvenes) frequens a nobis fiat methodi mentio. . . .' ('Since in these lectures of mine, my young friends, the subject of method is frequently mentioned . . .') he will proceed to treat of the nature and number of methods to be employed in the study of medicine.

Although Montanus had published as early as 1536 the first Latin translation of the sixteen books of Aetios of Amida and later (1546) a brief summary of the *Tegni*, none of his own medical teachings or *consilia* (see p. 266) appeared until after his death (1551). We are therefore dependent on collections of his works by several editors, of whom Girolamo Donzellini, Gaspar Peucer, and Martin Weindrich are responsible for the *Opera* in the Aberdeen collections. These *Opera* do not, however, include the *Consilia* which are contained in a separate handsomely bound volume (No. 460) edited by Ioannes Crato. Donzellini's (Basel, 1557) is the nearest in time to the years of the author's activity, but has the appearance of having been assembled as a sort of 'memorial volume' rather than as a definitive text, since it includes within the continuously paged text the *De Medendi Methodo* by John Caius (*Ed.P.*, Basel, 1544) and *Methodus Therapeutica* by Ioannes Crato, both of whom were his pupils. Both works are prefaced by discussions of method, the former at greater length than the latter, which in fact refers to the work of Caius for further details. Windreich's edition, a handsome folio, is more systematically arranged and lacks these two works and also the familiar form of address quoted above; otherwise the two versions do not differ much in respect of the matter with which we are chiefly concerned. While Donzellini states that Montanus was outstanding in the art of teaching and in the explanation of the ancient writers, as all who had heard him or read his writings clearly testified,

Windreich is more precise in emphasising that he 'deduced the principles of the art of medicine from the most recondite philosophy and from the very majesty of nature, in order that he might avoid putting forward anything, as the Arabs had been accustomed to do, without proof. By applying all the instruments of method, order, and teaching . . . by the definition of the essences of things, by demonstrating their affects, by the division and resolution of natural kinds, by bringing forward true causes, and whatever particular appearance of truth there was—by these methods and not by means of rhetoric he gave his hearers what they needed in concise and clear terms'. Windreich could bring forward the most glowing tributes to Montanus from Fracastoro, Brasavola, Trincavelli, Alexandrini, and many others. This is a claim the modern reader will readily endorse with the single reservation that if the exposition of texts of anything up to two thousand years of age was what his audience 'wanted', it was high time that someone told them that this method, admirable as it was, must be applied, 'not to the positions of philosophers but to the fabric of nature', as a later student of Padua, William Harvey, put the matter in the dedication of his great work to his colleagues. But it was a beginning, or rather a continuation, of an ancient and valuable method too long displaced by recourse to a purely deductive process. The key to the 'method' of medicine lay, as Montanus himself set forth, first in the clear recognition of the 'end' of medicine, which is the preservation or restoration of health in the 'natural' state of the body; therefore medicine is the art of preserving or restoring the 'natural' state. The method of an art is the rational means of attaining its end; but it is not sufficient merely to hear about it, and even in addition to learn about it (*addiscere*); it must become a habit of mind since it is concerned with discovery, and not merely with proof as is the syllogism.[1] Moreover, as Galen said, no one will ever comprehend an art from books of commentaries had he six hundred thousand; for art is concerned with particular problems, and these are infinite and can not be reduced to a universal art; and in another place, that method and practice are as the right and left foot of the

---

[1] Cf. Descartes, ' . . . ses syllogismes servent plutot a expliquer a autruy les choses qu'on sçait . . . qu' a les apprendres' (*Oeuvres*, ed. Adam and Tannery, 6, 17); and Francis Bacon, 'the syllogism . . . commands assent. . . to the proposition, but does not take hold of the thing' (*Works*, ed. Ellis and Spedding, Vol. IV, p. 49).

physician. This preamble, developed at what seems to us inordinate length, but which may have appealed to an audience of young men to whom syllogism was almost a second nature, was, as the citations from Plato, Aristotle, and Galen show, not notably original: but it emphasised a side of Galen's genius which had been lost sight of among those sycophants who had cultivated only his 'system'. 'Art' is to be based on the methodical generalisation from facts: how is it to be done? Not by the *Methodus demonstrativa*, which is proper to the sciences, since the end of these is knowledge; but the end of Art is action and is concerned with particulars, to which the demonstrative method is inapplicable, since it starts from unconditionally accepted truths (*ex necessariis*) and arrives at necessary conclusions. He then reviews the alternatives—rhetorical, divisive, definitive, resolutive, compositive—which were discussed in various combinations by the commentators, Alexander Aphrodisias and others. The rhetorical he dismisses as unworthy either for sciences or arts, but regards the remaining four as necessary and sufficient. Of these, however, two and only two, the divisive and resolutive, are necessary for medicine: the former, since the universals which are retained in the intellect may be applied to particulars; the latter, since the intellect, thus faced with the particular, can then promote a regress step by step to the first principles of things. We may wonder why Montanus leaves out the compositive and definitive methods. These, he shows, belong rather to the ordering and exposition of the art than to its creation: the compositive is more suited to the needs of younger students who are not practised in the more difficult resolutive method. Montanus is not altogether clear about the distinction between *method* and *order*, though he refers to the opening words of the *Tegni*. 'There are three orders of this doctrine'. According to Randall the distinction had been touched on by Achillini who thought that the order of exposition ought to follow the order of nature; but the radical nature of the dilemma (which is still with us today in the similar but surely ill-considered wrangles as to whether the teacher should impart 'facts' or 'principles') was first put in a clear light by Zimara. For him method was concerned with discovery and demonstration in the general sense, order with literary exposition and teaching.

The work of John Caius, which develops the subject on somewhat different lines, provides a useful supplement to the exposition of Montanus. But at the end one feels that one's failure to see clearly what exactly was the outcome of these discussions is not entirely due to weakness of intellect and the medium of an unfamiliar language. There seems little doubt that there remained latent confusions in the minds of these men themselves—confusions due in the last resort to an excessive reliance on words to which no clearly defined object or process corresponded; or obversely to the cramping effect of terms like *praeter naturam,* when what was 'natural' was too rigidly defined *à priori* without adequate recourse to experience. So progress was inevitably slow. But there seems to be equally little doubt that without the revival of these ancient controversies by men who were both masters of the original Greek and, as their other works manifestly reveal, constant observers of natural phenomena,[1] even if this was limited to the ills of human flesh, there might, in the sciences of the sublunary world have been no progress at all.

[1] Montanus was as famous for his clinical teaching at the bedside as for his 'method'.

CHAPTER XII

THE RISE OF THE ANATOMY SCHOOLS

THE year 1543 has been held, with about as much—and as little—justice, to mark the beginning of 'modern' biological science as of 'modern' physical science. For in this year, in which the Copernican 'revolution' was promulgated there appeared the *De Humani Corporis Fabrica* of Andreas Vesalius. The figure and achievement of Vesalius have been viewed through the same dazzling glow of reverence as were those of Copernicus: even Harvey Cushing[1] included him among those 'to be counted on the fingers of one hand' who rank highest in the history of medicine. This traditional thesis of meteoric translation of the spirit of medicine from the thraldom of Galen (who rather inconsistently appears as another of Cushing's 'fingers') has generated an antithesis that Vesalius was an anti-Galenist at most in policy and not in performance, in which he was largely a plagiarist more enterprising than profound. To clear away the legends and to give Vesalius his just place in the progress of scientific thought is even now hardly possible, and when it is will require a book to itself. All that can be done here is to review some of the least controversial evidence and to suggest a tentative estimate. To attempt more than this would be foreign to the purpose of this *Introduction*; to do less would be to ignore the fact that rightly or wrongly Vesalius became in his own brief lifetime a dominating figure and remained so until quite recently. And whatever may be the anatomical merits of the author, the *Fabrica* is undoubtedly one of the most inspiring, as it has been one of the most influential, monuments of scientific typographical and artistic enterprise: and evidence is available to prove that this was as much due to the care and insight of Vesalius as of the printer, Oporinus. Thus, to assess the progress of anatomy— perhaps the greatest scientific achievement of the sixteenth

[1] Cushing, H., *A Bio-Bibliography of Andreas Vesalius*, New York, 1943, p. xxviii.

century—is necessarily to assess its greatest single memorial, in itself, in its advance on previous works, and in its influence.

What has never been questioned is the unprecedented magnificence of the illustrations; of even greater importance perhaps is the new spirit which informs them. With a few, but not negligible, exceptions Vesalius was the first to use illustrations as *naturalistic representations* of the organs of the body. That he attached great importance to this is shown by the publication in 1538 of six folio sheets of which only two complete copies now exist—one in San Marco, Venice; the other in the Hunterian Collection, Glasgow. In his dedication he states that though it would be difficult, perhaps impossible, to learn anatomy by means of diagrams alone yet 'no one can deny that they are helpful in fixing things in one's memory'. This work, consisting only of six large plates (one comprising three diagrams) with extensive legends, included three studies of a skeleton which had been prepared by Vesalius himself. These studies, far surpassing any previously *published*, were the work of John Stephen Calcar, a fellow countryman of the author and reputed to have been a pupil of Titian. The great success of the *Anatomiae Tabulae sex*, as this publication is usually called, there being no title page, encouraged Vesalius to proceed with a greatly enlarged version which became in fact a completely new work—the *Fabrica*—containing an extensive text as well as a very large number of figures from woodcuts. But realising the need for a cheaper and more easily handled guide for students he produced, in the same year, an *Epitome* with fewer but actually larger plates and a more concise text. Such a policy appears to the modern teacher to be a great advance on previous practice. Many of his contemporaries, however, including his own teacher, Sylvius, who for a time drew crowds of students from all over Europe to Paris, publicly condemned it in withering and abusive terms. It is easy to say that this was the natural reaction of aged professors to the rapid rise to fame of a young man—Vesalius was under thirty at the time—as a result of his having had the wit to introduce a method which no one had previously thought of; but the force of this argument is broken by the fact that a similar method had been employed more than ten years previously in the herbal of Brunfels. Nevertheless, although identification and memorisation are important in anatomy, the recognition of

---

[1] Cushing, *op. cit.* p. 22.

morphological relationships is even more so: 'on the body let
your practice be first to discern the origin and insertion of the
muscle . . . the student must carefully do everything himself.' [1]
Thus, not Vesalius, but Galen; and, as Dr. Singer emphasises,
there is no evidence that Galen made any use of diagrams. Of
bones 'it is not enough to study them casually or read of them only
in a book: no, *not even in mine* [2]—a remarkable qualification
coming from Galen. Whatever may have been its real spring the
rejection of the Vesalian method was rationalised as being a
protest against the latter's rejection of Galen. Whether Galen,
had he been able to see Vesalius's figures of *active* skeletons and
muscles displayed so as to reveal their mode of traction, would
have sided with his sixteenth-century supporters is a matter for
speculation. For the *Fabrica* ('Working', as Cushing wished to
translate it [3]) had no greater merit than this: that its order of
exposition reversed the medieval sequence of anatomising—
viscera first and skeleton last [4]—since the skeleton is literally the
foundation of all else,[5] both of the shape and arrangement of the
viscera and of the power and direction of every movement.
In the absence of preservative (which was not commonly used
until the mid seventeenth century) and particularly in the warm
climate of Italy, the customary sequence of anatomising was unavoidable. In these circumstances the introduction of large illustrations of the soft parts, which the student could have at hand
while watching the demonstration and also as an aid in his
subsequent study of texts (the making of his own drawings being
then out of the question), would seem to have been even more
important than in the days of preserved specimens. But one can
measure the prejudice against this innovation by the absence of
any illustrations to the anatomical introduction to the *Physiology*
of that otherwise most enlightened physician, Jean Fernel.

That the *Fabrica* set a new standard in illustration and thereby
greatly improved the teaching of anatomy will hardly be questioned; what may not be so lightly passed over is the question of

[1] In Galen, *Anatomical Procedures*, a translation of *De Administrantibus Anatomicis*,
published for the Wellcome Historical Medical Museum by the Oxford University
Press, London, 1956, pp. 6 and 7.   [2] *Op. cit.* p. 3.

[3] *Op. cit.* Note 403a quoted by the editor, J. S. Fulton, from the *Times Literary
Supplement*, 29 May, 1943.

[4] Not so, Galen; see *op. cit.* p. 5.

[5] Cf. L. B. Alberti quoted above, p. 20.

the *extent* to which Vesalius himself stood alone in this enterprise. In the first place, who drew these lively, imaginative, and on the whole accurate, illustrations? For some time it has been almost assumed that they were the work of Stephen Calcar, doubtless, as the correspondence of Vesalius hints, supervised by the latter. Of Calcar's collaboration in at least some of the *Tabulae Sex* there is no doubt; it was, according to the colophon, at his expense that the work was printed. At the end of the dedication to his epistle on venesection dated 1539, Vesalius announces his intention to bring out a greatly enlarged version of the *Tabulae* 'if Ioannes Stephanus, the most admirable artist of our time, does not refuse his assistance '.[1] But that is the last mention of Calcar in any of the works of Vesalius: so the assumption that he was the artist of the *Fabrica* rests on conjecture, and has recently been seriously questioned.[2]

That the Vesalian plates were not the first of their kind has already been noted above. The first printed anatomical diagrams of any kind are those of the *Fasciculus Medicinae*, based mainly on medieval sources but omitting the interesting though crude attempts at naturalistic portrayal to be seen in the manuscript (dated 1314) of the works of the surgeon, Henri de Mondeville.[3] On an entirely different level are the manuscript drawings of Leonardo da Vinci, executed with artistic mastery and with such fidelity, indeed, that the composite nature of his displays of large areas of the human body is only too evident to the modern anatomist. In any event his work was almost certainly unknown to his successors for more than three centuries, though William Hunter was setting about the task of publishing an edition of the drawings he had acquired when his own death put an end to the project. There would thus have been hardly any need to refer to Leonardo's drawings but for the fact that Vasari (*Vite de Pittori*, 1568) states that Leonardo collaborated with Marc'Antonio della Torre, who was preparing what would probably have been the first 'modern' treatise on anatomy had Marc'Antonio not died. It has been alleged that Vesalius made great use of these drawings; if he did—of which there is no real evidence—he

[1] Quoted by Cushing, *op. cit.* p. xxxiii.
[2] E.g. C. Singer, and C. Rabin, *A Prelude to Modern Science*, Cambridge, 1946.
[3] L. Choulant, *History and Bibliography of Anatomic Illustration*, trans. M. Frank, New York, p. 59.

P*

failed to make the most of them, since in some respects they show deeper understanding than is revealed in any of the figures of the *Fabrica*. It is further known that Leonardo made casts of the ventricles of the brain, and by means of orthogonal projections of the valves of the heart 'knew more about them than Harvey'.[1] But the fact remains that Vesalius, though certainly anticipated by Leonardo in the provision of naturalistic figures, may never have seen the latter's, hence it might be argued that he should be given credit for the independent 'invention' of the method. But even this is claiming too much, since, apart from admirable studies by artists such as Michelangelo, Raphael, Dürer, and Domenico del Barbiere (pupil of Rosso de' Rossi), at least two books were published whose illustrations, not greatly inferior to, though far less numerous than, those of the *Fabrica*, were certainly prepared before its appearance: these were the anatomical works of Giovanni-Batista Canano (incomplete and undated, but almost certainly not later than 1543) and Charles Etienne (1545—but known to have been almost complete in 1539). Even earlier than these—earlier indeed than the *Tabulae Sex*— were those illustrating the commentary on the anatomy of Mondino by Berengario da Carpi (1523) and the *Anatomia Capitis Humani* by Ioannes Dryander (1536). The figures of the skeleton used in the former are not to be compared with even those of the *Tabulae Sex*, but Cushing describes the woodcuts of the brain and its envelopes contained in the latter as 'for the period truly remarkable'.

This brief survey of the works—published or prepared before 1543—does nothing to impugn the priority of the *Fabrica* in respect both of its scope and quality; but it does reveal that far from pioneering an entirely new approach to the study of human anatomy it had only made a great leap forward on a road already trodden by several slightly earlier workers. In respect of its influence, however, we can look upon 1543 as marking a watershed. After that date until the end of the century almost every work on anatomy made use of the illustrations, either overtly as in the cases of the *Compendiosa totius Anatomie delineatio* published by Thomas Geminus (London, 1545), or without acknowledgment, as by Felix Plater (No. 530). The compliment of piracy had already

[1] F. J. Cole in a review of K. D. Keele 'Leonardo da Vinci on the Motion of the Heart and Blood' *Nature*, **169** (1952), 1070.

been paid to the *Tabulae Sex* by Walther Ryff in his *Kleyner Chirurgi* (1542) and by Jean Tagault in his *De Chirurgica Institutione* (1543; No. 667 is of the 1549 edn.). These are but characteristic examples: the matter was fully dealt with by Cushing in his *Bibliography*.

We must now turn from this famous book to consider its author. To what extent can we now agree with Eric Nordenskiöld (*History of Biology*, English Trans., New York, 1928, p. 101) that he 'at once led anatomical research into a completely new direction, created an entirely original method of procedure, and thus started a new era in the history of science'? To appreciate the exaggeration of this statement—which is typical of many general histories—one can not do better than turn to Niccolò Massa's *Anatomiae liber introductorius* in which 'as many as possible of the parts, action and uses of the human body are now for the first time revealed, which hitherto had been overlooked by both ancients and moderns'. Though the copy (No. 426) bought by John Gregory in 1769 for one and twopence bears the date 1559, the British Museum copy is of the year 1536—that also of the dedication in both copies.[1] This work, though referred to by M. F. Ashley-Montagu (*Vesalius and the Galenists*, Singer, Vol. I, p. 374) as 'widely read' by Massa's contemporaries, and described in some detail by Singer and Rabin *op. cit.*, is not mentioned by Cushing, or in the standard histories of Garrison, Nordenskiöld, or Castiglioni. Yet in the dedication to Paul III the author states that *in former years* he took part in several anatomies in Venice and promised his collaborator, Hieronymus Marcellus, that he would write a book on the subject. 'I have shown', he adds, 'several members unknown to the ancients, and not only members but also not a few functions (*operationes*) overlooked by them'. In the introductory chapter he bewails the ignorance of contemporary anatomists who 'have merely tried to write down those things which they have neither seen with their eyes nor touched with their hands, but have smothered (*offuscarunt*) the light of the sun with texts copied from others, made useless by reason of their age, and the carelessness of authors and printers'. He has a word of praise for the Greeks and Arabs, but 'I am not one to claim that men have reproduced (*genuisse*) nature without error; ever since

[1] The discrepancy is accounted for by F. J. Cole, *History of Comparative Anatomy*, London, 1944, p. 399.

men have existed they have been liable to err'. There are (as Galen reminds us) many ways of dissecting, and Massa will follow the way of Mondino, preferring to study truth rather than the sayings of others. 'You will not see me defending the sayings of philosophers nor of the weightiest physicians, since they have sometimes fallen into error and could not know everything, consequently where I do not agree with the ancients the matter is otherwise (*aliter se habet*) than what they say about it.' He will be more concerned with truth than with men's authority. All this was written before Vesalius assumed the chair at Padua (1537), so that although the influence of that already famous youth [1] can not be absolutely ruled out, it seems more reasonable to assume that a highly critical attitude had already been established in Northern Italy. Moreover in the actual process of dissection Massa evidently was not accustomed to rely on the carving knife of the barber-surgeon but advised the use of wooden probes (*specilla*) of various sizes the better to explore cavities by the elevation of circumjacent parts (p. 84). Incidentally the dedication to the Pope disposes of the persistent myth that the 'Church' frowned on, if it did not actually forbid, dissection of the human body. And, if it be urged that Venice was in a peculiar position in regard to this, attention may be drawn to the case of Bologna where, in a city-state in which the only effective power was wielded by the Papal Curia, though the students retained throughout most of the sixteenth century the right to choose the anatomist, the regulation of the anatomies was the duty of the Podestà ('Mayor') or of the Cardinal-Legate himself. [2]

Massa's is a small book, and the text does not provide any spectacular 'corrections' of the Ancients; the promise that 'if God in His mercy shall continue to extend His aid to me I shall write about the remaining parts in a substantial volume' does not seem to have been fulfilled. What I am claiming for this book is not that it 'anticipated' the *Fabrica*, but that it is an important document in the still incomplete investigation of the degree to which Vesalius was not so much an innovator as the Man born in Due Season, sensitive to every indication of change, and able by his

---

[1] He was referred to as an anatomist of great promise by Guintherus of Andernach in the latter's very popular textbook *Institutiones Anatomicae*, 2nd edn. 1541, cited by Cushing, *op. cit.* p. xxvi.

[2] Webster and Gnudi, *op. cit.* pp. 59 f.

enthusiasm and urbanity to unite these diverse forces—critical, scholarly, artistic and instrumental—into a movement which ultimately swept everything before it. On such an assessment much light is shed by J. B. de C. M. Saunders and C. D. O'Malley [1] in the editorial introduction to their translation of the letter of Vesalius on blood-letting. The letter was prompted by the vigorous controversy on the presumably futile question as to whether bleeding should be resorted to at such a position as to drain the site of the supposed disorder ('derivative') or as far away as possible ('revulsive'). To the sixteenth-century physicians this was a matter of some moment, because it not only involved a fundamental point of physiological theory but the stand taken might involve a conflict of loyalties, since the former represented the original Greek position, the latter the Arab 'innovation'. A return to the Greek position had been started by Brissot, who was followed by Manardi, Fuchs, and Matteo Curti. It was when, in support of this position, Vesalius dissected the azygos vein in a human subject (about 1539) that he became convinced that Galen could not have based his anatomy on dissection of the human body. It was this conviction, and the gradual recognition of its implications, that constituted the foundation of 'modern' anatomy—the freeing of topographical anatomy from the misleading guidance of a falsely teleological physiology which could justify the assumption by Galen and his followers that the same function demanded the 'same' structure whether in animal or man. Unfortunately the history of anatomy has been obscured by the too frequent assertion, or at least implication, that it was the results of Galen's *incompetence* which the sixteenth-century anatomists were called upon to make good. What Galen saw, he described with a mastery perhaps never surpassed. What the sixteenth-century anatomists established was that no assumption, even of existence (e.g. of the *rete mirabile* beneath the brain, observed in the sheep and 'postulated' in Man on grounds of supposed physiological necessity), let alone of detailed form, can be made with regard to structure. If this be a fair assessment of the case, then the importance of Niccolò Massa is at once apparent: but it was because Vesalius brought vastly greater resources to bear that his name is associated with the anatomical 'revolution',

[1] In *Studies and Essays in the History of Science and Learning* (for George Sarton), New York, 1944.

despite the fact that even he (at any rate not until a later edition of the *Fabrica*) dare not storm the citadel of Galen's system—the alleged 'pores' in the auriculo-ventricular septum of the heart.

If from our present vantage-point we conclude that Vesalius was not the unqualified innovator he has until recently been regarded as, to his contemporaries, with the exception of a few disgruntled ones like Sylvius and Eustachio, he appeared pre-eminent. Looking back once again we can see to what extent this was justified. In the first place we are struck by the sequence of master and pupil which he created at Padua. Colombo his successor in the Chair was the first to gain publicity for the theory of the pulmonary circulation of the blood, previously announced by Servet in a theological work, all but three copies of which were burnt with him at the command of Calvin. Colombo's successor was Gabriele Fallopio, whose name is immortalised in that of the human oviduct, but whose elucidation of the auditory ossicles is by some held to be the most refined anatomical demonstration of the century. He was succeeded by his pupil Girolamo Fabrizio who first gave a detailed description of the valves in the veins already seen by Canano, Amatus Lusitanus, and drawn by Salomon Alberti. The persistence of a fundamentally Galenic outlook over half a century after the appearance of the *Fabrica* caused Fabrizio to give a wholly inadequate theory of their function, thereby missing the greatest opportunity in the history of anatomical physiology. Fortunately among his audience in the ingenious (and still extant) anatomy theatre built to his design there was a little later a young man on whom their significance was not lost—William Harvey.

But if the chief, Padua was not the only, medical school which drew crowds of promising young men from all over Europe. To what extent this invigoration of ancient institutions was due to the vision of Vesalius may be judged from a brief glance at the course of events at the University of Basel. From the foundation in 1460 there had been a Medical Faculty,[1] but apart from the 'irruption' of Paracelsus during the years 1527-30 little is heard of its activities until 1542 [2] when Vesalius took a year's leave of absence from

---

[1] F. Miescher, *Die Medizinische Facultät in Basel*, Basel, 1860. The following account is largely based on this work.

[2] Cushing says: 'Apparently he [*sc.* Vesalius] did not appear in Basel until early in January 1543', *op. cit.* p. 78.

Padua in order to superintend the printing of the *Fabrica* by Oporinus of Basel. During his stay here Vesalius undertook the first public anatomy of a human cadaver in Basel, the subsequently prepared skeleton of which is still to be seen in the University buildings overlooking the Rhine. Fifteen years were to pass before Felix Plater was to carry out another anatomy, and so little had the medical school advanced that he had attended what was then probably the greatest school outside Italy, Montpellier. From 1532—the year of the reorganisation of Basel as a protestant university—to 1560 there were only nine promotions for the degree of Doctor of Medicine, among whom however were Gesner in 1538 and Plater himself in 1557. During the next twenty-five years the number rose to 114, and from 1586 to 1610 it reached 454. 'From all parts of Germany, from Belgium, Holland, Hungary, Poland, Italy, France, England and Scotland came a steady stream of young Aesculapes.' Among those from Scotland were the Aberdonians James Cargill, the first recorded Scottish botanist (see Vol. II p. xvii) and Patrick Dun, Principal of Marischal College, whose diploma of graduation, signed by Felix Plater and other members of the Faculty, hangs in the Library of King's College. This astonishing increase in numbers and distinction was only in part the consequence of the happy circumstance of the sojourn of Vesalius in the city. Even before Vesalius had published his doctoral thesis (No. 708–1537) Sebastian Sinckeler had concluded a sketch of the *Reform of the Medical Faculty* with the wish that an anatomy should be held once a year, or at most in alternate years, and that the students should in summertime be taught the names and powers of herbs. The realisation of this prophetic wish, which was so long delayed,[1] might never have followed Vesalius's visit even after a score of years had it not been for two men of complementary talents subsequently assisted by a third, Plater, who, as we saw, started the tradition of public anatomies at latest in 1559, which, however, did not become annual events till much later. But it was the remarkable administrative sagacity and drive, aided no doubt by the best form of humanistic learning which included the Medical Doctorate of Padua, of Theodor Zwinger, which made possible

---

[1] Dr. Otto Bucher claims that an anatomy was first made at Basel by Oswald Bär, 'Die Anfänge der wissenschaftlichen Anatomie in Zürich', *Gesnerus*, 2, (1945), p. 131.

the emergence of a medical school ultimately second to none in Europe. In 1569 he recast the old laws, resolutions, and prescriptions of exercises into a well ordered set of statutes for the Medical Faculty, of which he was six times Dean. Plater, on the other hand, combined with the highest skill in anatomy a large medical practice which carried him far and wide in the surrounding country. In 1563-4, when the plague reached Basel with desolating effects, he remained with his wife in the city, earning then, as in later years, its undying gratitude for his devotion to the sick and his vigorous efforts to mitigate the worst effects of the visitation. During the period when Zwinger and Plater were in their several ways laying the foundation of Basel's greatness the Medical Faculty pressed for a third 'ordinary' Professor of Medicine to be added to the customary Chairs of Theory and Practice. In 1581 the brilliant performance of an anatomy by the young Caspar Bauhin (born in Basel in 1560 of a French father, Jean Bauhin) left no doubt as to who this third professor should be. But then as now academic changes came slowly, and it was only in 1589 that he became Professor *ordinarius anatomicus et botanicus*—the first chair of such a kind in Europe. In the same year a permanent anatomy theatre was erected and a botanic garden laid out. Nearly two centuries later William Cullen still combined the teaching of anatomy (on a much more modest scale!) and botany at Glasgow, as did his successor in the Lectureship in Chemistry, Joseph Black. Plater's work on anatomy, his first venture into print, (No. 530 is of a later edition) did not appear until he was almost fifty; by that time several anatomical works had been published by a younger man, Coiter, whose influence (see p. 205) on sixteenth-century anatomy has been rather generally overlooked.

The last fruit during the sixteenth century of the 'Vesalian Revolution' was a work (which Cole describes as being of Vesalian thoroughness) on Man's closest companion, the Horse. This was the work of Carlo Ruini of Bologna, published a few months after his death in 1598.

CHAPTER XIII

MEDICINE AND CHEMISTRY

I use this title with some hesitation for a section whose main concern is with pharmacology, since sixteenth-century *materia medica* was certainly botanical rather than chemical, as we understand those sciences today. But the century was not very far advanced before Paracelsus started the movement to extend the use of 'chemicals'—mainly of metallic origin—in the art of prescribing 'medicines'; on the other hand it was from the perfecting of methods for the extraction of the 'active principles' of herbs that the improvement of a great part of chemical technique arose. It is true that the former movement has been and is still seriously misrepresented and its importance in therapeutic practice exaggerated; but in the closing decade of the century it gave rise to an 'ideological warfare' whose place in the history of ideas has not as yet been adequately recognised. The outcome of this 'War of Ideas', which was ostensibly concerned with medical practice, was at least as important for the ultimate history of chemistry as for that of medicine: since for the next century and a half chemistry was to be mainly the handmaid of medicine. For the history of scientific ideas it is the chemical aspects of pharmacology which have special significance: the brief sketch which follows will therefore emphasise these aspects rather than those of medical therapy.

As the *Elements* of Euclid is the main fount, if not the origin, of geometry so the *Materia Medica* of Dioskurides may be regarded as for fifteen hundred years the basis of pharmacology. This view is supported by the fact that both Latin (1478) and Greek (1499) texts were available in print before the close of the fifteenth century. Yet the bare mention of this fact conceals an equally important one, namely, that several Arabic commentaries on, and extensions of, the original five books (see No. 199 for a note on the Greek additions) were printed (in Latin of course) earlier than the text of Dioskurides and subsequently in far more numerous editions within the same period. It is generally agreed that whereas the ultimate advantage to European medicine of the Arabic development of Greek *medicine* is open to question (it was already, as we saw in the case of Fuchs, hotly debated early in the sixteenth century) a large number of new and valuable drugs and modes of preparation were introduced. It will therefore be necessary to glance back over the centuries before the beginning of our period.

The *Materia Medica* of Dioskurides comprised a select list of herbs and a few materials of animal and mineral origin, together with instructions for their preparation and brief indications of their 'powers'. The appearance of this orderly and not uncritical survey in the first century A.D. was an indication of the change which medicine had undergone since the period of the Hippokratic corpus: for the latter relied more on diet and regimen and made sparing recommendation of drugs. Nevertheless, although written evidence is almost non-existent, archaeological investigation has brought to light a variety of utensils for pounding, straining, and storing drugs; also 'pictures' are extant of the highly organised trade in 'Silphium' carried on in Cyrenaica from the sixth century B.C., but which had died out, with the sudden disappearance of the plant, within living memory at the time when Pliny the Elder was writing.[1] The Greek words rhizotomoi, pharmakopoeoi, pharmakopoloi, myrepsoi testify to the existence of separate crafts: in their Latin forms these names can be traced down to the seventeenth century.

The drugs discussed by Dioskurides were mainly 'simples', that is, simple preparations of single plants, earths, etc. Galen made fashionable, though he did not originate, the practice of 'compounding' drugs, which even at a very early date reached a ludicrous degree of complication, and despite periodic opposition— usually associated with a 'back to Hippokrates' movement—remained the scandal of medicine until the end of the eighteenth century. None of these products of 'polypharmacy' attained a greater notoriety than 'theriac', which makes its first appearance in writing in the poem by the somewhat shadowy Nikandros of Kolophon printed, with the supplementary Ἀλεξιφάρμακα, together with the Greek *editio princeps* of Dioskurides by Aldus. The basis of theriac was a 'compound' of fifty ingredients devised

---

[1] A. C. Andrews, *Isis*, **33**, 232.

by Mithridates in such a way that the poison of every known animal was represented by its antidote—discovered, it is said, by experiments on prisoners. To this was later added by Andromachos the flesh of vipers prepared in a special manner. By the sixteenth century theriac had come to be regarded as a panacea, and was prepared in enormous quantities on regular occasions marked with all the signs of civic pomp, professional pride, and even social grace. The account given by Webster and Gnudi of the dispute concerning the proper characteristics of the vipers' flesh, and the authority—pharmacists or medical faculty—in which the ultimate responsibility was deemed to be vested, sheds a penetrating light on the 'emergence' of Renaissance medicine from the 'gloom' of the Middle Ages. That this was not merely a trivial clash of personalities is revealed by the fact that the dispute was resolved only after the dismissal of Aldrovandi from his university offices and his subsequent reinstatement by a decision of the Pope, to whom an appeal was made backed by the 'expert' evidence (on the question of the pregnancy of the vipers employed!) of Tagliacozzi.

Though the Greco-Roman tradition of pharmacology gradually lost its critical character by its transmission through well-meaning but not necessarily very learned monks, becoming debased by popularisation on the one hand (for instance in the Herbal of Apuleius Platonicus) and by magic on the other (as in the Anglo-Saxon leech-craft), the continuity was preserved locally in Southern Italy at Salerno. The origin of this repository of classical medicine has not yet been satisfactorily elucidated, but a manuscript of the eleventh century is extant of the well ordered book on remedies of all kinds, attributed to Gariopontos; since the manuscript is in Latin, it marks the beginning of a systematic 'Latinisation' of the Greek nomenclature of medicine. It is indicative of the subsequent swamping of this tradition by the Arabic physicians that this work, also known as *Passionarius Galeni*, was not printed until 1526. The work of Dioskurides seems to have been one of the first Greek medical works to be translated into Arabic, but the first 'definitive' rendering was that of Hunain ibn Ishaq. Since we are concerned not with the rise of Arab medicine but with what the Renaissance physicians made of it, we may achieve our purpose most satisfactorily by examining the contents of those works on pharmacology which were among the earliest to be printed.

The first thing that strikes one on looking through the surveys of medical incunabula is that works of primarily pharmacological interest are almost exclusively by Arab writers or by (mainly Italian) commentators on Arabic works. The only major exception is the *De Medicina* of A. Cornelius Celsus, one of whose 'books' contains a comprehensive list of compound medicines. Of course the incunable editions of the medieval physicians contain 'prescriptions' for specific ills, but no systematic treatment of drugs. The most notable omission is the epitome of classical pharmacy of Scribonius Largus not printed until 1528 (No. 635). In the Arabic tradition by far the most important was the work of the author known as 'Mesue'. This name was the Latin corruption of 'Maswijah', which was the name of two medical writers, the earlier of whom (IX–2) was physician to the successors of the Caliph Harun-ar-Rashid and was one of the first to translate medical works into Arabic: he is somewhat doubtfully identified with the 'Janus Damascenus' of the *Articella* (No. 47). The second was a Jacobite Christian (XI–1) about whom little is known. Failure to produce an Arabic manuscript of 'Mesue', together with other evidence, makes it highly improbable that either of these Arabic writers was the author of 'Mesue'. From the fact that Pietro d'Abano and Francesco Piemontese made 'additions' to the work it is inferred that like 'Geber' it was written under the name of a venerable Arab by a 'Latin' writer [1]—probably in the twelfth century in northern Italy. Whatever may be its origin, it was for centuries reckoned as 'the weightiest canon of the apothecary's art' (Choulant). The main parts of the text were on laxative medicines and general remedies respectively. The former shows a real understanding of the need to grade the drug as well as the dose, and gives instructions about 'correcting' the body after the use of purgatives. The latter, known as *Antidotarium* or 'Grabadin' (a Latin corruption of the Arabic *Aqrabadhin*, itself a corruption of the Greek γραφίδιον = a small treatise), contains all the new kinds of preparations—*loch, julep, syrup, rob*—introduced by the Arabs, and remained the model of all subsequent pharmacopoeias until the early nineteenth century. 'Mesue', however, was seldom printed alone, either in the fifteen Latin and five Italian incunables, or in the numerous editions which continued to appear every few years throughout the sixteenth century.

[1] Cf. Choulant, *Handbuch*, p. 351.

The contents of No. 740 may be taken as fairly typical: something must be said of each of those parts which are not merely additions to, or commentaries on, the 'Grabadin'.

The *Antidotarium Nicolai* was the pharmacological textbook of the School of Salerno.[1] In its earliest traceable form it was a small work believed to have been put together about 1100 (that is, before the full effect of the Arabic 'innovations' of Constantinus Africanus) by a scribe usually referred to as 'Nicolaus Salernitanus'; it was enlarged about fifty years later by the Salernitan physician, Matthaeus Platearius, in a work which from its *incipit* is commonly known as *Circa instans*: this accompanies the *Antidotarium* in No. 477. In 1075 Constantine,[2] a native of Carthage, who was probably engaged in the drug trade in the Mediterranean region, called at Salerno. As a result of his welcome there he probably continued his medical studies, and ultimately, after further journeyings, entered the monastery of Monte Cassino, where he passed the remainder of his life in translating Arabic works into Latin. He was an uncritical scholar, and it is difficult to disentangle his translations from compilations of his own; but the effect was incalculable: the Arabic medicine rapidly changed the character of the Salernitan teaching and spread through Western Europe with centres of dispersion in Lorraine and at Chartres. Thus less than a century later a list of the library of Bruno, Bishop of Hildesheim, contains twelve works introduced by Constantine. The *Antidotarium Nicolai*, also, as it is found in most printed versions, is much larger than that on which *Circa instans* is a commentary, the additional material having been added, it is believed, by Nicholas of Alexandria, also known as Nikolaos Myrepsos, that is, 'the maker of ointments'. This was not the end of the *Antidotarium Nicolai*; after about 1500 the author's name is often given as 'Nicholaus Pr(a)epositus', and the title of the further enlarged work as *Dispensa(to)rium ad Aromatarios*. The present view is that this was really the work of a late fifteenth-century French physician, Nicholas Prévost.

We must now return to the remaining 'additions' to 'Mesue' (See No. 740). These are: (1) *Quid pro quo*—an alphabetical list of certain drugs, followed in each case by the names of those which in

---

[1] But see bibliographical note on No. 477.
[2] Cf. J. W. Thomson, *Isis*, 12, 184-93 and H. Schipperges, 'Assimilations-Zentren Arabischer Wissenschaft in 12te Jt', *Centaurus*, 4, 325.

case of necessity may replace them in the usual prescriptions. This provides the historian with a clue to the principles on which the supposed properties of drugs were ordered. (2) *Synonyma*—an alphabetical list of alternative names, especially the 'classical' and Arabic equivalents: Choulant notes that it is sometimes seriously misleading. (3) *Liber Servitoris*—a treatise on the preparation of 'simples', attributed to the surgeon Alzahrawi (Albucasis).[1] (4) *Compendium Aromatariorum*, written by Saladino Ferro d'Ascoli in the middle of the fifteenth century, which might be described as the first comprehensive treatise on pharmacology of undoubted Western authorship, dealing with all aspects of the art.

Such then was the basis of Renaissance pharmacology; but reference to No. 477 will reveal that several other works similar in character to that of Saladino were written in Italy during the fifteenth, or early sixteenth, century; and in 1498 appeared *Ricettario Fiorentino* the first of the 'local' pharmacopoeias. Looking back at the works here briefly reviewed it is interesting to note that during the fifteenth century the Basel apothecaries were required to have copies [2] of 'Mesue', Avicenna, Serapion, Dioscorides, 'Macer Floridus', *Circa instans*, the *Synonyma* of Simon Januensis, and the *Antidotarium magnum et parvum Nicolai*. Of Avicenna's *Canon* there were more than a dozen incunable editions, and of 'Macer Floridus', the only work except Dioskurides not of Arabic origin, there was a flood of editions in the early years of the sixteenth century. Under the name 'Serapion' [3] were for a time, printed works by two different Eastern scholars— Yahya ibn Sarafyum, who wrote in Syriac in IX-2 and Ibn Sarabi (XII-2) of whom very little is known. These two came ultimately to be known as 'Serapion senior and junior' respectively, the latter's work on simples being the most influential, translated by Simon of Genoa and the Jew, Abraham of Tortosa, and printed as *Aggregator in Medicinis Simplicium* in 1473.

Throughout the centuries (XII-XV) during which 'academic' medicine was dominated by Arab pharmacology there had persisted a widespread 'lay' tradition of herbal medicine more or less independent of that developing in the universities and which

---

[1] But see Choulant, *Handbuch*, p. 373.

[2] J. A. Haefliger, *Pharmaceutica Acta Helvetiae*, 2, (1927), 140, referred to in Kramers and Urdang, *op. cit.* p. 29.

[3] Choulant, *Handbuch*, pp. 345, 371.

had grown out of a complex union of the corrupt tradition of Dioskurides deriving from the fifth century and the Salernitan tradition of *Circa instans*. The evidence for this lay tradition lies chiefly in the vernacular herbals, one of which, of special relevance to our period, has recently been edited.[1] This Middle English manuscript, on which the first part of Bancke's Herbal (printed 1526) was subsequently based is believed to have been written in Fransham Manor, Norfolk, in (XV-I). It is an excellent example of the complex tradition mentioned above. The descriptions of 248 plants include recognition marks, locality of growth, and uses—domestic as well as medicinal—'explained' in terms of their humoral characteristics. This practice of having at hand a systematic guide for the benefit of a large household and its dependants is paralleled over a century later by the manuscript compiled in the hand of the legendary beauty, Philipina Welser, wife of Archduke Ferdinand II of Tyrol, whose splendid castle of Amras (still to be seen on the hillside above Innsbruck in all its sixteenth-century magnificence) is believed to have been the regular meeting-place of physicians from the surrounding countryside (Karl Beer, *Gesnerus*, Vol. 7 (1950), p. 80). Further evidence of the importance of this tradition is the fact that when Fuchs and the other pioneer 'academic' herbalists set about the task of drawing up a definitive list of medicinal herbs available in Central Europe they freely admitted the valuable services of local herb-gatherers (Arber, *Singer*, I, 317).

On the question as to the real value of this prodigious activity in searching and cataloguing herbal remedies a certain amount of caution is still necessary. It is easy to point at the apparently entirely illusory character of the 'cures' of syphilis (see below, p. 281) effected by the widespread use of decoctions of the Guaiac tree, of which the most that could be said is well expressed in the mumbled incantation of the Scots sacristan as he scattered the Holy Water over the heads of the faithful, 'If it daes ye nae guid, it'll dae ye nae hairm'. Over the Peruvian 'Bezoar Stone', 'starred' in the title of Monardes's book (No. 456) and pictured in the translation by de l'Ecluse, it is better, perhaps, in this account of the century of the 're-birth of science' to draw a discreet veil.

---

[1] *Agnus Castus, a Middle English Herbal*, ed. with a long Introduction by Gösta Brodin, Uppsala and Cambridge, Mass., 1950. I am indebted to my wife for reading and discussing this work with me.

Yet, on the other hand, as Dr. Arber has reminded us (*loc. cit* sup.), the production and sale of drugs derived from the genus *Salix* (aspirin and phenacetin are both synthetic *derivatives* from the 'active principle' of these plants) has surpassed anything that Fuchs and his contemporaries could have imagined in their most optimistic moods; and the fascinating history of the use of *Ephedra vulgaris* and its derivatives goes back four thousand years.[1]

The almost completely Arabic origin of the pharmacological literature at the beginning of the sixteenth century posed a special problem for the humanist physicians. In almost every branch of science except alchemy (which was not quite respectable) and optics (in which few seemed to be interested) there was a Greek tradition which might plausibly be regarded as superior to the Arab deviation; a cry of 'back to Ptolemy, Aristotle, Theophrastos, Hippokrates, and Galen' could have been, and with the possible exception of Theophrastos was, effectively raised. But in pharmacology, all allowance being made for Dioskurides, on whom the Arabs had built, there was nothing in Greco-Roman literature on anything like a comparable scale to 'go back to'. Even an inveterate anti-Arabist like Fuchs had to admit that where drugs were concerned the Arab contributions had to be taken seriously. The Arabs had in fact done their job so thoroughly that there were only two ways [2] in which the structure of the science could be modified. One way was to examine the enormous number of drugs with a critical eye and weed out accretions and inconsistencies; the alternative was to reject the whole basis of Arab (virtually Galenic) theory and start again from the beginning. The former, conservative, course was taken by Antonio Brasavola, the latter by Philip Bombast von Hohenheim, who usually referred to himself as 'Theophrastus', but is best known by his ambiguous Latinisation of the latter part of his name as 'Paracelsus'.

The lives of these two men, so utterly unlike in most respects, had one significant common feature: they both [3] received part of

---

[1] H. Haas, *Spiegel der Arznei*, Berlin, 1956, pp. 6-8.

[2] No reference has been made here to later Arabic pharmacology (e.g. al-Idrisi, al-Malaqi, al-Gafiqi) who, though perhaps more original and comprehensive, were without recognisable influence on Western workers. Cf. Mieli, *op. cit.* pp. 198, 205-6, 212.

[3] Though the evidence for this is considerable, I. Ghibellini was unable to find at Ferrara any documentary record of the presence or graduation of Paracelsus (*Gesnerus*, **9**, (1952), 149-53. Cf. W. Pagel, *Paracelsus*, Basel, 1958, p. 10.

their medical training at the University of Ferrara, which at that time rivalled Padua in respect of independence of thought. Since Paracelsus probably graduated M.D. in 1515 when Brasavola was only fifteen, it is unlikely that their studies in medicine overlapped in point of time, but they were both taught by the same masters—Nicolò Leoniceno and Giovanni Manardi—noted for their recognition that the study of medicine could not be furthered by exclusive concern with books. On Brasavola, as eminent in classical scholarship as in medicine, the effect of this teaching was to induce him to work systematically through all the simple drugs and pharmaceutical preparations in the attempt to discover their real, as distinct from their imagined, virtues, and to publish the results in a series of monographs beginning with *Examen omnium Simplicium . . .* 1536 and ending with *De Medicamentis . . . Catharticis* 1555—six works in all, in numerous editions. That this was not a merely literary undertaking based on the opinions of the recognised 'authorities' is at once revealed by the opening passage of the first volume, in which it is shown that Brasavola recognised the importance of visiting the 'inhospitable and inaccessible Alps' to see the plants in their native haunts. But the effect of this work on the writer was not to dethrone the writings of Galen, but on the contrary to crown the old Master afresh by the compilation of an analytical index of the works of Galen, which, based on the first, was added to subsequent, editions of the works printed by the Giunti. The actual result of Brasavola's critical pharmacology is not particularly impressive; his virtue is that the criticism relies more on experience and even experiment than on the weighing of authorities: there are many valuable drugs not mentioned by Dioskurides, but equally their praise by Arab writers is not a sufficient guarantee of their value. That Brasavola, though critical, remained loyal to the classical tradition is revealed by the astonishing range of his honorific appointments—to Princes, Popes and Emperors.

How different was the reaction of Paracelsus.[1] What we know of

---

[1] The attempt made here and in the following chapters to assess the significance of Paracelsus in the science of the Renaissance was completed and submitted to Dr. Walter Pagel before I was aware of the imminent publication of his book *Paracelsus—An Introduction to the Philosophical Medicine in the Era of the Renaissance* (S. Karger, Basel, 1958). Dr. Pagel very generously drew my attention to two or three serious misconceptions, the correction of which appears below. I have since had the privilege of reading his noble work, but apart from the addition of a few references and one or two

his life is mainly a record or a rumour of his hurried departure from some town or other usually in consequence of the not unreasonable anger of the local authorities—ecclesiastical, academic or medical—at some new excess in his ceaseless denunciation of almost every person or opinion held in high regard by the orthodox. If there is any substance in the oft-repeated characterisation of the Renaissance as the liberation of the mind from the trammels of authority and tradition, it is not, in the case of Medicine at least, to the Humanists that we must look to exemplify the view, but to their arch-enemy who railed upon them as empty rhetoricians, bookworms, slaves of that servant of the Devil, Galen, *pseudomedici*, utterly ignorant of their craft, and far more concerned with fine raiment and academic ceremonial than with the care of the sick. Here, surely, is the embodiment of the 'liberation of the spirit' we are seeking; here indeed is one who unceasingly appeals to patient observation and experience, who on his own admission learnt far more from miners, farmers, wine-growers, peasant women, and metal workers than from any product of the universities: from everyone, in fact, engaged in *doing* things instead of ignorantly *talking* about them. Here it seems is the prophet of empiricism, of experimental enquiry, of natural knowledge—at least of those parts which are not founded on mathematics. Why then, it may well be asked, was not a sketch of Paracelsus added to round off the picture of 'Renaissance Man' provided by those of Alberti, Cardano, and Dürer, instead of being relegated to a corner of a department of Medicine. I confess that the temptation was great; but as in the case of Leonardo, though for different reasons, it had to be resisted. In the first place the passions which surged around his person in his lifetime have continued about his writings ever since: Paracelsus, like the 'Renaissance' he does in so many ways brilliantly represent, is still a topic concerning which a mass of confused and contradictory opinions is held, and about which a Cloud of Unknowing has been spread by writers, authoritative in their own spheres, who have either merely copied the time-honoured judgments of the general 'histories', or who have hidden the subject of their superficial study behind the dust raised by their own prejudices. In the writings of no character in the history of science is it easier to

amplifications I have thought it better not to alter anything I had written since to do so would have detracted from such small merit as it may possess in originality.

find evidence for some novel, daring, and enlightened 'anticipation'—or in another place to feed a conviction of his obscurantism, superstition, and utter blindness to the virtues of many of his
contemporaries. If he sought to liberate the mind from the thraldom of the logic-chopping of the later Schoolmen and the
unsupported theorising of the ancients, he was determined to replace these by an array of insensible active beings and occult
powers in things, the only certain consequence of whose adoption
would have been the strangling at birth of science as we have come
to know it. And for the authority of Galen and Avicenna he
exchanged the authority of 'Theophrastus', the interpreter of
God—'Mich hat nicht der Himmel zu einem Arzt gemacht.
Gott hat mich gemacht. Der Himmel hat nit Artzet zu machen;
es ist ein kunst ausz Gott, nicht ausz den Himmeln'—all this in
reply to those who called him 'Lutherus Medicorum'.[1] Clearly
neither of these assessments of Paracelsus is the true one; nor,
paradoxically, is their mere joint assertion. No one, in my view, has
the slightest chance of placing Paracelsus in the context of the
history, as distinct from the annals, of science until he has read and
re-read a few at least of the 'apologetic' works of the master, such
as the *Paragranum* and *Defensiones*, with a mind at once critical
and sympathetic—critical of his extravagant claims, sympathetic
with his struggle, which was determined by the peculiar circumstances of the times in which he lived, and which in his
obscure modes of thought he from time to time transcended.
Thus, as I see it, it is useless to thumb over the works to discover
whether he was the 'first chemist' or merely an aberrant
'alchemist' who made a few lucky shots: it is useless, since with
reference to Paracelsus these alternatives predetermine the
approach, thus forcing an answer in terms of categories inappropriate to his whole system of ideas. For, in my view, the
contribution of Paracelsus was, as I have already maintained in
the case of Copernicus, mainly *philosophical*; and this despite his
insistence on the appeal to experience—indeed because of it;
for the harvest of what we should call 'scientific' knowledge was

[1] Ed. Joh. Huser, *Ander Theil der bücher . . . Paracelsi*, Basel, 1589, p. 16. Sir William
Osler and others used the expression 'Luther of Medicine' in a complimentary sense;
but Paracelsus himself says: 'Mit was Spott habt ihr mich auszplasimiert ich sey
Lutherus Medicorum . . . (*ibid.*). Cf. the Latin edition—'Quanta cum contumelia me
proclamastis pro Luthero Medicorum'—*Op. Lat. Red.* Basel, 1575 vol. II, p. 469.

not really very impressive. This, to a large extent novel, attitude, preached with daemonic fervour and mixed with a mass of details irrelevant to the empirical method itself but touching his contemporaries to the quick, caused so great a stir as to ensure that the lesson should never again be wholly forgotten. But this again is something less than half the truth. For the astounding success of the empirical method (combined, indeed, a century later with the 'mathematical way' of which Paracelsus had no inkling) ensured the almost complete neglect of his prior insight, namely of the pre-eminence of the spirit in man's nature, and of the way to knowledge through natural piety. Of this something will be said in the final chapter.

The complexity of the Paracelsian question is clearly such that no attempt could have been made to resolve it here even had it been within the author's competence: hence the omission of this great man from those chosen as representative types of the Renaissance. What has been said of him must be taken as a warning against accepting at their face value the partial judgments that are still widely current. There remains the question as to why he has been included where he has.

My reason for relegating the consideration of Paracelsus to the section of medicine and chemistry is mainly that I believe it possible, without drowning in the sea of Paracelsian polemics, to give point in this particular field to the rather ill-supported protests I have made in regard to the wider problem of his place in the history of science. Also, as has already been hinted, towards the end of the sixteenth century there arose a violent controversy, between his disciples and the self-appointed custodians of medical orthodoxy, whose importance for the history of ideas has, I believe, not been sufficiently exploited. This could not even be touched upon in any useful way without a previous attempt to present the issues freed from the over-simplification which not uncommonly characterises references to this *cause célèbre*.

The traditional account of the importance of Paracelsus in the history of chemistry and medicine is commonly based on the following propositions: (1) He lectured at Basel in German and publicly burnt the books of Galen and/or Avicenna. (2) He said that the object of chemistry is not to make gold but to prepare medicines. (3) He introduced metallic compounds into pharmacy. (4) He was a successful surgeon, and effected numerous startling cures with the aid of laudanum. In each of these statements there is sufficient truth to ensure their having been handed on since the beginnings of the history of medicine: but taken out of their context they still seriously mislead.

Of Paracelsus's habit of 'verteutschen',[1] as he himself called it, there is of course no doubt. The use of the vernacular does not seem to have been repeated in a university until William Cullen opened his course as Lecturer in Chemistry at Glasgow in 1747. The tradition of the 'burning of the books' appears in many forms. Paracelsus himself claims to have thrown 'die Summe der Bücher' on to the students' bonfire (Huser, *op. cit.* p. 11)—a claim supported by a witness as close to Paracelsus as Sebastian Franck.[2] But more important than such a symbolic gesture was Paracelsus's systematic and detailed attacks on Galen (and Avicenna) scattered about the *Labyrinthus Medicorum* and other polemical writings—'Sagen Sie mire welches ist zur rechten thür hinein gangen in die Artzney? Durch Avicennam, Galenum, Mesue, Rasim, etc. oder durch das Liecht d'Natur? Dann da sind zwen Eingang: ein ander eingang ist in den bemelten Büchern, ein ander eingang ist in d'Natur . . .' (Huser, *op. cit.* p. 195). Though Paracelsus and Galen may have agreed in their insistence that the object of the physician is the cure of a sick *person* rather than a 'disease', yet their means of attaining this end had nothing in common. Whereas Galen relied upon a highly rationalised system in which every thing followed with logical rigour from the largely fallacious hypothesis of indwelling humours, Paracelsus based his treatment upon a wide and varied experience of actual cases. The need to release Medicine from the stranglehold of the humoral *system*—though it took more than two centuries to achieve—was perhaps the greatest of Paracelsus's insights.

'The object of chemistry is not to make gold but to prepare medicines' is of all the sayings referred to Paracelsus the most important, and, wrenched from its context and mistranslated as it usually is, the most liable to mislead. To many a modern reader it probably summons up a picture of a forerunner of W. H. Perkin trying to synthesise quinine. A typical example of what Paracelsus wrote is: 'Nicht als die sagen *Alchimia* mache Gold mache

[1] Huser, *op. cit.* p. 70.
[2] My attention was drawn to this by Dr. W. Pagel.

Silber: hie ist das fürnemmen Mach *Arcana* und richte dieselbigen gegen den kranckheiten' [1] (*Italic* in original). Clearly it is *alchemy* Paracelsus was talking about—there was nothing outside mining circles that could properly be called chemistry until, say, half a century later (see p. 179). Also the word 'medicine' as an equivalent for *Arcanum* misleads to an even greater degree; for what were these *arcana*? 'Diss *Arcanum* is weiter ein *Chaos* und ist den *Astris* möglich zu führen wie ein Federn vom Windt. . . . Und darnach soll das wissen da sein was *Astrum* in diesen *Arcano* sey unnd darnach was Astrum dieser Kranckheit sey, was *Astrum* in der Artzney sey wieder die Kranckheit' ('This *Arcanum* is furthermore a *chaos* and is able to be driven by the *Astrum* as is a feather by the wind . . . and accordingly is knowledge given of what *Astrum* is in this *Arcanum* and what is the *Astrum* of the disease, what *Astrum* in the medicine works against the disease'). 'The *arcanum* is a *chaos*'—a little further on Paracelsus says that the *Arcana* are *Volatilia*. Whatever he may have meant by this [2] it is perfectly clear that it is not vitriol, flowers of antimony, or iron that effects a cure, but some occult influence directed by the *astrum* and of which the 'chemical' is only a vehicle. 'Astrum' is a technical term as untranslatable as 'arcanum', but it is of central importance in the attempt to assess the significance of Paracelsus in the history of science. The *astra* are neither stars nor planets, as such, since Paracelsus disagreed with the majority of his contemporaries in their belief that men's lives are determined by the 'dominance' of individual planets at the time of birth or on other critical occasions in their lives. The *astra* are not created by the stars—they are not created at all—but have always existed in God's 'nature'. The stars, however, provide the conditions for their development. Herbs and metals likewise are only the signs of the complementary *arcana*. Yet the various *astra* and *arcana* are associated with particular stars; hence the specificity

---

[1] Huser, *op. cit.* p. 65.

[2] Dr. W. Pagel has warned me against attaching too great significance to the juxtaposition by Paracelsus of *chaos* and *volatilia*. Despite the (probably correct) philological identification nothing which Paracelsus wrote, he believes, justifies any close analogy between the *specific* Paracelsian *chaos* and the universal *gas* conceived by J. B. van Helmont at the end of the century. (See W. Pagel, 'The Religious and Philosophical Aspect of van Helmont's Science and Medicine' Bull. Hist. Med. Suppt. 2 (1942). This is a most suggestive study of the transition to 'modern' modes of thought of the seventeenth century).

of the former and the significance of the latter. And it is this postulation—for as such it must appear to us—of a *specific* [1] origin and cure of each disease which most concerns us here. It is true that the conception is expressed in the fantastic 'correspondences' of the ancient conviction that the whole being of Man is a microcosmic image of the macrocosm, but it is one of the chief functions of the historian of science to recognise the formal pattern of relationships in all creative thought when freed from the accidents of contemporary modes of visualisation: hence the fascination of Paracelsus for so many modern scholars, not counting those who would make of him a cult, even to the extent of attributing to him the 'discovery' of radioactivity and cosmic rays!

No attempt can be made here to unravel the unthinkably complex—and often inconsistent—pathology and therapeutics which Paracelsus developed over the years. To me it appears as a phase in the eternal dialectic of thesis of 'disease as disturbance of natural balance' and antithesis of 'disease as specific entity'. The former was expressed by Galen in *terms* of non-existent entities ('humours') defined only formally ('hot-dry', etc.); therapy was based on a purely hypothetical and equally formal armoury of herbal 'powers'. Reform was blocked by the vagueness and arbitrariness of the characteristics: nothing but a revolution could open the way. This Paracelsus provided. And through the equal confusion of his doctrine and the even more fantastic nature of *his* terms there shone the prospect of a system of *testable* relations: 'this disease is due to the "virtue" having gone out of the blood; here is the metal (iron) which is the sign of the "virtue" which will restore it.' The Galenic notion of 'harmony' has not been so much superseded, as the necessity of *specific* definition of its elements affirmed. We have travelled far—perhaps not always in the right direction—from Galen and Paracelsus. Our present phase of synthesis in the dialectic emphasises less the Paracelsian 'disease as entity' than the Galenic '*individual* harmony of humours'; the synthesis consists in the fact that our 'humours' are not the vacuous notions of the 'hot-and-the-dry' but the Paracelsian *quintae essentiae* in the concrete and testable form of vitamins, viral toxins, and the like. Though Paracelsus made

[1] I am indebted to Dr. Pagel for pointing out to me the importance of this conception.

little enough progress in the development of a chemical pathology he at least showed that it was possible.

So much then for the *astra* and *arcana*, which it must be admitted resemble 'chemicals' about as little as they did, in Paracelsus's elegant phrase, the 'soupy muck' (*Suppenwust*) [1] of herbal decoctions prescribed by his contemporary 'rhetorical prescription-writers '. How then are we to justify the claim that he showed the way to a chemical pathology? The answer lies in his views as to the nature of *alchimey*. Alchemy is the art of removing the dross (the four Aristotelian *corpora*) and leaving the *quinta essentia*, which is the *arcanum*, behind. The alchemist-physician is here not the efficient cause, which is the *astrum* directed by heaven, but is adept in providing the right conditions. . . . This seems no more promising than the *arcanum*. But if we are patient enough to listen to Paracelsus pointing out the natural models, we may agree that here, hidden within a mass of almost psychopathic symbolic dross, the seed of alchemy is beginning to germinate into the future fruitful plant of chemistry. For it is in the rotting of the seed in the earth to release the plant, the fermentation of the grape whence comes the wine (and its marvellous spirit first named by him 'alcohol'), the refining of the impure gold and silver in the fire, releasing of the iron from the ore—in these and many more are we to see alchemy; though it is only to those processes of *perfecting* by man's agency—smelting and cooking, for instance—that the name 'alchemy' in the strict sense is to be applied. 'Also volgt d'Archeus der inwendig *Vulcanus* hernach der weisz zu circulirn und Preparirn nach den Stucken und ausztheilung wie die kunst in ihr selbst vermag mit Sublimiern, Distilliern, Reverberiern etc.' ('And here follows the *Archeus*, the indwelling *Vulcanus*, the fire-alchemist, who knows how to circulate and prepare according to the fragments and their distribution, as the art [*sc*. alchemy] itself effects by sublimation, distillation, reverberation etc.'). Paracelsus tells us more about this 'Alchemist' inhabiting the stomach in his *Buch von den Tartarischen Kranckheiten*, the third of the books accepted by the provincial government (*Landleute*) of the Grand Duchy of Carinthia (*Kärnten*) for publication but actually never printed in his lifetime. In this work on diseases caused by obstruction

---

[1] Huser, *op. cit.* pp. 77 *passim*, 159, 64 f., 212 f., 216.

through any kind of coagulation Paracelsus put forward the view that all such diseases are due to the spontaneous separation of the 'impure' from the 'pure' such as may be observed in wine (whence the name), fruit sap, and water. If, for instance, the wine has not been 'perfected' before consumption then the *Archeus* 'whom God has endowed with such arts and *Magnalia*' will carry out the separation, in urine and faeces. Unfortunately the *Archeus* has his 'days off'—then a 'tartaric' disease is to be expected. This introduction of a superfluous animistic principle by Paracelsus has naturally been regarded as 'unfortunate' by modern historians, even as 'in a measure inconsistent with his central theory' (Kremers and Urdang). 'Unfortunate' for the emergence of chemistry it may have been; but, as has already been urged, Paracelsus was not thinking in terms of chemistry but of an enlightened extension of alchemy: his 'central theory' was animism run riot, in a manner characteristic of much renaissance thought (cf. Cardano, and on the cosmic scale, even Kepler—see below, p. 284) but which would have caused a shudder among the despised 'scholastics' of the thirteenth and fourteenth centuries.

With the third claim for Paracelsus—that he 'introduced' metallic remedies for internal use and more efficient methods of extraction—we can deal with much more briefly. Of his *use* of metallic remedies on a much more extensive scale than previously there is no doubt; nor of his use of alcohol for the preparation of tinctures; our only concern is to assess the degree of his originality and the reason for the misleading emphasis which I believe has marked most accounts of his contribution to knowledge. Metallic preparations—of mercury, iron, lead, arsenic, antimony, for instance—are described in the Fourth Book of Dioskurides, indications of their 'powers' being, however, somewhat vague and in some cases absent: such evidence as there is points to the restriction of their use to *external* treatment. That their use never completely died out may perhaps be inferred from references in the *Antidotarium Nicolai*. In the version 'Nicolai Praepositi' (which may have been written about the time of Paracelsus's birth) there is a list of more than fifty 'mineralia', with which the apothecary ought to provide himself. These include a number of precious stones (as in Dioskurides) and different 'forms' of the same material, for example, 'calx'. Of special importance is the impression given by some writers that Paracelsus *introduced* mercury and antimony: this view is at once corrected by the presence in the *Dispensatorium* of a complete 'chapter', *De Antimonio*, and a section on the dangers of excessive use of mercury, suggesting a long previous history. Similar warnings (with the signs of danger) are given in the printed version of the *Conciliator* of Pietro d'Abano, which even if they were an editorial interpolation certainly antedated the birth of Paracelsus. Any question of 'introduction' of metallic remedies can therefore not be sustained. The case for 'progress' in their administration must rest on the demonstration of improved means of preparation and a clearer understanding of their application.[1] Paracelsus's use of 'alcohol' was certainly frequent and skilful: his tinctures must have been far more effective than the *Suppenwust* he so often declaimed against. His rationale likewise was sound up to a point, namely, that there exists in every natural product an essential part, the remainder being useless dross. The limit of usefulness was passed when he naïvely made preparations of the 'essence' of gold, antimony, and other simple (and insoluble!) substances; but there is no more justification in pressing this point against him than there would be in denouncing all endocrine therapy on account of the exaggerated hopes (based on ignorance of the interconnections of the secreting glands) held out in the third decade of this century. But a more formidable count against Paracelsus-worship is the fact that there was nothing original in this. We have already seen that a detailed account of the theory of the quintessence and of the use of alcohol as an extractive was available in manuscript by the mid fourteenth century, written almost certainly by Ioannes de Rupescissa. Though this did not appear in print till after Paracelsus's death the essentials were available in 1500, and in a greatly expanded form in 1512 (No. 102) in the works on pharmacology and distillation written by the surgeon, Hieronymus Br(a)un-

---

[1] Paracelsus's recognition of both the efficacy and the dangers of mercurial treatment of syphilis reveals a critical appreciation based on extensive observation—see Pagel, *Paracelsus*, p. 24, and for an assessment of his improved methods of preparation and administration of existing remedies, p. 276. Of special interest is Dr. Dobler's repetition of several of Paracelsus's preparations with apparatus sufficiently similar to what would have been available to Paracelsus. These have confirmed in a marked degree the latter's insight and his discovery of tartar emetic long before Mynsicht, (*Pharm. Acta Helv.* **32** (1957), 245). Dr. Dobler kindly supplied me with off-prints of several articles.

schwig, in the German language so beloved by Paracelsus, so hardly to have been overlooked by a young student voracious for 'new' ideas, and, especially, practical arts. Moreover in a similar work published in 1526 (No. 694) Ulstadt candidly admits that it is largely a development of the earlier ideas of Ioannes de Rupescissa, Ramon Lull (but see below, p. 299), Arnald de Villanova and others.[1]

Looking at Paracelsus's output with a dispassionate eye—if this is yet possible—one finds it difficult to pick out any single innovation, except in regard to a few new remedies, such as 'spiritus vitrioli' (ether), whose analgesic properties might have assisted the cure of some diseases (Pagel, *Paracelsus*, pp. 276 f), together with a few much more efficacious preparations, particularly of antimony and iron: he is also credited with the discovery that goitre is a mineral deficiency disease. His 'laudanum' was the subject of a special study by H. E. Sigerist,[2] who claimed that whatever it was that Paracelsus used, allegedly with such remarkable success, it was not the preparation of opium to which the name was later given. Sigerist's reasons for this view were that there is evidence that Paracelsus did actually prescribe opium, but that the characteristics ascribed to his 'laudanum' fitted much better the ancient 'ladanum'—a gum resin prepared from certain plants of the family *Cistaceae*. Perhaps in relation to pharmacology and chemistry we may not unfairly compare Paracelsus with Vesalius in anatomy: neither of these great men added any outstandingly important item to the sum of human knowledge, but each combined a wholesome contempt for *mere* authority with an uncanny sense of more effectively harnessing existing knowledge, techniques, and ideas in the service of discovery. Paracelsus, less cautious and more imaginative, provided the basis for far more serious errors than did Vesalius, but obversely sowed the seeds of further progress, the harvest of which is still being gathered. Of the harvest which followed more closely on his death we must now take notice—both of the good grain and the tares.

Apart from his *Grosse Wundartznei* (1536), the tracts on the use of guaiac wood and mercury in the *Frantzosische Kranckheit*

---

[1] After the above was written I found that Dr. R. P. Multhauf had actually claimed that Io. de Rupescissa took the decisive step of turning alchemy towards the preparation of medicines, *Isis*, **45**, 359.   [2] H. E. Sigerist, *Bull. Hist. Med.* **9**, 530.

(1529-30), and a sketch of his course of lectures at Basel (1527-8), no major work by Paracelsus was printed in his lifetime. Despite the friendship and respect of Erasmus, the elder Froben, and even a confirmed Galenist like Guinther of Andernach, local pressure was brought to bear to prevent the publication of his manuscripts. As a consequence it was not until towards the close of the century, by which time according to Sudhoff's reckoning well over 200 editions of his very numerous works had been printed, that his influence became sufficiently powerful to provoke a more or less organised reaction. Meanwhile the orthodox pharmacology had been greatly strengthened by the establishment of the first pharmacopoeia by a local government (see No. 174 of Valerius Cordus), and of the, in their way, admirable critical works by Sylvius, Vesalius's teacher at Paris (No. 664), and Mattioli—the latter's being nominally a text and commentary on Dioskurides, but actually an 'up-to-date' and largely original work. It is significant that in neither of these works is there any protest against the wider use of metallic remedies; Mattioli, on the contrary, provides a most interesting and detailed case-history of a physician, who, when all else had failed, saved his own life, as he thought, by the use of antimony. About the same time appeared a book called 'Euonymus . . . on Secret Remedies': there was no author's name, but in 1569 there was a new edition (including a second 'book'), in which the editor, Caspar Wolph, made it clear that Gesner had more or less completed the work before his death. Whether the latter was loth to attach his name to an 'unorthodox' work on medicines (it contains a great many 'chemicals' and information about their preparation) during his lifetime is uncertain, but it does not seem to have attracted very wide attention, though it was Englished (somewhat loosely) by Sir George Baker under the title *The Newe Jewell of Health* in 1576.

It is unlikely that a definite date [1] could be assigned to the outbreak of Ideological Warfare between the 'chemists' and the orthodox physicians; but the year 1575 saw the first exchange of shots in print. The diatribe of Jacques Aubert 'contra chemistas'

---

[1] As late as 1571 Ioannes Guinther of Andernach, in his *De Medicina veteri et nova* . . . could write of the Art of Chemistry as being suited to the treatment of the most intractable diseases, adding the typical 'humanist' comment: ' . . . quam olim diu obscuratam Paracelsus Eremita nostra tempestate rursus illustrare augereque coepit . . .'. (*Praefatio.* This interesting work does not seem to have been given the attention it deserves.)

has already been referred to in connection with the Paracelsian theory of the origin of metals; but it was accompanied by an attack on the Paracelsian remedies. To both of these Joseph Duchesne, physician to Henry of Navarre, replied in the same year. In his reply to the 'slanderous letter in which Aubertus tried to overturn some remedies of the "Paracelsians", as he calls them' Duchesne makes clear two points which some comparatively recent historians have overlooked: first, that he was not prepared to be described as a 'Paracelsian', though he believed that several of the latter's remedies were 'almost divine'; and second, that the 'laudanum' then being prescribed by the iatrochemists *was* soporific *and* did contain 'suc de pavot' (opium—see above, p. 255). Both points are important; the former because it shows that even at the *beginning* the controversy was not, as it has so often been represented, a straight issue between 'Paracelsists' and 'Galenists'; the second, because although an experienced physician like Duchesne, well aware as he shows himself to have been of the dangers of 'laudanum', might well have used it with valuable results, the true 'Paracelsians', undisciplined by a university career, may well have spread havoc by its indiscriminate use. Though the contestants in this first exchange were both French, the *casus belli* seems to have been recognised on the other side of Europe, for in 1585 Iohannes Crato wrote from Breslau a vigorous onslaught on 'the iniquities of the chemists' in a foreword to a revised edition of the posthumously collected works of Falloppio.[1] But it was of course the Faculty of Medicine at Paris which about 1575 forbade the use of antimony as an internal remedy. This in itself might have been justified as a precautionary measure pending further investigation; that, however, was not the way of official bodies in the sixteenth century. But quite apart from any question as to how such a ban should be applied the issue was raised to a far more serious level by the publication in 1603 of Duchesne's *De Priscorum Philosophorum verae Medicinae Materia. . . . (On the 'Matter' of the True Medicine of the Ancient Philosophers . . .* 'materia' may involve a conscious play on words, namely, 'Materia Medica'

---

[1] The stimulus to this long and seemingly irrelevant effusion seems to have been a doubt whether Falloppio, or at least his followers, had not started meddling in matters better left alone (Falloppio's tract on Fossils is included in the edition). Crato gives a clear account of the theory of the *tria prima* (see above, p. 167) but is shocked at the implication that these form the ultimate basis of the human body.

R

in its technical sense and also an 'affair' or (legal) 'cause'. The point at issue was no longer metallic or any other 'new' remedies, but whether or no the rising science of chemistry should be allowed to play any part in the ancient discipline of Medicine. On the appearance of Duchesne's work the elder Jean Riolan, having persuaded the Faculty of Paris to appoint him *censor*, published within the year an anonymous pamphlet *Apologia pro Hippocratis et Galeni Medicina* (No. 572). He was hardly likely to be an impartial judge, seeing that he had already in the dedication to his *Methodus Medendi* (1598) referred to 'quidam chymista, qui suo stibio morbos deploratos suscipit sanandos' ('a so-called chemist who undertakes the cure, with his antimony, of diseases given up as incurable'), ending with the objurgation 'ut vestrum nomen sit terrori impostoribus qui . . . faciunt (que) per mortes experimenta' ('let your name be a terror to those impostors who . . . make experiments by sacrificing the lives of others'). Confusion was at once introduced into the dispute by the title of Riolan's abusive pamphlet, which implied that Duchesne was attacking Hippokrates and Galen as such. This allegation the latter categorically denied in a reply published in the following year (No. 216 is of a later edition). In the *Lectori* of this work he claimed that never had he strayed from the 'Royal and broad path of the Dogmatics' [followers of Hippokrates] but numbered himself among the 'Hermetics', in whose ranks were numerous English and Scottish members, Dee being specifically named, perhaps because he had lectured to large audiences in Paris. This defence 'stirred up Riolan's hornets' as Libavius put it, and within the year another anonymous tract appeared (No. 574). At this stage the elder Riolan seems to have handed over Duchesne to his son who continued the struggle with two tracts (Nos. 575 and 576) in 1605. The following year Libavius brought out a greatly enlarged version of his *Alchymia* (No. 396), in which, by way of an introduction to his *Commentaria* on the art, he wrote a *Defensio alchemiae et refutatio objectionum ex censura Scholae Parisiensis*. This brought the elder Riolan back into the fray with his *Ad Libavimaniam* (No. 573). According to the 'history' of the affair, with which Riolan opens, Turquet de Mayerne, at one time physician to James I in England, came to Duchesne's aid after the *censura*. Riolan then addressed Libavius, accusing him, as author of an attack on the Paracelsian, Gramanus, of inconsistency. Enraged by what he considered a studied misrepresentation of the whole issue and a personal attack on himself in particular, together with other eminent physicians, Libavius in the course of a year drew up a detailed refutation of Riolan's indictment running to 926 pages (No. 397). As a personal counterblast it missed fire; for in his *Lectori* Libavius admitted that 'when the book was almost finished and revised the news of Riolan's death spread abroad', whence, with a show of generosity, he agreed to 'leave his bones to rest in peace and deal only with that Riolan whom, in his books against chemistry, he had himself devised (*pinxit*)'. *Alchymia triumphans* nevertheless will always have an important place in the history of science; since it not only provides a comprehensive (and seemingly objective) account of the successive stages of the War of Ideas, but probably played a decisive part in establishing *iatrochemistry*—hence chemistry itself—as a discipline, not yet indeed wholly in its own right, but as a more and more honoured handmaid to medicine. For Libavius was a many-sided man: originally a doctor of medicine, he later combined the practice of medicine with direction of the Latin school at Rothenburg; at his death in 1616 he was Director of the *Gymnasium* at Coburg. With a thorough knowledge and critical appreciation of the 'Ancient Medicine' he combined a command of a vigorous and fluent, if occasionally somewhat barbarous, Latin style; so that he was able to meet the academic Riolan on his own ground and to demonstrate the confusion and bigotry of his attitude. A brief review of some of the points raised in the *Alchymia triumphans* should enable us to get a fairly clear picture of the real nature of the issues which were at stake, and thus to assess the quality of iatrochemical thought at the turn of the century.

In his *Lectori* Libavius makes clear his belief that Riolan's attack on Duchesne, the 'growing splendour' of alchemy and of the remedies prepared by means of its study, was due at least in part to envy, in part to fear that the substitution of the name 'Hermetic' or 'Chymiatric' for the more usual 'Dogmatic' would lead to the gradual banishment of Hippokrates and Galen from the art of medicine. But he pointed out the vanity of this fear, when you considered that it was in any case no longer mere Hippokratic or mere Galenic medicine, since it had undergone revision and enlargement by the Arabs. Again he is accused of defending, not alchemy, which, apart from those of its adepts who use metallic remedies, Riolan had no quarrel with, but Duchesne, Turquet de Mayerne, Israel Harvet and other *chymiatrici*. But Libavius had no wish to make it a personal matter—Duchesne was perfectly able to look after himself. Nevertheless, when he denied that he was supporting the cause of Duchesne he was called an advocate of Paracelsus; and that, despite the fact that formerly he had written in defence of the Galenic medicine against the invective of the 'Paracelsian', Gramanus (*Neoparacelsica*, No. 392). 'I want you', he writes elsewhere in his *Lectori*, 'to realise that there is a middle path between the simple unadulterated Paracelsian and that unadulterated Galenic, in which Galen is dictator and high priest, from whose words these unbending and finnicky sycophants think it wrong to deviate in the slightest degree.' But that he was no passive eclectic he proved by the further elaboration of this 'middle way' (the text has 'medio vero vita est'—presumably for 'via') wherein the false would be rejected from both extremes and the truth re-established by shedding light on them (*illustrare*) and adding to them where necessary. 'But, you say, I notice that you more often speak like a Paracelsist than a follower of Hippokrates. Look a second time, I reply, and again, and don't jump to conclusions. Consider also that Paracelsus often says things which are true, Hippokrates not a few that are false. You will see also, perhaps, things which are not to be found in either Paracelsus or Hippokrates. Often the same words have a different meaning. I also speak of principles in which the fundamentals of the powers and properties of mixts lie hidden, but not as Paracelsus did, nor as Gramanus, with the greatest fervency against Galen. The "principles" of chemistry are true as are essences, but not exactly in the way that Paracelsus and his new disciples make out. . . . The more complex the matter the more opinions there may be about it. Our knowledge in this life is imperfect: hence our pronouncements about things which are more deeply hidden (*abstrusioribus*) and removed from observation frequently carry the possibility of contradiction. The greater our debt, therefore, to him who brings forward reasons nearer to the truth. Hence we do not despise Hippokratic and Galenic truths and principles.' And once again he affirms that his aim, and that of Duchesne (a letter from whom he quotes), is neither to accept slavishly, nor to reject, but to reform.

The body of the text opens with a 'brief comparison of the Hippokratic-Hermetic medicine with the spurious Galenic'. The former is based on Hippokrates and the 'genuine Galenic of the Arabs' (in the main text he frequently refers to Mesue in confirmation of the use of metallic preparations, etc., but see above, p. 256). There are also 'spurious Hermetics', that is, the Paracelsians, who mix magic madness with their medicine.

In the remainder of the text he takes up the indictments of Riolan, mainly from the *Ad Libavimaniam*, casts them into syllogistic form, and refutes them by denying one or both of the premises. Sometimes he shows that Riolan is ignorant of, or goes far beyond, the tradition even of the Paris school: sometimes he calls up great names to testify on his own side. The work is unfortunately unduly repetitious and sputtered with invective in which the language degenerates into wordy obscurity. Boyle may have had this in mind when, fifty years later, setting about a similar task of clarification, he insisted on courtesy in controversy. Nevertheless, apart from the extraordinary thoroughness with which the whole question is examined, there are to be found many pages in which valuable light is thrown on points of cardinal interest. For instance, in our histories it is often at least implied that the Faculty of Paris performed a valuable service in placing an absolute ban on the use of antimony in internal remedies. Libavius (p. 200) is at once ready to admit that in the hands of the inexperienced any mineral essence is 'as a sword or a fire in the bosom of fools'; but after all the same argument might be applied to Galenic medicine 'whose errors cover the earth' (Cullen reversed the terms!) The argument is given more general application on p. 628 f. where Libavius reminds Riolan that many Galenicals—such as Hellebore, Colocynth, and Scammony—are violent in action and just as dangerous in the hands of the inexperienced. Again, to the modern reader, Libavius appears in a particularly favourable light when (p. 407 f.) taking Riolan to task for his delicate aversion to the smells and dirt of alchemical operations which the latter regarded as beneath the dignity of the physician and fit only for menials. Has not the physician to face far more loathsome tasks, Libavius asks, and points out the level to which pharmacy had sunk before it was rescued by those like Tragus, Gesner, and many others, who were willing to go and study plants in the wilds. But of course, he continued,

R*

the Parisians were content to let the surgeon dissect while the physician presided; yet did not those great anatomists Vesalius, Colombo, and Valverde themselves carry out the dissection? Riolan might think surgery and pharmacy arts subordinated to medicine; but Libavius replied that they were all members of one body of knowledge. In another fundamental question Libavius showed himself a master of compromise. The distinguishing mark of the Paracelsians is usually and with justice held to be the belief in the existence of three chemical principles—sulphur, mercury, and salt (see above, p. 167): it is these, rather than the four Aristotelian elements, on whose proportion the qualities of materials depend. To Riolan's allegation that he accepted them in one book, but violently rejected them in his diatribe against Gramanus, Libavius replied that he accepted three *chemical* principles [1] but denied that *medicine* should be founded on them. In such a way he was of course able to maintain his respect for Galen whose 'humours' Paracelsus had utterly repudiated; at the same time his belief in the existence of the Philosophers' Stone (capable of effecting transmutation of base into rarer metals) appeared to be given a sounder theoretical basis in the mercury-sulphur concept of grades of metallicity. Libavius's reasoning may sound over-subtle and a mere casuistical shift, but he shows (p. 715) that he was moving towards a more empirical basis than the current Aristotelianism permitted: 'Chymici istas logicas causas [*sc.* "materia", "forma", & "contraria privantia"] non negant. Quando autem de natura corporea est disserendum, & physica scientia constituenda vident non sequenda esse figmenta nostra sed id ponendum quod sensus cum ratione & experientia in natura corporum monstrant' ('The chemists do not deny those causes and depriving contraries assumed in logic, but when it is a matter of expounding corporeal nature and the construction of a science of nature they see that our fictions ought not to be followed, but that that should be posited which the senses, together with reason and experience, show to be in the nature of bodies'). In the same mood he comments on the observations of Duchesne and others on the formation of salt 'coagulations' and 'concretions' both in nature and chemical operations: 'Those who have not

---

[1] It is significant that in his introductory chapter (p. 21) Libavius writes, '. . . liquor oleosa, pinguedo, & sal, quae *symbolice* dicuntur mercurius, sulphur & alcali seu sal' (my italic).

seen experiments of this kind nor have been occupied with artificial investigations of nature, resolutions, and compositions, believe nothing unless it lies under their very noses; the philosophy of these people is concerned rather with the outer rind than with the inward essence of things' (p. 852). This reveals a new attitude on the part of a physician associated with the classical tradition of education and medicine: it is doubtful whether it could be paralleled elsewhere at so early a date.

Such was this involved war of ideas, which has usually been given a 'meaning' only by ignoring all the apparent inconsistencies of the disputants. Here, on the one hand, is the academic pedant, a slave to authority of ancient books, who uncompromisingly defends his belief that the operations of surgery and pharmacy are beneath the dignity of the physician. His opponent, on the other hand, subjecting all previous authority to the test of experience, opens the door to a new world of chemical enterprise. Yet it is the former who soundly rates the chemists for wasting their time in attempts to extract the *quinta essentia* of natural bodies, 'since there is no such thing in nature'[1]; and the latter who (in the *Alchymia*) becomes almost lyrical on the subject of the search for the Philosophers' Stone. The paradox is only lessened when we read on to discover Riolan's reasons—aprioristic and Aristotelian—for his rejection of the *quinta essentia*, namely, that it belongs only to the heavens. Again, after what we have lived through in recent years, we ought to be less surprised at Riolan's puzzled annoyance at the fact that a comrade who had denounced in violent terms one enemy of the Ancient Medicine (Gramanus) was actually showing sympathy with another suspect (Duchesne): could there be a clearer anticipation of Right Wing Deviationism? Truly the illumination of this 'unscientific' brawl serves only to darken the shadows of human inconsequence; but the historian must concern himself with the shadows as well as with the highlights, and in such cases it is more than usually necessary to discover *wie es eigentlich gewesen*.

[1] *Apologia pro Hippocratis et Galeni Medicina . . .*, p. 12.

CHAPTER XIV

OF MIASM AND CONTAGION

WITH pathology and therapeutics in general we are not concerned, but in a study of the sixteenth century we can not ignore two major preoccupations which not only dislocated human life, but enlisted the scientific imagination to a degree unsurpassed by any other problem. These were the Pest and the Great Pox. Since the latter was, and is, frequently regarded as a novelty unknown before the close of the fifteenth century, whereas the former had been a recurring menace for perhaps two thousand years, they may conveniently be discussed separately. But since each was a particular instance of the larger question of the widespread outbreak of disease, I shall try to relate them to other forms of epidemic disease. First then to the ancient scourge—the Pest.

The word 'Pest' is a common translation of the Latin *pestis*, which throughout our period connoted a recurrent visitation made familiar in England by 'the' Plague of London—only the worst of a number of such outbreaks in the capital. It has been necessary to refer to the 'Pest' or 'Plague' as a 'visitation', since it is not 'a' disease in the sense of being represented by a well-defined syndrome of signs and symptoms.[1] There are two 'typical' forms—pneumonic, which is highly infectious by air-borne droplets and almost invariably fatal; and bubonic, probably one of the least infectious of diseases, and characterised by the development of a painful *bubo* commonly in the groin: recovery occurs in a considerable proportion of even untreated cases. Were these all the facts there would seem little justification for supposing that they represented two extreme forms of a single disease; this supposition was however based on the facts that seldom did the pneumonic or bubonic form appear in isolation throughout a single visitation—though after the so-called 'Black Death' the

---

[1] L. F. Hirst, *The Conquest of Plague*, Oxford, 1953, pp. 28 f. This work has been an indispensable aid in the preparation of this section.

bubonic form does seem to have preponderated in Europe—and also that cases of an intermediate character were common. There is also a third form, rather misleadingly called *septicaemic plague*, which, though invariably fatal, may be accompanied by hardly appreciable physical signs and few symptoms of illness until within a few hours of death. This protean manifestation is even further complicated in respect of its history by the fact that the bubonic form may be accompanied by dark 'tokens' under the skin (actually subcutaneous haemorrhages) which at a certain stage would be described as 'red spots', thus giving rise to possible confusion with typhus: there is no doubt that some visitations of 'pestis' or 'febris pestilentialis' were in fact typhus, and not 'plague' in the more usual sense.

In view of the impossibility of referring to 'plague' as a well-defined 'entity' (a conception which in any case was foreign to physicians before Sydenham, and which attained its somewhat tyrannical hold only after the demonstration of the necessary presence of specific microbes in conjunction with well-defined syndromes of diagnostic characters) it is not surprising that in addition to general works on the theory of plague-like diseases there grew up a considerable literature relating to particular outbreaks. The latter was however mainly a product of printing as a going concern. The 'tracts' which, as we have seen (p. 209), formed so large a proportion of 'contemporary' writing printed before 1501 were of a more general character. Of the approximately forty *authors* reviewed by Klebs[1] about thirty had died later than 1400, and the majority of the remainder not long before. Also, it is to be observed that there were 130 items altogether, including a number entitled *Ordnung* copied from the *Regimen Sanitatis Salerni*. It is a reasonable guess that this relatively large output was started by the incidence of the Black Death, which entered Europe *via* the Black Sea port of Kaffa in 1347, and, as Boccaccio records in the introduction of the *Decameron*, was already devastating Florence in the next year. Only one comparable disaster has been recorded in the history of mankind—a similar pandemic in the reign of Justinian (VI-1). The influenza

---

[1] A. C. Klebs and K. Sudhoff, *Die Ersten Gedruckten Pestschriften*, Munich, 1926. The discrepancy between 30 and 21 (see above, p. 209) authors is mainly due to the fact that authors of tracts appearing only in collections (e.g. Tossignano and Ioannes Itrensis) were not included in the earlier general estimate.

pandemic of 1918-19 may have killed a comparable number of people, but proportionately the devastation was much less. This conjecture is strongly supported by the 281 tracts (the Klebs list of course comprises only those that were *printed*) discovered by Sudhoff up to 1925. The first appeared as early as April 1348, and one of special value, by John of Burgundy, in 1365. A brief but authoritative eye-witness account by an eminent physician and surgeon is that of Guy de Chauliac who was in Avignon in the early months of 1348. In addition to the titles *Tractatus, Regiment, Ordnung,* the word *Consiglio (Consilium)* begins to appear, especially in the case of the Italian masters, Gentile da Foligno, Francesco da Siena, etc. It is difficult to give a precise definition of a *Consilium*: at no time did it approximate very closely to what came later to be called a *Consultation*; it was rather an 'appreciation of the situation' in the military sense of noting, and diagnosing, but generally included a concise summary of what the classical writers had to say about that sort of case, and an outline of regimen to be followed. There was at least before the sixteenth century an air of unreality about them since the whole procedure might be conducted 'by correspondence'; it had indeed some of the marks of a legal 'brief'. In course of time the term came to be restricted to the 'case' of a single patient, and in the sixteenth century many collections of these were published as a contribution to knowledge; these are by no means devoid of interesting and acute observations clearly distinguished from the usual Galenic theory, which for the modern reader vitiates so much early medical reporting. In the plague literature, however, the *consilium* does not appear to differ in form from the *tractatus*: indeed one does not usually find the former term employed where it would seem to be most appropriate, namely, in respect of those numerous studies of local outbreaks which were undertaken throughout the sixteenth century. Thus in a well-known collection of plague tracts (No. 753) the first two, written in the most general terms,[1] are called *Consiglii*; of the remainder, which are reports on specific outbreaks, two are called *consiglii*, one a *ragionamento* ('theory' rather than 'regimen') and the other has the simple *De Origine et Causa Pestis Patavinae*: these six tracts cover a period of about eighty years. The earlier (1473) *Ordnung* of

[1] Though Marsilio Ficino does refer in passing to 'la presente peste del 1478 & del 1479' (p. 5). (First printed 1481—Sudhoff.)

Heinrich Steinhowel is in general terms, whose character is
indicated by the sub-title 'wie sich der mensch halten sol zu den
zyten diser grusenlichen kranckheit' ('how to conduct oneself in
the times of this horrible—lit. "shuddering"—illness'). Lastly,
as a late example I take the *pièce d'occasion* written by Rodericus
de Castro and called *Tractatus brevis*, on the outbreak at Hamburg
in 1596.[1] (No. 139).

Looking through these works, which cover over a century, one
is hard put to it to find any notable change in either the reporting
or the theory. The Hamburg tract of 1595 claims that *pestis* (as
distinct from *febris pestilentialis*, a fever merely similar to true
plague) is characterised by being a disease which attacks whole
communities (*populariter*), which not only contaminates neighbouring people by means of contagion but sometimes also by the
breath; is invariably accompanied by *internal* fever and usually by
bubos in the groin, armpit, or neck. The proximate cause is a
putridity of the humours especially in the blood, which in the most
severe cases attacks the heart. The predisposing cause is the lack of
harmony of the humours brought about by lack of moderation—
particularly to excess—in the way of life, aggravated by certain
combinations of wind, moisture, and temperature. Though the
stars themselves can not be said to *cause* plague, nevertheless
certain conjunctions, as for instance that of the conjunction of
Jupiter and Mars in a 'warm' sign, are likely to bring about a
corruption of the air. Also earthquakes releasing noxious vapours
have been regarded as a probable cause.

The emphasis is thus on the presence of a *contagion* introduced
into the body, not only in the breath but even (as was in any case
supposed to happen to the *pneuma* providing the 'vital spirit')
through the pores of the skin. For this reason the daily exercise,
recommended as a preventive, must not be so violent as to
induce sweating. The contagion can be transmitted from one
victim to another by breath, direct contact, or by 'fomites'
(literally 'tinder', used figuratively for clothes, etc., contaminated
by the sick person—see below, p. 277 for the origin of this term).
This theory of *contagion* produced in the humours, and only
secondarily by contamination of the air, was opposed to the
Hippocratic theory of *miasma*—a general corruption of the air

---

[1] A similar report for a municipal authority was that of Io. Ewichius for Bremen, of
which a full report is given by Dr. John Ritchie, *Edin. Med. J.* **60** (1953), 437.

itself which was held to be the immediate cause of the disease.
The theory of the need for predisposition of the humours goes
back to Galen, but the emphasis on transmissible *contagion*
generated in the sick probably originated with the Arab Ibn
al-Khatib (1313-74) and became more and more marked during
the subsequent two centuries. In this theory the blood 'fights
back' in varying degrees, victory being signalised by the appearance of the bubo through which the poison was expelled. The
gradual shift of emphasis from *miasma* to *contagion* was probably
promoted by observation of the plague-track from the port of
entry, and of the more frequent *local* outbreaks of the sixteenth
century—often restricted to *urban* centres, in apparent defiance of
the fact that a planetary conjunction must cover the whole
earth, or at least be effective in the whole area involved in a
particular set of the wind. The contagion theory, though just as
faulty in principle as the miasmatic, had the important consequence that the urban authorities took more and more pains to
effect isolation of infected centres and disposal of bodies and
fomites—a procedure which would clearly be useless in the presence of a general miasma. The importance of this lay not in the
control of contagion, which in bubonic plague is normally non-
existent, but in the control of infected *fleas*, without whose bite
there is normally no chance of infection—normally, since metamorphosis into the highly infectious pneumonic form, though rare,
is not unknown. Until 1576 the two theories had not been
mutually confronted, and accounts of the 'cause' of plague
in the tracts had usually been of an eclectic nature. But in that
year an outbreak at Venice followed by one at Padua provided
the occasion for a course of lectures by Mercuriali (No. 450)
at Padua in 1577, in which he strove to establish a purely miasmatic origin of plague. Alessandro Massari replied in a tract
written in 1578 (contained in No. 430) in which, on the basis of a
careful examination of the sequence and circumstances of the
recent outbreaks, he put forward an unqualified version of the
contagion theory. Though even a sketch of this highly significant
work would occupy us too long, it includes a passage of so great
interest in relation to the general question of the science of the
sixteenth century that I shall quote it in full. It was in Vicenza
that Massari's investigation began; here, though Venice and
Verona were afflicted in the summer of 1575 and Padua in the

following summer, it was only at the end of December 1576 that a man died 'without reason'. Within a few weeks the three members of his family had succumbed, so their bodies were handed over by the magistrates for inspection by the physicians. Black 'papulae' having been found on them, the house was burned to the ground. It was discovered that the 'good-for-nothing fellow', who had been the first victim, had secretly introduced contaminated linen and wool from Padua. When the disease broke out in the neighbouring house Massari took charge of the affair at the request of the magistrates; the more readily, 'partim quod charitatis et humanitatis officium id maxime postularet, partim quod haud contemnendam occasionem mihi oblatam esse viderem qua morbi omnium saevissimi et quem ante nunquam & nusquam vidisse mihi contigerat diligenter observare possem progressiones symptomata nec non experiri & in usum revocare illa praesidia, quae ad illius praeservationem & curationem maxime accommodata viderentur' ('partly because the duty of charity and humanity most expressly demanded it, partly because I saw that an opportunity had been offered to me, not lightly to be set aside, by which I might be able to observe diligently the progress and symptoms of the most cruel of all diseases, which I had at no time or place previously seen, and both to test and bring into use those aids which seemed best suited to its prevention and cure').[1] Here then was a physician of high academic standing who was more than willing to risk his life for the sake of the sick and to study the disease systematically and in the 'light of nature'. Doubtless he was not the first to think or to act like this; but I know of no earlier published record in which the ideals of modern clinical medicine are so explicitly exemplified. Even Paracelsus would have had to admit an exception to his wholesale condemnation of the products of the *Hochschulen*.

That this controversy did not involve an immediate 'line-up', as had the earlier dilemma in regard to venesection (p. 233), is shown by the persistence of an eclectic treatment in the clear and able Hamburg tract of Roderic à Castro. Nevertheless, according to Hirst (*op. cit.* Ch. III) the dilemma remained a living issue, liable to break out with recurrent visitations of the plague and sometimes accompanied by a degree of heat rivalling that engendered by the latter.

[1] *Tractatus de Peste*, p. 2.

The course of this controversy thus belongs to the centuries following our period, but a somewhat casual phrase in the Hamburg tract reminds us that before 1595—indeed by 1546—a theory had been put forward whose ultimate exploitation and clarification were to provide one of the major insights into the 'secret causes of things' whereby mankind gradually rid itself of the 'terror that walketh in the night season'. After referring to the possibility of corruption arising as vapour (*halitus*) from various sources, the author warns the reader that unless such vapours are rapidly got rid of a worse disaster may follow, 'praesertim cum civitas sit maritima, & in ea loca pleraque reperiantur, fimo & coeno plena, in quibus . . . *hujus mali seminaria* adhuc versari credendum est, ita ut sit verendum, ne, adveniente calore veris, in alias aedes & lautioris conditionis homines propagetur ac ita incrementum suscipiat. . . .' (R. à Castro, *op. cit.* sig. B 1v-2r, ital. mine) ('particularly when the city is on the sea coast and many places are to be found in it, full of dung and filth, in which it is to be believed the *seminaria* of this evil were dwelling up to that time, and thus it is to be feared that on the advent of the warmth of spring the contagion may be propagated in other buildings and among men of a higher condition, and thus wax . . .'). The writer passes straight on to a further consideration of the signs of the disease; but from his use of the term *seminaria* it may be plausibly inferred that he was not unfamiliar with the theory of transference of material bodies put forward by Girolamo Fracastoro in 1546. This theory was one intended to be applicable to a number of diseases, including the *morbus Gallicus*; it will be convenient therefore to refer to it in more detail after we have considered the latter.

Space permits of only a superficial comparison of the Hamburg tract with the earlier ones referred to. There is more evidence of objectivity—separation of the characterisation of the disease in terms of its epidemiological features and case-signs—than in the earlier ones; but this may be a virtue in the writer himself rather than of the times in which he wrote. On the other hand Steinhowel (*vide sup.* p. 267) prefaces his text with a prayer to St. Sebastian; but again this is in keeping with the more devout approach to medical study characteristic of German works well into the sixteenth century. Doubtless also, Steinhowel may have been hampered in his treatment of the subject by the limitations of New High German which was at that time even less settled as a medium of accurate communication than the other vernaculars—especially of course Italian. Nevertheless though using homely terms he gives a clear and accurate picture of some at least of the peculiarities of the plague, as for instance of the absence of the *outward* signs of fever in the worst cases—'Von erst so ist ein grosse inbrunstige hicz inwendig aber uszwendig ist sie lydig und nit so schynlich wann der kranckheit wurczel ist in dem herczen und geblut' (Facsimile pp. 8-9—unnumbered), and again in the failure of that medieval 'stand-by'—the urine—to reveal an abnormal state —'. . . oft so belybt der puls als an einem gesunden menschen und der harn gelychet des gesunden harn und stirbt der mensch als bald' (p. 9). Both Ficino and à Castro record these facts, and the latter especially discusses alternative theories to account for them: the point of interest is the fact that despite the lapse of over a century à Castro still has to say in respect of the anomalous urine sign 'illud vero mirum alicui videbitur' ('to some people it will seem a marvel') (Sig. B2r) instead of 'it is well known that'. Moreover he was writing an 'official report' and not a 'home physician'. Also, one must be impressed by the accuracy of clinical observation in the fifteenth century of a phenomenon in flat contradiction to the accepted dogma of the omnicompetence of urinary diagnosis.

On 7 August 1495 in an edict of the Emperor Maximilian I occurs the first printed reference to a disease 'genant die posen plattern die vormals bey menschen gedechtnusz nye gewesen noch gehort sein' ('called the evil pox, never previously existing, nor heard of, in the memory of Man'). Probably before the end of the year appeared the first of a number of consilia or tracts dealing with the 'new' disease which is variously referred to as *Malus de Francia, Morbus Gallicus, pudendagra* (cf. *podagra* = gout) *malafranzos*, etc. Ten of these tracts, published 1495-8, were edited in facsimile by Sudhoff,[1] who in an introduction drew attention to the importance of this corpus, not only in relation to the great syphilis epidemic which slowly swept over and for perhaps half a century inundated Europe, but as the first demonstration of the cultural importance of the press, whose production had previously been restricted to works, whose value had been supposedly established before the age of printing. Though Sudhoff has here done a little less than justice to medicine in general, his claim

[1] K. Sudhoff, and C. Singer, *The Earliest Printed Literature on Syphilis*, Florence, 1925.

seems to be more or less substantiated, and as such demands the historian's attention. Space permits of detailed reference to only one of these tracts—*Libellus de Epidemia, quem vulgo morbum Gallicum vocant*—by Niccolò Leoniceno and printed in June 1497. This is not perhaps the most original, but the circumstances out of which it arose—a disputation at the University of Ferrara—and the eminence of the author (see above p. 245) lend it an authority and guarantee a breadth of treatment above any of the remainder: not the least advantage is its elegant Latinity. It is not the first time, says Leoniceno, that a completely 'new' disease has been reported, for Pliny states that a kind of ringworm (*lichen*), unknown before the age of Claudius, had appeared in Italy and almost the whole of Europe. He believes Pliny to have been in error. 'Something similar has happened in our time, for a disease of a nature now unfamiliar has invaded Italy and many other regions. There are pustules beginning in the *pudenda*, soon spreading to the whole body, especially the face, bringing for the most part, besides foulness, severe pain. To this disease the physicians of our day have not yet assigned an accurate (*verum*) name, but call it by the vulgar name of *malus Gallicus* implying either that its contagion had been brought into Italy by the French, or that Italy had been infested by both the disease and French arms at the same time. There are not lacking those who think that it is the same as that which the ancients called *elephantiasis*; others think the *morbus Gallicus* to be the *lichen* of the ancients. . . . Which ambiguity of names and disagreement about the thing itself has caused many to suspect that it is a new disease never seen by the ancients, nor yet handled by a physician, Greek or Arab, among other kinds of diseases. Just as I do not agree with those who have applied to this disease various names by no means consistent with its nature; so likewise when I reflect that men are endowed with the same nature, born under the same skies, brought up under the same stars, I am compelled to think that they have been always afflicted by the same diseases; neither can I comprehend how this disease has suddenly destroyed our age as none before. For if anyone thinks otherwise than I do, what, I ask, would he say this is other than a revenge of the gods? For if the laws of nature are examined, they have existed unchanged on countless occasions since the beginning of the world. Wherefore I am prepared to show that a similar disease has arisen from similar causes also in past ages.' Leoniceno proceeds for over forty pages to enjoy himself in exposing the errors of the Arabs in particular, but not omitting Dioskurides and others. This is all largely irrelevant (as is his oft-quoted eulogy of the printer, Aldus Manutius) except in so far as a decision on the nature of the *morbus Gallicus* is bound up with the wider question of the reigning confusion of terminology and nomenclature in medicine and botany. But Leoniceno, then nearing seventy, doubtless like Theodoros in the *Theaetetus*, enjoyed the digressions more than the argument. His conclusion was that the *morbus Gallicus* could not be regarded as either new or necessarily of a constant nature. Such diseases, he thought, arise either by the wrath of God, as the theologians believe, or by the power of the stars according to the astrologers, or as a result of a certain boisterousness of the air, as the physicians judge. He would follow the physicians in this respect, and assign it to the proximate (*proximiores*) causes of nature. In agreement with this view was the fact that in the year in which the disease began to spread (*pululare*) the waters arose (*magnam aquarum exuberantiam*) all over Italy. Evidence for this view was that at Rome, where the effects of the disease were first felt, the Tiber rose to such a height that the fact was celebrated by the poet Pomponius; and rivers rose above their accustomed height in several other towns. This was in keeping with much that Hippokrates and Galen had written about diseases that included pustules on the *pudenda*, so it could safely be attributed to a disturbance of the humours; for which reason Leoniceno could not agree with the use of external unguents, which by driving the disease inwards merely increase the danger.

This little book by Leoniceno, though conservative in outlook and adding nothing to scientific or medical knowledge, nevertheless provides us with an almost complete picture of contemporary views on this new problem. It is characteristic of the best type of humanistic medicine, showing both its strength—accurate, critical, comprehensive, free from superstition or quackery, even 'scientific' in preferring proximate to remote causes—but also its weakness, namely that in consequence of its blind reverence for the classical writers the possibility of transfer of contagion in the sexual act is not even entertained:[1] the appearance of pustules

---

[1] The Town Council of Aberdeen knew better—at first—for in an edict of 21 April 1497 in respect of the 'infirmitie cum out of Franche & strang partis . . . all licht

on the *pudenda* being 'explained' (ut inquit Galenus!) as a result of the excessive 'warmth and moisture' of those parts.

So far it was only to the 'vulgar' that the name 'French disease' had been attributed. In the tract *cum consiliis contra pudendagram seu morbum Gallicum* written by Gaspar Torella in 1497, which Sudhoff reckoned to be the most original of the contemporary publications, a more careful scrutiny of the origin of the disease is made. These *consilia* were written by Torella at the request of Cesare Borgia, his fellow countryman and son of Roderigo de Borgia, who, on his assumption of the papal tiara as Alexander VI, appointed Torella his body physician. In these circumstances it might be supposed Torella would not have had much opportunity for the study of the disease, which was almost entirely transmitted by sexual contact, nevertheless he claimed to have treated successfully seventeen cases in two months, the description of five of which was regarded by Sudhoff as a very valuable part of the treatise. Of special importance for us, however, is the early reference to the first appearance of the disease: 'Incepit ut aiunt hec maligna egritudo anno 1493 in Francia; et sic per viam contagionis pervenit in Hyspaniam, ad insulas, in Italiam et finaliter serpendo totam Europam peragravit; et si fas dicere est totum orbem' ('They say this malignant disease began in France in the year 1493, and thus by means of contagion reached Spain, the islands, Italy and finally spread over the whole of Europe; or, if one may rightly say so, the whole world'). This is significant coming from a physician who, in the following pages, shows himself to be well versed in, if not wholly bemused by, the prevalent humoral theory. But Sudhoff's linking of what was rumoured to have happened in 1493 with the fact that (as he alleges) there was in southern France as early as the fourteenth century a clear conception of the distinct character of syphilis is not altogether convincing as an explanation of the origin of the name; especially as he adds that a similar distinct disease, *scabies grossa*, was recognised equally early in Italy.

women be chargit & ordanit to decist fra thar vices & syne of venerie'. Later, however (on medical advice?), they attributed the spread of the disease to simple contact—even with food. I am indebted to my colleague, Dr. M. G. McEntegart, for drawing my attention to this citation in T. Ferguson, *The Dawn of Scottish Social Welfare*, London, 1948, pp. 107 f. Dr. McEntegart tells me that contemporary accounts of the spread of the Great Pox have many of the indications of introduction into a virgin soil, also of a high degree of non-genital transmission.

It will have been noticed that no reference has yet been made to the still widespread belief that the disease was introduced into Europe from America by some of Columbus's sailors—the details of the port of entry and subsequent dissemination vary in the different accounts, all of which seem to be based on the statement of three Spaniards more than twenty-five years after the first epidemic appearance of the disease. Of such stuff are historical dreams made. Of course the *possibility* of this mode of entry can not be disproved; only the persistence of the legend under the not infrequent guise of an authentic record is a matter of concern to the serious historian. The flimsiness of this evidence must not be confused with the belief, still held by some medical authorities, that previous instances of the disease in Europe remain unproven, hence it must either have been introduced or have been a 'new creation'; and of these alternatives the former appears to be the less improbable. Sherrington went so far as to say that Fernel was 'quite right' in accepting the American origin.

The name *morbus Gallicus*, and its vernacular variants, was of course neither universal nor has it been used in more recent times. From the first the French naturally preferred *morbus Neapolitanus* or *morbus Italicus*; though, rather strangely, no French medical writer published anything on the subject until 1527,[1] when Jacques de Bethencourt introduced the term *morbus venereus*,[2] which, in slightly varied forms (e.g. *lues venerea*, used consistently by Fernel), was the commonest term until the nineteenth century, when *syphilis* gradually displaced it. The origin of this term is the name given to a youth by Girolamo Fracastoro in his poem (1530) *Syphilidis, sive morbi Gallici lib. tres*. This is one of the most important contemporary testimonies to the horrors of the disease; but the 'cause' is treated poetically as a vengeance taken by Apollo on the youth, Syphilis. It was however the same author, in a work on contagious diseases written in his old age, who approached most nearly to a 'scientific' determination of the cause of syphilis and of many other transferable diseases. Before dealing with this it may be as well

---

[1] J. K. Proksch, *Geschichte der Geschlechtskrankheiten* (a separate publication, originally included in *Handbuch der Geschlechtskrankheiten*, Vienna, 1910), p. 48. De Bethencourt's work had the deceptive title *Nova penitentialis quadragesima*. It is a highly critical and lucid study. A French translation—*Nouveau Carême de Penitence* was made by A. Fournier, Paris, 1871.

[2] Proksch, *op. cit.* p. 46, who says that there was no English publication before 1575 (No. 164), p. 48.

to mention that although the other well known venereal disease, gonorrhoea, is unmistakably recorded in classical times, it was not finally distinguished from syphilis until the present century after their correlation with two profoundly different microbian agents had been demonstrated. The long delay was due in some measure to John Hunter's unfortunate inference that gonorrhoea and syphilis are different stages of the same disease: on self-innoculation from a supposed case of syphilis he developed symptoms of both diseases, not being aware that double infection may occur.

The work of Fracastoro, *On contagion*, has given rise to much fruitless speculation as to whether he 'discovered' the germ theory of disease. It is easy to extract from its context the famous second 'chapter' to show that he did; it is even easier (as, *proh pudor*, I did myself) to rely on secondary sources to prove that he did not. The question itself is of relatively little importance, since whatever the answer given it is the case that progress towards the modern theory actually occurred along a different road—that of the problem of 'spontaneous generation'. On the other hand the manner in which the question is approached is of the highest importance in the attempt to understand the renaissance attitude to what we should call 'biological' questions—hardly less so than the appreciation of the Copernican 'Revolution'—hence the rather detailed discussion which follows.

A first point to notice is that Girolamo Fracastoro was and is held in honour in Italy as one of the outstanding intellects of the sixteenth century. Of noble blood on both sides he was born in 1484 and from an early age excelled in all that he put his hand to. In geometry skilled enough to make the last attempt to revive the theory of homocentric celestial spheres; an artist in letters, his name may be linked with Giovio Pontano and Pietro Bembo; soldier and country gentleman (for although he took part in disputations he held no university appointment) he passed his later years at his villa near Monte Baldi, twenty miles from Verona. Here, 'graviori aetate ac plane senex',[1] he wrote the work which should ensure his immortality in the history of science, the second chapter of which contains the following oft quoted passage: 'The first distinguishing mark of all contagions seems to be threefold: for some exert their influence (*afficiunt*) by contact alone, others

[1] *Vita* prefixing *Opera omnia*, Juntae, Venice, 1555.

by this means and in addition by *fomites* also; and the remainder
are contagious in themselves, such as *scabies, phthisis, areae,
elephantiasis* and such like. I call by the name *fomes* clothes, pieces
of wood and things of this sort, which, though indeed by themselves
are free from corruption, are nevertheless fitted to retain the
first *seminaria* of contagion and by means of the latter exert their
influence; furthermore there are some which do so not by contact
alone, not by *fomes* alone, but also at a distance, such as pestilential
fevers, *phthisis*, and certain affections of the eyes (*lippitudines*),
also those *exanthemata* which are called *variolae* and the like.'[1] This
is a remarkable beginning; certainly the origin of a science of
epidemiology may be discerned in the acute observation that
those which are contagious at a distance are contagious by the
other two methods, but not necessarily *vice-versa* and so 'videntur
autem ordine quadem se habere haec. . . .' ('these things seem to
be characterised by a certain order . . .'). Nevertheless a classification does not constitute a science, and the main passage does
little more than generalise and clarify the sort of knowledge well
understood in particular cases ever since the Black Death—though
the humanist physicians of the early Renaissance may have
hesitated to adopt such an un-Hippokratic theory. All turns upon
the exact meaning of *seminaria*, which had never before been used
in quite the sense the passage seems to suggest. The first hint comes
from the first 'chapter', where it is asked 'whether all contagion
is a kind of putrefaction?' This was not wholly new: there was a
hint of it in Ficino's *Consiglio*; but it is more completely worked
out in various places in succeeding chapters, and first in Chapter 3,
De contagione quae solo contactu afficit ('Of the contagion which acts
by contact alone'), which concludes thus: 'In fructibus igitur
quae contagio accidit, per haec principia fieri putandum est, at
vero, & in aliis quoque omnibus, quae putrescentia sese tangunt,
si analoga sint, idem evenire, & per idem principium existimare
par est: principium autem sunt particulae illae insensibiles, quae
evaporant, calidae quidem, & acres, sed humidae commistione,
quae deinceps seminaria contagionum dicantur' ('And therefore
the contagion which happens in fruits must be supposed to be
brought about by the same " primordia " [2] but indeed in all other

---

[1] *Op. cit.* fo. 105ᵛ.

[2] The use made by Fracastoro of the word *principium* suggests that he was strongly
nfluenced by the work of Lucretius, *De Rerum Natura*. I have ventured to suggest

s*

cases, if they are analogous, in which putrefying bodies are touching each other, it is proper to think that the same thing happens and by the same primordia. Now the primordia are just those insensible particles which evaporate, hot and sharp indeed, but wet as a result of mixture, which hereafter shall be called the *seminaria* of contagions' (*op. cit.* fo. 106ʳ). Contagion is thus held to be very like, if not the same as, putrefaction: both are transmitted from one body to another by insensible particles. How easy to call these 'germs'! But whatever *seminaria* are (and in classical Latin the word means seed-*bed*, hence 'seminary'), they are not 'germs', or at least not microbes, for there is no suggestion that they are parasitic on the infected organism; and it is only towards the end of the book that the view is put forward that they are capable of self-multiplication. Their origin and mode of action is characterised as follows: '. . . omnino enim tale in secundo fuit, quale in primo principium et seminarium est, quoniam dictum est eam seminariis inesse vim, ut sibi simile propagare, et gignere possint, sicuti et spiritus faciunt. In primo igitur causae fuerunt illae, quae passim solent putrefactiones in nobis facere, obstructiones, plenitudines et humorum pravitates, a quibus facta putrefactio sordida et conclusa plurimum, accidit inde seminaria enasci, quae apta sint in alium contagionem transferre, sive in eo fuerint causae et dispositiones, quae in primo fuere, sive non; quare analogum humorem nactae in secundum & tertium et alios contagionem apportant' (*op. cit.* fo. 112ʳ). ('There was certainly in the second [*sc.* infected body] the same sort of thing as is the cause and seminal principle as in the first, since it has been said that a power of such a kind resides in the *seminaria* that they are able to propagate and generate something like themselves just as spirits do. In the first, therefore, the causes were those which commonly cause putrefaction in us, namely, obstructions, plethora, and foulness of humours, whereby is brought about a stagnant and filthy corruption; thence it happens that *seminaria* are born, which are of a nature to transfer contagion to another, whether in it there were the causes and predisposing factors which existed in the first or not; whence, having acquired a similar humour, carry contagion to a second, third, and more men.')

'primordia' as an equivalent for 'principium' or 'principia' in the present context instead of 'first beginnings' as used by Munro in his well known translation of *De Rerum Natura*.

To judge (as for instance F. H. Garrison did in his *Introduction to the History of Medicine*, 2nd edn. Philadelphia, 1917, p. 220, though he virtually retracted the statement in a footnote!) that 'Fracastoro states with wonderful clairvoyance the modern theory of infection by means of micro-organisms' is to ignore the assertion that the *seminaria* are 'born' as a result of a 'stagnant and filthy corruption'. Such a view of their origin was of course entirely in line with contemporary notions of the generation of organisms of many kinds (see above p. 184), but it is hardly 'modern'. That Fracastoro's *seminaria* differed radically from the micro-organisms now recognised as the causative agents in contagion appears from his attempt to indicate their specificity with respect to various diseases: they are to be regarded as 'crassiora, minus acria' or 'subtiliora, acria, magis, & ad spiritualia magis analoga' according as they affect the outward or deeper parts of the person infected—a further proof of Fracastoro's leaning towards the atomic theory.

If, however, it is gravely unhistorical to regard the theory of Fracastoro as an 'anticipation' of the modern germ theory of communicable disease, it is just as easy—and just as vicious—to write him off for his suggestion that the *seminaria* are compact of the Aristotelian elements—the 'hot' and the 'moist'; for in his day everything 'under the moon' was assumed to be compact of these elements.

Where Fracastoro is so 'modern' is not so much in his concepts, which he failed (as was almost inevitable) to rid of irrelevancies associated with the contemporary 'physics', as in his persistent attempt not to dodge such of the evidence as failed to fit neatly into the theory. Thus in the section *De contagione quae fomite afficit* he admits that whereas in fomites the poison (*virus*) can be preserved for two or three years, none of those particles (*particulae*) which 'evaporate' from putrefying bodies seem to be able to persist (*perdurare*) so long. Nevertheless the possibility that putrefaction is due to the same cause should not be rejected for this reason alone, since those which evaporate may by being held in fomites ultimately act in the same manner as they would have done at the time of evaporation. It is not necessary to go to the length of claiming that Fracastoro is here 'anticipating' the notion of resistant resting stages or 'spores' to recognise that he is performing the even more important task of showing how subsidiary hypotheses must frequently be developed to adapt a particular theory to diverse circumstances. Moreover it is at least plausible to claim that he is here applying to a field more profitable than those in which it was usually exercised the *method* of the medieval disputation.

I have dealt with Fracastoro's work at what may seem inordinate length since it provides, I believe, an admirable example of the necessity of 're-thinking' such ideas as nearly as may be in the context of the original thinker's cultural environment and attitudes. Perhaps I may be permitted to clarify this point by reference to a lapse of my own. On a previous occasion, ill prepared for such a judgment, I rejected the usual claim made on behalf of Fracastoro on the ground that he 'combined the theory with the customary renaissance abracadabra of astrological signs and portents'.[1] Reference to Chapter 12 of *De Contagione* shows that, granted that he could not escape the almost universal concern with the influences of the celestial bodies (see above p. 273), his handling of the problem reveals remarkable insight: '. . . videbimus a caelo nullas contagiones per se fieri posse, per accidens autem nihil prohibet quasdam ab ipso fieri, ac praedici etiam ab astrologis posse . . .' (*op. cit.* fo. 113*r*) ('we shall see that no contagion as such can be created by the heavens; on the other hand nothing prevents their being brought into being by the heavens *per accidens* and even the possibility of their being forecast by astrologers . . .'). The stars of their own accord can produce an elevation of temperature, whereby may come a profusion of vapours which in turn may be the cause of diverse forms of corruption. Here surely, *within the context of his age*, is as good a piece of scientific thinking as one could hope for—one indeed looking ahead to the time when the redundant (if it is!) influence of the stars could be dispensed with.

One final point (illustrating incidentally the value of thorough bibliographical investigation in the history of science) is the fact that the 'book' *De Contagione*, in which the theory of *seminaria* was developed, was not a separate treatise, but was part of a composite work dedicated to Cardinal Alexander Farnese, and was preceded by *De Sympathia et Antipathia, Liber* I; it was itself '*Liber I*' of a set of three, of which *Liber* II and *Liber* III were respectively called *De Morbis Contagiosis* and *De Contagiosorum Morborum Curatione*. The numbering of the title-headings was carried out in a

[1] W. P. D. Wightman, *The Growth of Scientific Ideas*, Edinburgh, 1950, p. 448.

manner liable to lead to confusion, but this was rectified in all later editions. Now that this preliminary book, though numbered separately, was not intended to be regarded as a separate work is made clear in the dedication (p. 78), where it is said that without a consideration of Sympathy and Antipathy it does not seem possible to investigate or demonstrate the nature of contagion; the point is made once more in the opening sentence of the book *On Contagion*. Now this preliminary discussion on *Sympathy and Antipathy*, though full of acute observation and apt comparisons, ranges so widely as to include many phenomena—the action of amber (electricity), the magnet, the inability of certain plants to grow together, the dissolution of gold by mercury but not by water, and such mental characters as anger and joy, that we may well wonder what it all has to do with contagion. The fact is that, as we now believe, it has nothing to do with contagion; but that Fracastoro regarded its understanding as an essential pre-requisite to the study of contagion is clearly of the utmost importance in any attempt at a properly *historical* assessment of Fracastoro's thought; but with the notable exception of Thorndike[1] it is commonly ignored. On the other hand Thorndike is perhaps a little less than fair to Fracastoro in regard to the latter's attempt to 'explain' the facts of contagion (the truth of which had been assumed by many municipal authorities in their plague regulations for more than a century[2]) in terms of the current Aristotelian philosophy. The attempt was not as successful as is commonly made out; but his substitution of a material agent, which could be controlled, for the classical *miasma* or general corruption of the air, which could not, was a notable step towards a scientific explanation.

The question of therapy in the *morbus Gallicus* is not without general historical interest. Modern clinicians agree that mercurial treatment under regulated conditions of dosage was the only effective one—in the hands of a bungler the cure would have been literally worse than the disease. In the early years of the fifteenth century a 'miraculous cure' by concoctions of guaiac wood was announced from Spain. Ulrich von Hutten testified to its effectiveness in his own case, though he finally succumbed to the disease; Nicholas Pol (see above, p. 73) reported favourably on

---

[1] *Hist.* Vol. V, pp. 493 f.

[2] See for instance, A. C. Crombie, *From Augustine to Galileo*, London 1952, pp. 204-5.

it; yet it is doubtful whether it could have had any effect [1] except as a result of suggestion fortified by the exceedingly unpleasant character of the regimen. What was of course not understood is that the primary signs and symptoms of syphilis disappear spontaneously after a time, and the onset of the secondary ones may be long delayed.

Space does not permit of even a sketch of the study of other infectious diseases: the reader's attention may, however, be drawn to a few other points of special relevance to the question of science and the Renaissance. Of these one was especially the concern of surgeons, namely the problem as to whether gunshot wounds were freed from the risk of infection by virtue of the heat of combustion of the powder which drove the missile. This gave rise to a good deal of wordy argument and a few acute observations; but the consensus of opinion was so strong that the appalling custom of dressing wounds with boiling oil might have persisted in perpetuity had not a young military surgeon, Ambroise Paré, run out of oil after the assault on Turin (1537) by the forces of Francis I. Fearful of the result, Paré applied a 'digestive of eggs, oil of roses, and turpentine', but, to his surprise, it was these patients who next morning were comfortable and on the mend; those dressed in the conventional way were feverish, swollen, and in pain. The discovery was of course purely empirical. The use of hot oil was theoretically justified; since, whatever the temperature of the missile, infection might occur from the clothing; but doubtless the necrosis consequent on the use of the boiling oil would nullify the antisepsis. It is significant that Paré had a hard struggle to reach the highest position in his profession on account of his ignorance of Latin. It is at least doubtful if he would ever have succeeded had it not been for the interest of influential military commanders who early noted his outstanding skill.

Of other infections that were of frequent concern to the sixteenth century the following may be specially mentioned: [2] The 'English sweats', of which a model description was given by John Caius, and which seems to have been most probably an exceptionally virulent strain of influenza; small pox (*petite vérole*, so

---

[1] Except in filling the coffers of the Fuggers (who had a monopoly in the import of the wood) as Paracelsus was quick to recognise.

[2] The information in this paragraph is drawn mainly from E. W. Goodall, *A Short History of the Epidemic Infectious Diseases*, London, 1934.

called to distinguish its pustules from those of *grosse vérole* or *morbus Gallicus*); typhus (*lenticulae, puncticulae,* etc.); and tuberculosis (*phthisis contagiosa*), carefully described by Fernel in his *Pathologia,* who noted in one place that 'often the exhalation corrupts by contagion those who are not careful'—a truth, which, on account of the non-epidemic character of the disease, was ignored by the medical profession in Great Britain for three centuries.[1] With the frequently used designations 'putrid' and 'hectic' fevers no single disease can be connected, though one of the syndromes which the former comprised was almost certainly typhoid fever.

[1] E. R. Long, *Jean Fernel's Conception of Tuberculosis,* Singer, Vol. I, pp. 401-7.

CHAPTER XV

THE EMBODIMENT OF THE
SPIRITUAL WORLD

'IN that age many things that, later on, were to be divided by a critical effort were still closely interrelated: the view of the universe was not yet split into a religious one and a scientific one.'[1] Wolfgang Pauli is here speaking of the first years of the seventeenth century when in the mind of Ioannes Kepler the birth struggle was proceeding of the first *epoch-making* discovery in astronomy since the age of Ptolemy. The purpose of Pauli's extremely important monograph is to show that the driving force behind this struggle to frame a concept of planetary motion which turned out to be the fundamental basis of modern quantitative astronomy was essentially a religious creed springing from archetypal ideas on the relation between God and the world. It is immaterial whether or not Pauli's contention will stand up to detailed criticism; what can not be denied is the importance of his emphasis on the necessity for considering this kind of evidence in the history of science. The case of Kepler is crucial, since he stood on a plateau dividing the Old from the New in natural science: of the latter he was one of the architects, though one shudders to think with what dismay he would have viewed the outcome. It is always possible, and this was the almost invariable custom until the recent past, to ignore such 'confusions' in the mind of a creative genius as human weakness over which it would be kinder to draw a veil.[2] Sometimes indeed there may be good reasons for regarding such aberrations as merely incidental;

[1] C. G. Jung and W. Pauli, *The Influence of Archetypal Ideas on the Scientific Theories of Kepler, The Interpretation of Nature and the Psyche*, trans. by P. Silz, London, 1955, p. 155. Original German, 1952.

[2] Cf. P. O. Kristeller, who emphasises the necessity of reporting and understanding the errors as well as the successes of a thinker like Kepler, 'otherwise the history of science becomes nothing but a catalogue of disconnected facts, and a modern version of hagiography.' *The Classics and Renaissance Thought*, Cambridge, Mass., 1955, p. 67.

but what can never be justified is to ignore them; not only because to do so is to abandon the historian's task at the outset, but for a reason which may carry even greater weight with men of science whose interest in history is often only pragmatic. 'In contrast to the purely empirical conception according to which natural laws can with virtual certainty be derived from the material of experience alone, many physicists have recently emphasised anew the fact that intuition and the direction of attention play a considerable role in the development of the concepts and ideas, generally far transcending mere experience, that are necessary for the erection of a system of natural laws. . . . What is the nature of the bridge between the sense perceptions and the concepts? All logical thinkers have arrived at the conclusion that pure logic is incapable of constructing such a link. . . .'[1] Even if the precise formulation of this view may be open to criticism these words of Pauli bear the authority of one who himself undertook a leading part in the fashioning of the contemporary conceptual framework of physics. He continues: 'The process of understanding nature as well as the happiness that man feels in understanding, that is in the conscious realisation of new knowledge, seems thus to be based on a correspondence, a "matching" of inner images pre-existent in the human psyche with external objects and their behaviour. . . . These primary images which the soul can perceive with the aid of an innate "instinct" are called by Kepler archetypal ("arche-typalis").'[2] Pauli's emphasis on 'happiness' seems to me specially significant, since it points to the essentially *emotional* origin of creative activity in science: it is supported by Einstein's admission that for him a 'faith in the unique intelligibility of the cosmos was required to provide the necessary incentive'[3] to the sustained effort it demands. Kepler's positive contributions to science belong to the seventeenth century; but he was born in 1571 and the publication in 1595 of his *Mysterium Cosmographicum* placed him at once in the front rank of theoretical astronomers. His system of ideas, which he never wholly renounced, was therefore mainly the product of the sixteenth century. This system of ideas was squarely based on the faith that there is 'one spirit in all

---

[1] Pauli, *op. cit.* p. 151.

[2] *Op. cit.* pp. 152-3.

[3] See M. K. Munitz, *Space, Time, and Creation*, Glencoe, Ill., p. 117, note 6. The words as quoted are those of Professor Munitz.

things' and that the outward forms of all mundane things, including Man, in some sense embodies the modes of this creatorspirit; it is the pervasiveness of this cultural attitude which I wish
to examine in this concluding chapter.

The simple way of accounting for Kepler's 'unscientific'
approach to science is of course to say that renaissance thought
was at last freeing itself from 'Aristotelianism' and reverting to
'Platonism' and 'Pythagoreanism'; but this is not quite good
enough. Plato did not indulge in judicial astrology,[1] which
Kepler certainly did, and not merely to supplement his income,
though doubtless he had to compromise his inmost astrological
faith in order to accommodate his employer, Wallenstein. Nor
was Pythagoras an alchemist, which Tycho Brahe, whose positive
discoveries were the basis of Kepler's laws, certainly was. Also
it is hard to see Plato and Paracelsus seeing eye to eye on many
issues; yet Kepler regarded the latter as one of the greatest
ornaments of the Germanic nation. In this matter there seems to
be an unusually good case for writing history backwards—at any
rate as a beginning.

Though the opponents of astrology in Kepler's youth were almost
certainly less numerous than its adherents, it must not be assumed
that the majority of these adherents had any carefully articulated
scheme of ideas to justify their belief: they probably accepted
the conventional sequence of sign and event as the common
man accepts the fall of rain after the fall of the barometer. Also
it is necessary to distinguish those who believed that the influence
of the heavenly bodies was restricted to what we might describe
as purely physical changes such as the seasons, weather, biological
cycles, etc. This view might appeal to a thorough-going empiricist
like Francis Bacon[2] no less than to an academic partisan of the
Counter-Reformation such as James Cheyne.[3] Nevertheless,
when all allowance has been made, the number of outstanding
men for whom the configurations of the heavenly bodies were a
sign of the operation of spiritual powers is quite impressive. No
period of the sixteenth century is without some distinguished

---

[1] Cf. *Timaeus* concerning the various planetary configurations which 'send to men,
who can not calculate, panic, fears, and signs of things to come'. Quoted by M. K.
Munitz, *Theories of the Universe*, Illinois, 1957, p. 81.

[2] *De Augmentis Scientiarum* in the translation of Ellis and Spedding, Vol. IV, p. 351.

[3] W. P. D. Wightman, 'James Cheyne of Arnage', *Aberdeen Univ. Rev.* 35 (1954), 382.

representative. An early contemporary of Kepler was Giordano Bruno, whose unsubstantiated vision of an infinite universe filled with innumerable systems of suns and planets has already been alluded to (p. 43)—a vision Shakespeare may have had in mind when he makes Lorenzo call upon Jessica to 'look how the floor of heaven is thick inlaid with patines of bright gold: there's not the smallest orb which thou beholdst but in his motion like an angel sings . . .' for in the classical 'harmony of the spheres' it was only the planet-bearing orbs which emitted music; the same of course being the view of Kepler who denied the infinity of the universe. A little earlier than Bruno, was John Dee, who, though hard-headed enough to be the inspiration of the English school of navigation, held extreme views on the possibility of solving the riddles of the universe by the interpretation of the symbolic truths displayed in the astral and elementary relationships; such pre-occupations did not however prevent Tycho Brahe referring to him as 'my singular good friend', though Brahe seems to have had little use for judicial astrology as such. We have already seen (p. 29) the extent to which (on his own admission) Cardano was obsessed by belief in marvels, portents, and the adequacy of genitures. These names are sufficient to span the century; many others could be cited, notably Fernel, who, however, seems to have turned away from astrology in his later years.

Cardano was born in 1501; during his youth there was being thrashed out in the universities of Northern Italy that basic issue of the relation of nature and spirit to which reference has already been made. In 1520 Pietro Pomponazzi had completed his work rather misleadingly referred to as *On Incantations* (the full title being *De Naturalium Effectuum admirandorum Causis seu de Incantationibus*) which, though numerous earlier manuscripts are extant, was not printed until 1556, perhaps significantly under the editorship of Gratarolo, famed for his editions of alchemical 'classics'. Thorndike (*Hist.* Vol. V, pp. 94-110) gives a full and not unsympathetic analysis of the work, but it was Cassirer (*Individuum und Kosmos*, pp. 108-12, etc.) who emphasised its great importance as marking a new stage in the attempt to reduce all types of manifest experience to some kind of *order*. As Cassirer so sagaciously observes, there are two different steps (*Stufen*) towards the renunciation (*Überwindung*) of the astrological world-view, namely, either by demonstration that it is empty of content, or by giving it a new methodological basis. Moreover, there has been no steady 'progress' in this liberation, the two methods having been prosecuted side by side. Pomponazzi's approach was not wholly new. It developed out of, and in some degree in opposition to, that of Averroes; but he leaned more heavily on the Greek commentators on Aristotle such as Alexander of Aphrodisias. What is especially significant in this work of Pomponazzi is not, as is so frequently claimed for the 'Renaissance', an emphasis on accurate observation of nature; quite the contrary: marvels are accepted for the most part uncritically. Its importance is the deeper philosophical one of seeking a single causal principle as the basis of all those phenomena whose causes are not manifest: namely, the influence of the celestial powers. No unmediated action of any spiritual agent, except that of the astral intelligences, is to be accepted as valid: God Himself works His wonders only through the agency of the celestial powers.[1] This dogmatic demand for a *single* causal principle may be, as Bacon was to point out, an Idol of the Den; but it is hard to see how the deterministic attitude characteristic of science as it developed in the seventeenth century could have been otherwise assured.

The exact degree of insight and appreciation of a 'scientific' mode of thought possessed by Pomponazzi can now never be estimated. He seems at times to have been prepared to do away entirely with *all* the paraphernalia both of the medieval Church and of primeval superstition. But even in Padua he had to walk warily, and doubtless even more so in Bologna, while his work on the *Immortality of the Soul* was publicly burnt even in Venice; so in the concluding chapter he had to admit the existence of whatever the Church affirms, for what might be true in philosophy might be false in theology. Yet however this may be, Pomponazzi's works provided a methodical basis for an ordered system of nature by which an intuitive belief in the pervasive influence of the supernatural (as the celestial bodies were by definition) on the natural could be rationally justified. The ascription of spiritual powers to the celestial bodies, though to us a work of supererogation, was wholly consistent with contemporary modes of thought, whether paying homage to Plato or to Aristotle. Nor is it to be so easily brushed aside: it is merely a virtual admission of the

---

[1] *De Incantionibus*, Basel, 1567, p. 122, quoted by Cassirer, *op. cit.* p. 109.

inconceivability that power to effect motion and change is able to reside within natural bodies. After all, Newton said as much in respect of gravitation.[1]

I have paid rather more attention to this work of Pomponazzi than it usually receives in the history of science, since although it added nothing whatever to knowledge either of the heavens or of the earth it does seem to show that astrology was a probably unavoidable avenue to science, as we know it. The metaphor may perhaps be pursued; for the astrologer may be likened to a traveller passing along a winding avenue composed of trees densely planted on either side. From time to time he may catch a glimpse of the castle he is seeking: shall he keep to the 'safe' but tortuous roadway, or strike off into open fields where all is clear? If he does the latter, a dip in the ground may once again hide the castle from him. At times he reaches side tracks leading towards the castle; we need not specify those who took the side tracks and lost themselves in enchanting but impenetrable thickets! At last a break in the trees gives promise of a passage to the castle; but there is no path, and many hills lie between the traveller and his objective. He alone, therefore, who is willing to proceed cautiously by measurement and calculation, seeking the nearer hills as observation points for further progress, will ever, if at all, reach the Castle of Knowledge. For of that new country there were no maps. What Pomponazzi taught his companions was the necessity for the faith that the castle really exists; that it is the same castle viewed intermittently through the trees; and that there are no magic carpets, wishing stones, or elfin voices to guide them. What neither he nor they recognised was that this faith was useless as long as they remained in the avenue. Nearly a century had to pass before people began to break out into open—and uncharted—country. But, to conclude the metaphor, it may well have been their walking along the avenue with Pomponazzi's message—perhaps diffusely rather than directly communicated—echoing in their ears that they ultimately came to such a view of the open country as to provide the illumination needed.

Before leaving Pomponazzi we must recall that it was as a *Neo*-Aristotelian that he composed his books: to his acquaintance

[1] 'It is inconceivable that inanimate brute matter should without the mediation of something else which is not material operate on and affect other matter without mutual contact.' Letter to Bentley, 25 February, 1692/3.

T

with Aristotle is probably due the closer approach in the *De Incantionibus* to the modern principle of causality than is to be found in the Neo-Platonic views of the 'Platonic' Academy of Florence. In some respects it is an 'advance' on both Aristotle and Plato: the former's world system suffers from the radical cleavage between celestial and sublunary spheres, the latter's from the fact that it is purely mathematical, hence has very little relevance to the sublunary sphere as it was known at that time. Pomponazzi's causal theory, since it still lacked any settled principle for the selection and appraisement of its *data*, was still very far from science—further than were the Greek masters; but in its formal aspects it showed the pattern of relationships on which science was ultimately to build.

Paracelsus was dead before *De Incantionibus* was printed; but it is unlikely that the noise of Pomponazzi's challenging views should not have reached him while he was at Ferrara. So striking is the resemblance between their attitudes to the celestial origin of all terrestrial changes that a later commentator, Jacques Fontaine, was to accuse Paracelsus of plagiarism (Thorndike, *Hist.* Vol. V, p. 645). But into the world-view of Paracelsus there entered a factor with which Pomponazzi would have had no sympathy: this was alchemy. We have already (p. 166) noted that this term covers a considerable range of experience and operation, from matter-of-fact practical handbooks for the guidance of miners and metal-workers to esoteric phantasies where any merely practical outcome would probably have been regarded as sordid. We have considered the former in so far as they relate to the nature of the physical world; we come now to those which seem almost wholly detached from any such consideration. But it must be remembered that these are only the extremes of an unbroken series; a practical textbook such as the *Alchimia* of Libavius might be written in the hope of furthering the quest for the mythical Philosopher's Stone.

As an example of 'mystical' alchemy we may consider *The Compound of Alchymy* (No. 577) written in the second half of the fifteenth century and dedicated to Edward IV by George Ripley, Canon Regular of the Augustinian Priory at Bridlington in Yorkshire, where the fumes from his laboratory are said to have caused annoyance to the rest of the community. I have chosen this work for the sufficient reasons that its authenticity and origin are unquestioned, it exists in several near contemporary manuscripts, and was printed in 1591. It has the further advantage of having been written in English. The editor of the first printed version, Ralph Rabbards, of whom little is known, signs himself 'Yours in the furtherance of science'. It may well have been the first alchemical work to be printed in England; it was followed in the seventeenth century by a steady flow of such works, of which the collection by Elias Ashmole is one of the best known. The book opens with Ripley's *Vision* of a toad which, swollen with excess of grape juice, gradually died and was committed to 'a gentle fire: which done . . . the Toade with colours rare through every side was pear'st' becoming white and at last 'rudde for everymore did last'. This colour transition was a constant theme in the alchemical work, and it is not surprising that in his own vision Ripley obtained from this sequence transmuted 'venom', a sort of homoeopathic 'medicine'. After the *Vision* comes a *Prologue* containing the injunction:

'Therefore with God looke thou beginne
That he by grace may dwell with thee
So shalt thou best to wisdome winne
And knowledge of our great privitie
Nourish vertues and from vices flee
And trusting thou wilt thee well dispose
Our secrets to thee I will disclose.'

Then follows a *Preface* opening with a prayer and proceeding without break into the main part of the text, which consists of *Twelve Gates* or stages through which the Work must proceed. It is written in verse, but, as space does not permit of long quotations, I shall ignore the divisions. The purpose of the poem is to answer the question 'What is our stone?' to which Ripley replies, 'Mercurie it is I wis, but not the common called quicksilver by name'. There are three mercuries, two of them are 'superficiall', the third 'mercurie of metals essentiall is the principle of our stone materiall. In Sunne and Moone our menstrue is not seene. It appeareth not but by effect to sight. That is the stone of which we meane. . . . It is a soule, a substance bright. Of sunne and moone a subtill influence whereby the earth receiveth resplendence.' So far there is nothing that might not be interpreted as contemporary chemical theory. The *Prologue* and opening prayer do not necessarily betoken an introduction to a spiritual exercise *as such*: a German plague tract would probably open in a similar way, or even a 'family physician'. The opening sentences reproduce one well known contemporary theory of transmutation—that the mercurial 'essence' is the principle of the purest gold. A 'menstruum' (a term in use in ordinary chemistry till late in the eighteenth century) was anything which brought other substances into intimate contact, so was equivalent to a solvent in the widest sense; hence ordinary mercury was a menstruum (by amalgamation, a term later used by Ripley and still current in chemistry) for gold, copper, silver etc. but not for iron. But the 'menstrue' effective for the action culminating in the production of the stone was invisible (which was not surprising!) except by its effects: that is, its presence could be inferred from changes observed in the mixture, which is after all a perfectly good chemical concept. 'Sun', 'Moon', and 'earth' may be intentionally ambiguous here, implying (perhaps), as well as the ordinary sense, an influence of gold and silver, or their *essences*, on the earthy character of the substances present.

In the first 'Gate' called *Calcination*, however, Ripley gives a hint that it is not with the ordinary operations of chemists that he is concerned, for it is *not* to be carried out with fire alone, corrosives, or 'waters ardent'. Nor are such things as eggs and blood to be used, but gold and silver 'wisely', that is, 'philosophically' not 'manual'. Other things must first be separated by putrefaction. This caution against the common practices is repeated under *Putrefaction*, where he waxes eloquent on those who lose their own and others' money with 'fires, corrosives, odours, smoakes and watchings': especially significant here is his objurgation against 'false multipliers promising earthly riches of coin'. He returns to it yet again in *Sublimation*: 'Some do mercury from vitriol and salt sublime and other spirits from scales of yron and steele, from egg shells and from quicklime . . .' but 'we sublime not so'. Finally, in an *Admonition* following the main text, he gives a detailed list of the chemicals he himself had used, 'weening so to make the Philosophers' Stone, but finally I lost every deele'. . . . 'In smokes and smell thou shalt have much woe.'

It is clear from the above and other similar warnings that the kind of alchemy Ripley is telling about has only a formal relation to chemistry, even to the contemporary Arab or Aristotelian versions. Such connection as it has with chemistry is also eclectic: for while 'sulphur' and 'mercury' are 'coessential', their transformations are visualised in terms of turning 'earth into water, water to air, air to fire, then reverse'; this may, however, be no more than a picturesque description of distillation and condensation of some originally solid substance. More precisely Aristotelian is the statement that every metal was once water and 'as yce to water doth relent' since it was water before 'so each metal . . . with water they turne to water all'. In the account of these transformations there is also a strong biological strain: for *Dissolution* is to be carried out 'in one glasse . . . like to an Egge in shape and closed weele'; also 'let never thy glasse be hotter than thou maist feel'—a mode of operation going back at least to the Alexandrian alchemists near the beginning of the Christian era. The usual sexual symbols are present—Sun and Moon are husband and wife. But the main emphasis is on putrefaction and regeneration: 'Sith Christ doth witness without the graine of wheate dye in the ground, encrease maist thou none get. . . . Seeds both rot and spire . . . that they may be separate. The water used must be seven times sublimate, else no kindly dissolution nor putrefying.' In *Congelation* following *Putrefaction* water plays a dominant part: earth is 'revived' by it; the 'Fire of our philosophe named now oyle now water mysticalie'. 'Water is the secret and the life of everything' as witness the 'birth water' and the water which with the substance of the egg nourishes the chick within the shell.

The 'death and corruption' of the seed as a preliminary to new life are paralleled in the production of the stone; but it is also paralleled in the life of the spirit. After the frequent (reflux?) distillation 'by itself' in a closed vessel described in the Gate called *Separation* the vessel in *Conjunction* is allowed to stand for five months that the 'Soule' may be 'cleansed from sin'. Later, after several 'gates', including *Putrefaction*, have been passed, a similar process is carried out in *Sublimation*, in which the substance driven to the top of the vessel, is to be left for forty days, whereby is a 'cleansing of spirit' and a joining of spirit to matter. In *Exaltation*, which follows, the 'elements' are 'circulated' and taken 'up to heaven' in a manner which reads very like a modern reflux distillation. Of projection we are told little that is intelligible except that it must not be made on 'mettals uncleansed' but for

T*

'profitable projection . . . the psalmes of the Psalter example thou take.' After such a series has been propounded Ripley says that 'by this mustie talking I meane nothing else, but that thou must cast first the lesse on the more' which does not seem to take us much further. Nor does the *Recapitulo* provide any further enlightenment as to the nature of Projection; but there is further reference to the part played by the astronomical influences which are to be calculated by turning the 'wheel'. The work concludes with an epistle to Edward IV telling him that this is written for him alone and was learnt at the University of Louvain. Lastly comes the 'astronomical wheel in paradise outside the sphere of Saturn where the Red Man and White Wife will be spoused with the Spirit of Life.'

In this condensed account of *The Compound of Alchemy* I have tried to avoid special pleading. In support of my belief that it describes a probably material projection of a spiritual exercise I have consciously abstracted similar sentiments from their contexts in different 'gates': I have done so with the less concern for possible distortion since the author is apt at any stage to digress into side-issues, and one gets the impression that the number twelve was chosen first and subsequently an attempt was made to concoct an equal number of stages—hence a good deal of repetition. This 'spiritual' interpretation is of course original only in the sense that I could not avoid the conclusion that, viewed merely as a recipe for the Philosopher's Stone, this rig-marole could never have achieved the reputation that it did: it must have satisfied some other need both in reader and author. Dr. C. G. Jung's *Psychology and Alchemy* provides a highly plausible hypothesis of what this satisfaction may have been. Very roughly this amounts to the view that alchemy provided a release for those archetypal urges of the unconscious for which the relatively sudden 'spiritualisation' of Christianity provides inadequate means of expression. The wealth of evidence for this hypothesis can not even be summarised here. I add only one gloss. In his discussion of Myth (*Philosophy of Symbolic Forms*, Vol. II) Cassirer emphasised the importance of recognising that for primitive cultures the distinction between original and 'copy' is not made: an image does not *represent* the god, but *is* the god. Similarly, rites are more important than operations; since, although the latter are known to be *necessary*, their effectiveness is believed to be wholly dependent on the former. Cassirer goes on to show a partial persistence of this 'identification' in the rise of alchemy, referring the reader to Lippmann's *Enstehung und Ausbreitung der Alchemie* (Berlin, 1919, pp. 318 f.) where it is shown that the Platonic-Aristotelian 'elements', with their conjugate 'humours' in living creatures, provided the theoretical justification for the alchemical 'substantiation of qualities'. In this mode of thought the 'fluidity' potentially present in every metal had to be looked upon as 'carried' by *a* 'mercury' and so on. The mode was enriched, and doubtless at the same time confused, by the Stoic conception of τὸ πῦρ τεχνικον ('craftsman fire', i.e. creative, in contradistinction to destructive) and λόγοι σπερματικοι (fragments of the 'seminal reason' which proceed from the πνευμα or 'world soul').[1] Now, if we compare Ripley's 'alchemy' with Io. de Rupescissa's (see above, p. 171), or even more strikingly, with the *Preciosa Margarita Novella* (*A New Pearl of Great Price*) (No. 682), written by Petrus Bonus of Ferrara in 1330, we are struck by the relatively matter of fact and lucid character of the products of the medieval 'gloom'. The *Margarita* represents scholasticism at its best: the arguments *against* alchemy are set out with searching thoroughness, but they are subsequently rejected. The arguments rest of course more on verbal and logical distinctions than on appeal to observation; but the author is honest enough to admit that, though he is convinced that transmutation is possible and the method can be quickly learnt, he has never succeeded in achieving it himself. What caused the degeneration (if it was degeneration) from the near empiricism of Io. de Rupescissa and the rationalism of Bonus into the hocus-pocus of Ripley? It would hardly carry conviction to suggest that the England of Caxton and the Switzerland of Froben and Amerbach had 'gone primitive' to the extent of reviving *mana* and *consciously* identifying object and image. The key to my gloss is the word 'conscious'. Is it not possible that at a period in which there was proceeding, as I have argued, a break-up of traditional modes of thought, a transvaluation of all values, the archetypal images relatively repressed by medieval rationalism emerged into the consciousness of a larger number of more gifted individuals, finding expression there in various related ways of which Ripley's *Compound* gives one of the clearest instances? Though neither Paracelsus nor

---

[1] For a development of this relationship see Pagel, *Paracelsus*, esp. p. 84 f.

Cardano had any truck with transmutation as such, each of them, in different ways, saw the working of 'demons' (in the Greek sense of personal unembodied forces) in the world of nature. The route largely pioneered by Ripley was ultimately followed by an increasing number of pilgrims (many, such as Robert Fludd, belonging to a definite spiritual community called the 'Rosicrucians'—still active—of whom it seems not wholly improbable that Isaac Newton was one. As Pauli has clearly brought out, where Kepler (and doubtless Newton) differed from Fludd and a host of camp-followers was that, whereas the former drew generously on the archetypes of the unconscious as an inspiration towards the 'discovery of the great ocean of Truth', they had the moral courage to drop these double-edged weapons when they were seen to break against facts firmly established by observation.

In all this Paracelsus seems to me to hold a special place. If one may appropriately use the Jungian categories of personality-structure, he is the *extrovert* complement to the *introvert* Ripley. For although there is a striking similarity of the symbols employed by the two men, especially in respect of the putrefaction and regeneration of seed and soul, one gets the impression that, although he is willing to share his 'secrets' with the king, Ripley is seeking 'sublimation' by the 'projection' of his own unconscious needs on to the materials he is operating with. For Paracelsus, on the other hand, nothing less than the human race will suffice; hence his concern rather for the alchemic 'medicine' to 'perfect' the human individuals on to whom he is 'projecting' that aspect of the 'Stone' which has the power to 'perfect' metals. Hence also his vastly greater importance for medicine and chemistry, since a great variety of natural objects—metals, precious stones, plants (of which he made far more use than his dogmatic assertions would suggest) became the medium for his 'perfection', and a great variety of 'imperfect' human beings the objects. Thus he knew that the 'Light of Nature' [1] must be his guide, as well as the light

---

[1] This concept, as Dr. Pagel has warned me, is highly complex. It does *not* mean merely the 'light of experience', but rather the innate nature in so far as it is other than 'material'. The context for the present application is Huser *op. cit.* p. 88: 'Nun folgt hierauff das diese Bequemligkeit und Verfügung der Ordnung Soll gehen aus der Arth des Leibes auch des Liechts der Natur: dann das der Leib hat ein ander Liecht für sich selbst, ein anders das Liecht der Natur betreffend die Arth' . . . 'So ist die Art des Liechts der Natur dasz sie in der Wiegen eingehet . . .' Cf. Newton, *Opticks* Reprint of 4th edn., London, 1931, p. 405.

of his own nature which God had created for the work. Despite his fantastic 'theory' he made a great number of striking observations (such as the first relatively systematic account of pneumoconiosis in mine workers) and seems to have effected far too many striking 'cures' for these to have been the result of mere chance. Nor was his 'theory' *merely* fantastic. Though he failed to realise it, it was a return to the Greek (especially Hippokratic) conception of the physician as guide, philosopher, and friend, and of the patient as an embodied spirit; of the physician as the wise councillor, who could at most provide the best conditions in which the patient's 'nature' could work for the re-establishment of harmony. Paracelsus was in advance of Hippokrates, in that he made use of the fact that for most people a 'faith that worketh all things' is one of which the Crown is a Loving Creator; and of Galen, in that he stripped off the meaningless polypharmacy with which Galen had obscured the nature of the problem, which in other respects he well understood. Paracelsus was in advance of both the masters in possessing a greater understanding of the subtlety of the relations between Man and Nature in respect of which only a far-ranging search, backed by genius for seizing the essential, could hope to discover the keys which fit the several locks. In this 'theosophic medicine' Paracelsus was only applying in a special field modes of thought and feeling more widely current among his contemporaries than has as yet been sufficiently taken account of. This is well brought out in a study of *Mystiques, Spirituels, Alchimistes* recently brought together by Alexandre Koyré (Paris, 1955). Among these Koyré singles out Sebastian Franck as one of the many who came to find in the Reformed Churches a tyranny no less than that from which they had escaped. Born eight years later than Paracelsus, Franck resembled him most closely in his insistence on the need for each man to strive to replace the 'old Adam' by the 'Light of Christ'. Franck was concerned with spiritual sickness, Paracelsus primarily with physical, while emphasising that they are essentially inseparable. As Koyré notes, the doctrine of the 'casting out of the old Adam' was far from new; but the novelty of Franck's teaching was that if in all men there abides the old Adam there abides also the Light

The contrast of *Liecht der Natur* to superstition is illustrated, by Paracelsus's 'theory' of the alleged curative power of Mumia—fragments of a human body, preferably after sudden death. See Pagel, *Paracelsus*, pp. 55, 56, 101.

of Christ; and that true self-knowledge—which is spiritual
health—is identification with the inner light: 'Nimand kennet
sich selber als wenn er sihet und wisset durchs licht und wort
Gottes das in ihm ist und Gott selber sehet. Sich in Gott und Gott
in sich.' Even closer to the central doctrine of Paracelsus is: 'Wer
in der Natur bliebe der bliebe in Gott, denn Gott ist die Natur.'
Such sentiments are easily dismissed by the blanket word 'pantheism'; but, as Koyré is quick to point out, this is to tell us
nothing, since the term can be stretched to cover even certain
aspects of the teaching of St. Thomas. What Koyré brings out
more convincingly than any other writer in my experience [1] is
not the remarkable resurgence of Pantheistic modes of thought in
the Renaissance, but the almost unique position of Paracelsus
within that company of 'pantheists', in being the *epitome* of *all* the
non-literary aspects of that not wholly fictitious creation of historians, 'Renaissance Man'. Restlessness of body and spirit,
mistrust of authority, 'seeing for oneself' combined with an almost
pathological credulousness, arrogance and a hyper-sensitive
awareness of the ubiquity and *individuality* of hidden natural
powers—all are developed to a marked degree in this protean
spirit. It is utterly remote from renaissance 'humanism'; but was
it a 'new Birth', or merely a new constellation of old ways 'emergent' in an environment which must certainly be reckoned as
new for them? Reference has already been made to Io. de Rupescissa and to what I believe to be the as yet undervalued importance
of the nature-philosophy of the Stoics.[2] No one is likely to under-
emphasise the influence of what is somewhat equivocally called
'Neoplatonism', so frequently rearing its head, and as frequently
pushed back with varying degrees of firmness by the orthodox.
Some have seen in the revival of the mystic numerology of the
Kabala by Reuchlin an important factor in the less respectable
(since not Greek!) aspects of Renaissance thought. This was
undoubtedly much 'in the air', and the fact that two eminent
Greek scholars—Pico della Mirandola and Reuchlin—were responsible for the movement, gave it a wider circulation (especially
in Germany) than it would otherwise have had. But though not
'humanistic', the supposed clues to the sacred realities provided
by numbers and geometrical figures associated with certain

---

[1] This was written before Dr. Pagel's *Paracelsus* was published.
[2] See note 1, p. 295.

numbers belonged to a wholly literary and pseudo-historical tradition far removed from the mines and wild nature where Paracelsus sought inspiration. More important, perhaps, and one whose influence has so far been peculiarly difficult to assess, was the Lullian Art. The way is strewn with pitfalls, since the supposititious nature of the *whole* alchemical corpus attributed to 'Lullius', 'Raimundus', etc., has now been demonstrated by the discovery of warnings against the vanity of alchemy by Raimundo Lull himself—that is, within books whose authenticity can not be doubted. What then could be the significance of 'Lullism' to the 'theosophic medicine' we are here concerned with? First, that both Paracelsus and Brunschwig refer expressly to the writings of 'Lull', as do Pico, Cardano, Cornelius Agrippa, Bruno, Dee, Descartes, and, more so than any other thinkers of the seventeenth century, Leibniz; and second, that, though the authentic Lull warned against alchemy, he explicitly recognised the value of his Art to the alchemist. Indeed this fact expresses the importance of the Art, namely that by an ingenious process of abstraction and system of parallel relations it is recognised by its founder as, though primarily *for* theology, 'good for law, astronomy, and medicine'. Careful examination of these categories indicated that 'astronomy' means 'astrology' in so far as this is concerned with the influence of the indwelling powers of the heavenly bodies on terrestrial creatures. 'Medicine' is that part of the subject concerned with the calculation of drugs from the relations between the 'elements', 'humours', 'astral influences'—whether benign or antagonistic—and the 'temperaments' of the patient. It is no far cry from this 'astrological medicine' to the 'alchemy' which Paracelsus claimed to be one of the corner stones of medicine. Indeed it seems likely that Lull would not have disclaimed the books subsequently written in his name, and evidently under his influence, except in so far as they held out promise of material wealth to be gained by means of the 'Stone'. The case seems to be parallel to that of 'astrology', which he condemned only in so far as it was represented as implying an astral pre-destination of individual men and their enterprises.

The cry wrung from Paracelsus on more than one occasion, 'Man must bring everything to perfection. The work of bringing things to perfection is called "ALCHEMY",'[1] has been greatly

[1] Cf. Huser, *op. cit.* p. 61 and again on p. 70.

realised. About twenty years after his death commenced the flood of editions of his works, culminating in the splendid and still indispensable collected (but far from complete) editions of Huser and Palthenius. But, as happens to all prophets, his memory suffered grievously from those who heard only the words he uttered and failed to understand their message, the application of which must be modified with the march of knowledge. Libavius was right to dissociate 'alchemy' from the grosser superstitions and uninspired quackery of the 'Paracelsians'; possibly the denunciations of the less liberal Erastus were even more influential. In any case, as the seventeenth century wore on, the works of Paracelsus became of less interest both for medicine and chemistry; though his more positive teaching received a new support from the Flemish recluse, J. B. van Helmont,[1] who nevertheless on general grounds repudiated a considerable part of it. Before we take our leave of this meteor of the Renaissance, who to the Fellows of the Royal Society would have seemed to have burnt himself out in his fiery passage a century before their day, we must take a final, if fleeting glimpse at the author of *Astronomia Nova*—Ioannes Kepler.

It was not only in respect of time that Kepler stood upon the bridge between 'renaissance', and the 'modern', science of the Royal Society. For if it is true that his thought was shaped by the archetypal ideas—microcosm and macrocosm, signatures, number mysticism, astral influences, and world-soul—it is significant, as Pauli has emphasised, that he was selective in respect of those ideas on which he drew. In regard to astrology he was closer to Paracelsus in rejecting the crude judicial theory still widely held: his inconsistency in practice, as in the horoscope he drew for Wallenstein, may perhaps have been forced on him by the exigencies of gaining a livelihood. In respect of 'signatures' he echoed Paracelsus in regarding the form of plants as inborn and derived by a natural instinct (*ex instinctu naturali dependere iisque connasci*). But whereas Paracelsus poured forth a jumble of ideas, some individually suggestive but without any inner coherence, Kepler's world-view was disciplined by his Platonising respect for the regulative power of the eternal rationalities expressed in quantitative relations. In the application of this principle he was apparently unique among the mystics of his generation, in that,

[1] See Pagel, *Paracelsus* for many examples.

unlike for instance his opponent Robert Fludd, he saw the Cabbalist number-mysticism for what it was—a diverting figment, but essentially *uncontrollable* in the modern sense of the term. His quantitative images were exclusively geometrical—the point-sphere analogy of Nicholas of Cues (whom surprisingly Pauli does not mention) and the 'radiation cosmology', so prominent in the philosophy of Plotinus and given a more precise physical significance by Robert Grosseteste and Roger Bacon. This idea of an 'axis of power' (if I may borrow Faraday's expressive term for an electrically conducting path) was used by Kepler as an image of the motive power of the sun upon the planets, and as a means of determining points of special cosmic significance due to the intersection of special rays: by the latter expedient he justified the alleged importance of the *directiones* (cf. Regiomontanus, No. 559) in astrology. The same *potency* of geometrical regularity was shown, so he believed, by the constancy of the number and arrangement of floral organs in certain plants (cf. Turneisser, No. 691) and by the regularity of crystal form of 'fossils', 'generated' by the *vis formatrix* within the earth. All this was indeed mere schematism; vital perhaps for the mental struggle through which Kepler brought the 'New Astronomy' to birth, but superficially remote from the 'modern' science which was to follow it. Yet this was not all. The cosmic faith of Paracelsus shone again in the following *credo*: 'Nothing exists or happens in the visible heavens, the significance of which is not extended further by way of some occult principle to the earth and the faculties of the natural things; and thus these animal faculties are affected here on earth exactly as the heavens themselves are affected.'[1] Neither the *credo* nor the schema are by themselves sufficient; but combined they afford the suggestion and the discipline which ultimately led to a new faith: 'Therefore to the same natural effects we must as far as possible assign the same causes. As to respiration in a man and in a beast; the descent of stones in Europe and in America; the light of our culinary fire and of the sun, the reflection of light in the earth and in the planets.'[2] The points of view of the two faiths are strikingly different: from the latter the 'occult principles' and 'faculties' of the former have been banished. But is the result so different in the two cases? From both there has disappeared the

---

[1] Kepler, *op.* ed. Frisch, Vol. II, p. 719, quoted by Pauli, *op. cit.*
[2] Newton, *Principia*, Rules for Philosophising, II.

baneful influence of the Aristotelian dogma expressing the complete disparity between the 'order' of the heavens and the 'physics'
of the sublunary 'elements'. For Kepler, as probably for Raimundo
Lull and Paracelsus, this dogma is replaced by one in which the
image of the heavens is as it were stamped upon 'natural things'.
With Newton the whole *distinction* between the heavens and
'natural things' seems to have gone: all are included in one
'natural philosophy' by means of 'mathematical principles'.
But this did not mean the *rejection* of the spiritual—'That gravity
should be innate, inherent, and essential to matter, so that one
body may act upon another at a distance through a *vacuum*,
without the mediation of anything else. . . . is to me so great an
absurdity that I believe no man who has in philosophical matters a
competent faculty of thinking can ever fall into it' (Newton, in
letter III to Richard Bentley). Newton never categorically asserted
his belief that the cause of gravity was spiritual, but since in another
connection he puts forward the view that (God) 'is more able
by his Will to move the Bodies within his boundless uniform
Sensorium, and thereby to form and reform the Parts of the
Universe, than we are by our Will to move the parts of our own
Bodies',[1] it is pretty clear where his sympathies lay. Is it therefore
too much to suppose that the mystical strain so characteristic of
Renaissance thought had as important a part to play in the final
establishment of 'Natural Philosophy' as the more abstract
geometrisation of Galileo? This enquiry has as yet been too little
cultivated. The labour will be immense, but the value of the
results might well be commensurable; for they may help to reveal
how shabby has been the betrayal of those great men of the
Renaissance who, while enlarging Man's vision of the universe,
still regarded it with wonder and awe. To 'Modern' Man was it
left to rob it of all spiritual significance, degrading it and himself
to the soulless task of exploitation. Yet 'the thing is not altogether
desperate': recognition of the disease is half way towards its
cure. More and more are the great men of our time who have
demonstrated their prowess in the wielding of the weapons of
'modern science' turning to the past where 'Natural Philosophy'
meant what it said and not, as now, merely one road towards it.
It is the task of the historian and philosopher of science to bring
to life the great figures of the past, not, as so often heretofore, as

[1] *Opticks*, Reprint of 4th edn. London, 1931, p. 403.

embodied categories of truth or folly, but as men of like passions as ourselves, yet often with insights and sympathies which modern Man has deliberately shunned. In such a light can we now see Paracelsus, who through the clouds created by his own undisciplined imagination nevertheless saw undimmed the truth from which our eyes have so long been turned, that the 'beloved physician' leading the unquiet spirit may over a great range of human ills effect far more than the 'scientist' for whom the patient is reduced to a mere disordered system of electrolytes.

At a superficial glance the searchers of the Renaissance, surrounded by the many paths their own efforts had once more cleared or had opened up for the first time, chose the wrong path towards modern science. But the path you choose depends at least to some extent on where you want to go: it is clear that throughout the sixteenth century there was no settled conviction of where they wanted to go. If this brief study of Science and the Renaissance has succeeded in pointing any moral, it is, or should be, that in so far as the term has any application beyond a mere chronological convention the Renaissance in science denotes neither a rebirth of Greek ways of thought nor the new birth of modern science, but rather the clearing away of settled land marks and the search for new viewpoints. In the following century one of these aspects became dominant: it was that whereby in 'enlarging the bounds of human empire' men should become 'masters and possessors of nature'; the unanimity of the protestant empiricist Francis Bacon and the catholic rationalist Descartes has not always been sufficiently noted. It is not at all clear that the path thus pointed out is the one many of the great thinkers of the Renaissance would have wished to tread—at least with such blinkered self-assurance. In another mood even Lord Chancellor Bacon reminded his readers that knowledge is 'a rich storehouse for the glory of the Creator' as well as for 'the relief of Man's estate', and that although no limit is to be put upon men's study in 'the book of God's word or in the book of God's works' 'let men beware that they apply both to charity, and not to swelling'. Among the many reasons for treading once again these paths of the Renaissance is that of listening to the talk of those great men who with all their faults had not yet identified the task of natural philosophy with the means whereby Man might expropriate the universe. The task of finding a road leading to a nobler prospect is urgent; for a consummation threatens in which, in a sense undreamed of by Karl Marx, the expropriators will be expropriated.

BIBLIOGRAPHICAL NOTE AND SUPPLEMENTARY BIBLIOGRAPHY

THE author of a work covering the period of the 'Renaissance' is faced with the problem of the 'correct' spelling of Greek, Latin and Arabic names. The view adopted here is that of the late Georges Sarton (*The Appreciation of Ancient and Medieval Science*, Philadelphia, 1955, p. xiii f), namely, that there is no 'correct' method. The line dividing pedantic rigour from needless looseness will be drawn by different authors at different points: I have tried as far as possible to follow Sarton in not writing the names of Greek thinkers in their Latin forms in a book written in English, nor those of Arabic thinkers in the crude phonetic equivalents concocted by the medieval 'Latins'. But like Sarton I have halted this side of pedantry by writing 'Plato', 'Aristotle', 'Ptolemy', and 'Averroes' instead of 'Aristokles', 'Aristoteles', 'Ptolemaios' and 'Muhammad ibn Ahmad' or even 'ibn Roshd'. The only excuse for my 'Hippokrates' and 'Galen' is that the latter is at least English and not Latin; but I fear that inconsistency will 'break in', for which the reader's indulgence is asked.

The following Supplementary Bibliography is divided into two parts. The first includes the titles of books alluded to in more than one place in the text, to facilitate reference; in this list also will be found works not referred to in the text but from which further information may be derived on topics for which there was not room to provide adequate discussion.

The second list comprises a few works which became available only after the text was completed, but to which reference would otherwise have been made.

ALBERTI, L. B., *On Painting* (tr. J. R. Spencer), London, 1956.
ARBER, A., *Herbals*, 2nd edn. Cambridge,
BARRACLOUGH, G., *History in a Changing World*, Oxford, 1958.
BLUNT, W., *The Art of Botanical Illustration*, London, 1950.

BOLGAR, R. R., *The Classical Heritage and its Beneficiaries*, Cambridge, 1954.
BURCKHARDT, J., *The Civilization of the Renaissance in Italy* (tr. from 15th edn. by S. G. C. Middlemore), London, 1929.
CASSIRER, E., etc., *Ed.*, *The Renaissance Philosophy of Man*, Chicago, 1958.
CURRY, W. C., *Chaucer and the Medieval Sciences*, 2nd edn., London, 1960 (esp. Ch. I, The Doctor of Physic and Medieval Medicine).
DREYER, J. L. E., *History of the Planetary Systems*, Cambridge, 1906.
DUVEEN, D. I., *Bibliotheca Alchemica et Chemica*, London, 1949.
FERGUSON, J., *Bibliotheca Chemica*, 2 vols., Glasgow, 1906.
GILMORE, M. P., *The Age of Humanism*, New York, 1952.
GOLDSCHMIDT, E. P., *The First Cambridge Press in its European setting*, Cambridge, 1955.
GRANT, A. J., *History of Europe from 1494 to 1610*, 4th edn., London, 1948.
HALL, A. R., *The Scientific Revolution*, London, 1954.
HUSER [The works of Paracelsus—refs. to 'Ander Theil', 1589].
KOYRÉ, A., *From the Closed World to the Infinite Universe*, Baltimore, 1957.
KÄSTNER, A. G., *Geschichte der Mathematik*, Vols. I and II, Göttingen, 1796-7.
KLEBS, A. C., *Incunabula scientifica et medica* (OSIRIS) Bruges, 1938.
LORIA, G., *Histoire des Sciences Mathematiques dans l'Antiquité Hellénique*, Paris, 1929.
MIELI, A., *La Science Arabe*, Leiden, 1938.
PUTNAM, G. H., *Books and their Makers during the Middle Ages*, 2 vols., New York and London, 1898.
SARTON, G., *A History of Science—Hellenistic Science and Culture in the last three centuries B.C.*, Cambridge, Mass., 1959. (Especially useful for early printed editions of Greek classics of mathematics and medicine.)
SARTON, G., *The Appreciation of Ancient and Medieval Science during the Renaissance*, Philadelphia, 1955.
SARTON, G., *Six wings—Men of Science in the Renaissance*, Indiana, 1957 and London, 1958.
SARTON, G., *Horus—A Guide to the History of Science*, Waltham, Mass., 1952.
SINGER, C., etc., *Ed.*, *History of Technology*, 5 Vols. especially Vol. III (1957), Oxford, 1954-8. (Referred to in text as *Hist. Tech.*)
SMITH, D. E., *Rara Arithmetica*, London, 1908.
THORNDIKE, L., *History of Magic and Experimental Science*, 6 vols., New York, 1923-41.
UNDERWOOD, E. A. *Ed.*, *Science, Medicine, and History*—2 vols. Papers in honour of Charles Singer. (Referred to in text as *Singer*.)
WEBSTER, P. and GNUDI, M. T., *The Life and Times of Gaspare Tagliacozzi*, New York, 1950.
WIGHTMAN, W. P. D., *The Growth of Scientific Ideas*, Edinburgh, 1950.
ZINNER, E., *Geschichte und Bibliographie der Astronomischen Literatur in Deutschland zur Zeit der Renaissance*, Leipzig, 1941.
ZINNER, E., *Deutsche und Niederländische Astronomische Instrumente des 11-18 Jahrhunderts*, München, 1956.

RECENT WORKS

BONJOUR, E., *Die Universität Basel*, Basel, 1960.
CROMBIE, A. C., *Medieval and Early Modern Science*, 2 vols. Doubleday Anchor Books.
CLAGETT, M., *The Science of Mechanics in the Middle Ages*, Madison and London, 1959.

Henry the Navigator, B. M. Catalogue of an exhibition, 1960.

HUIZINGA, J., *Men and Ideas*—(History, the Middle Ages, the Renaissance:) Essays, London, 1960.

KUHN, T. S., *The Copernican Revolution*, Cambridge, Mass., 1959.

LLOYD, H. A., *Some outstanding Clocks and their Makers over Seven Hundred Years* (1250-1950), London, 1958.

NEEDHAM, J., et. al., *Heavenly Clockwork*, Cambridge, 1960.

PANOFSKY, E., *Renaissance and Renascences in Western Art*. 2 vols., Stockholm, 1960.

PARTINGTON, J. R., *The History of Gunpowder and Greek Fire*.

SCHOLFIELD, P. H., *The Theory of Proportion in Architecture*, Cambridge, 1958.

VOLKMANN-SCHLUCK, K. H., *Nicolaus Cusanus: die Philosophie im Übergang vom Mittelalter zur Neuzeit*, Frankfurt am Main (1957).

INDEX OF NAMES AND DATES

The Index of Names consists mainly of those of persons and places. Dates have been appended wherever possible to the names of all sixteenth-century workers and also to those historically related to them in the text. The dates of emperors, kings, and popes are *regnant* years, except in a few cases where the life-span seems more appropriate; for the latter *Italic* type has been used. The names of authors of secondary sources have been given without dates in all cases.

'Arabic' authors have been alphabetised under the headings of 'al-' and 'ibn' in the shortest form necessary to avoid ambiguity; 'Latin' equivalents have been added in some cases. Medieval writers generally appear under their Christian names except where a familial name has become established (e.g. '*William* of Heytesbury' but '*Bacon*, Roger'). Attention is drawn to the Bibliographical Note on p. 304.

Where (as frequently happens) there is inconsistent spelling of names in the sources, no attempt has been made to impose an artificial consistency; but rare variants (e.g. 'Neper' for Napier, 'Valopius' for Fallop(p)io) have been ignored. Similarly no two writers are likely to agree on the choice as between Latin and vernacular names in any particular case: an attempt has been made to include relatively common alternatives (e.g. 'Iacobus Faber Stapulensis' and 'Jacques Lefèvre d'Etaples') where these might not easily be recognised.

INDEX OF TOPICS